# BASIC ALGEBRAIC CONCEPTS

**F. Lynwood Wren**
Professor of Mathematics
San Fernando Valley State College

**John W. Lindsay**
Associate Professor of Mathematics
San Fernando Valley State College

**McGraw-Hill**
**Book Company**
New York
St. Louis
San Francisco
London
Sydney
Toronto
Mexico
Panama

## BASIC ALGEBRAIC CONCEPTS

*Library of Congress Catalog Card Number* 68-9050

71908

1234567890 HDMM 7654321069

To ALLEYNE and KATHLEEN

# PREFACE

This book has been designed to provide background for more effective instruction in mathematics in the upper elementary and junior high schools. It presupposes one year of high school algebra and one year of high school geometry, supported by a one-semester college course equivalent in coverage to the first six chapters of F. Lynwood Wren, *Basic Mathematical Concepts*, McGraw-Hill Book Company, New York, 1965. The content has been checked carefully against the "Recommendations for Level I" of the Committee on the Undergraduate Program in Mathematics (CUPM). A person completing a two-semester program based on the first six chapters of *Basic Mathematical Concepts* and the content of this book will have met in a substantial manner the CUPM recommendations pertaining to the study of the structure of numbers and algebra.

Chapter 1 provides a brief historical orientation to the evolution of the concept of an algebraic system and its basic structure. Chapter 2 presents a minimum preparation in the logical concepts and techniques essential to the treatment of algebraic systems and a careful analysis and detailed discussion of the more fundamental aspects of problem solving. In Chaps. 3 to 5 the concepts of group, ring, integral domain, field, and vector space are considered within the context of the mathematical maturity assumed of the reader. These particular algebraic systems were selected as being those of greatest significance to the evolving mathematical programs of the upper elementary schools and junior high schools. After this preparation, the remaining chapters treat, with reasonable detail and precision, the concepts of relation and function, polynomials and polynomial equations, systems of equations, and systems of inequalities. A large number of carefully selected exercises are presented in great variety to illustrate the concepts discussed, to afford opportunity for application of the techniques developed, to motivate a study in greater depth of topics presented, and to direct attention to related areas of mathematical interest.

The treatment might be said to be semiformal, rather than either formal or informal. No great effort is made to give the basic concepts of algebraic structure a strict rigorous development. However, some effort is made to bring the reader into contact with the nature of proof, both through description and use. There are several theorems whose proofs are given, both in formal and informal patterns. In no case, however, does the proof place any heavy demands on the use of logical processes. This treatment of the deductive process, while relatively brief and not formidable in technical detail, is sufficient to encourage and develop precision of thought, and hence is adequate for the purpose of the book.

It has been assumed that the reader is familiar with some of the more common notation associated with the study of sets and the number systems of arithmetic. Part 1 of the Glossary lists the symbols and notation which are prerequisite and which will serve to orient the reader with respect to the material in this book. Furthermore, many of the examples in Chaps. 1 and 2 have been selected to effect a review of some of the fundamental concepts which are assumed known.

A prefatory section, Guidelines for Careful Study, appears at the beginning of each chapter. These guidelines include questions designed to assist the reader in getting the most from the chapter. In the main, they point out key concepts and principles which the discussion of the chapter develops. Some of the questions serve as refresher ties with previous chapters. Each set of guideline questions thus can serve (1) as a partial review of previous chapters, (2) as a preview of the new chapter, and (3) as an outline for a detailed review upon completion of the chapter. The marginal notes also serve as a distinct study aid and key for ready reference.

At the end of each chapter is a section entitled Invitations to Extended Study. Here the reader will find questions and suggestions for pursuing the development of the preceding material in further detail and in greater depth. Also, in some cases there are opportunities for study of more advanced, but closely related, topics. It is hoped that at least some readers will be challenged to accept some, if not all, such invitations.

Although the content of the entire book has been developed with a carefully planned sequential pattern of treatment, there are opportunities for flexibility in selection. If there is no desire for an orientation of the course in its historical perspective, Secs. 1-1 and 1-2 can be omitted with no serious interference with the continuity of treatment. Similarly, the omission of Secs. 3-2 (Groups from Geometry), 3-3 (Mapping and Permutation Groups), 6-7 (The Reciprocal Function), and 6-8 (Diophantine Equations) would not disturb too seriously the sequence of development. If time is at a premium, the content of Chaps. 7 to 9 can be appraised against the desires and demands of a particular course to determine what selection to make among these chapters.

We wish to express our appreciation to those of our colleagues who gave us the benefit of their discussions of content and patterns of development; to students, in each of four different uses of the manuscript, for frank discussions of the appropriateness of content and treatment; to Professors E. Muriel Wright, John McGhee, and Jack Kifer, for their careful review and criticism of the manuscript; to Jan Shorey, Pat Weary, and Phyllis Willame for their cooperation and assistance in preparing the manuscript for classroom use; and to certain unknown reviewers for their helpful evaluation and criticism. Also, we owe a deep debt of gratitude to our wives, Alleyne Wren and Kathleen Lindsay, for their efficient typing of the manuscript and for their patience and critical help in seeing it through to its final form.

**F. Lynwood Wren**
**John W. Lindsay**

# CONTENTS

# CHAPTER 1

# ALGEBRA AS A MATHEMATICAL SYSTEM

## Guidelines for Careful Study

Algebra is an area of mathematical thought and endeavor which has evolved from a crude beginning as nothing more than a sort of theory of equations into a powerful logical structure of mathematical content. Since its basic language is symbolic, the reaction of some people to algebra is somewhat like that of the atheistic French philosopher Denis Diderot when he was confronted by the mathematician Leonhard Euler in the court of Catherine the Great. According to tradition,† Diderot's efforts to convert his hearers to atheism had made him rather objectionable to the court, and Euler was summoned to silence him. Diderot was informed that he was to meet a mathematician who, through the use of algebraic techniques, could prove the existence of God. Upon being presented to Diderot, Euler stated in a very serious tone, "Sir, $(a + b^n)/n = x$; hence God exists." Confused and humiliated, the philosopher departed from the company of the court.

Had Diderot oriented his thinking to the context of the symbolism used, he would have recognized Euler's statement as one entirely void of meaning or one subject to very simple interpretation, and in either case not very convincing support of the conclusion drawn. For example, he could have challenged Euler's failure to specify the domain of definition of the symbols used, or, providing his own context for interpretation, he could have demonstrated the irrelevancy of the formula by

† E. T. Bell, "Men of Mathematics," pp. 146–147, Simon and Schuster, Inc., New York, 1937.

selecting values such as $a = 5$, $b = 1$, and $n = 2$, which produce 3 as an interpretation of x. A bit of intelligent reflection rather than irrational impetuosity might have resulted in a mockery of the mathematician rather than the philosopher.

The topics of this book have been selected and developed with the hope of dispelling some of the mystery that so frequently enshrouds algebraic terminology and techniques. When this is done, the groundwork will have been laid for clearer comprehension and deeper appreciation of the significance of algebraic structure.

Following is a list of questions intended to aid in careful study of the subject matter of the chapter by providing: (1) a brief preliminary review of pertinent prerequisites, (2) a preview of important concepts and principles to be developed, (3) guidelines to significant content, and (4) upon completion of the chapter, a review in the form of questions which the reader should be able to answer with clarity and conviction.

1. What is meant by the cardinal number of a set?
2. How does the concept of place value contribute to the formation of a system of numerals?
3. What is meant by the base of a numeral system?
4. For what purpose is the symbol 10, read "one-oh," used in a numeral system?
5. In what sense are words and abbreviations used as symbols in everyday life?
6. What are the properties of the equality relation?
7. What are the properties of an equivalence relation?
8. What does $a \equiv b \pmod{m}$ mean when applied to integers?
9. According to the historian Nesselman, what are the three periods into which the history of algebra can be separated?
10. What is the etymology of the word "algebra"?
11. In what ways are the names Descartes, Gauss, Abel, Galois, Peacock, Hankel, Hamilton, and Grassman associated with the liberation of algebra?
12. In what ways have the concepts of symbolic arithmetic and theory of equations been associated with algebra?
13. During what period did the modernization of algebra begin to take place?
14. What is meant by the statement that there are many different algebras?
15. What is a mathematical system?
16. In what sense is algebra a mathematical system?
17. What is the definition of each of these concepts: term, constant, variable, proposition, and propositional form?

**18.** When are two terms said to be equivalent?

**19.** What is the Term-replacement Rule?

**20.** What is meant by disjunction, conjunction, and negation as used in the structure of propositions?

**21.** What is a conditional proposition?

**22.** What is the domain, or replacement set, of a variable?

**23.** When is a list of postulates said to be consistent?

**24.** What are some of the advantages to be derived from the study of different algebraic systems?


## Introduction

The use of symbols is a basic requirement in the creation of effective media for the communication of ideas between individuals, communities, and nations. This has been true through the ages, as it is today. The Egyptians used a heelbone symbol (∩) to indicate the same number concept for which the Babylonians used an arrowhead symbol (<), the Greeks used the letter iota ($\iota$), the Romans used X, the Maya Indians used =, the Chinese use +, and we use 10. Such symbols continue to provide a meaningful framework for the description of quantitative concepts. Similarly, the words we use are merely symbols to convey thoughts and express ideas, whether we are speaking the narrative language of the man in the street or the quantitative language of the scientist and mathematician.

*Significance of symbolism*

To the general public the symbol 10, read "one-oh," normally carries the meaning "ten," whereas to the operator of an electronic computer it may mean "two." This difference in meaning is not the result of any confusing ambiguity; rather, it underscores the true import of the symbol which has evolved as a representation of the cardinal number of the basic set used in any given pattern of numeration that employs the principle of place value. Thus the symbol 10 may represent "ten," "two," "twelve," or any such number concept, at the mercy of the context in which it is used. Similarly, whether any set of symbols constitutes a series of meaningless marks or a systematic presentation of intelligible ideas depends to a very great extent upon the studious effort of the reader to orient his thinking to the framework within which it is fashioned.† Numerals and other numerical symbols, traffic signals, highway signs, radio signals, signs of the Zodiac, scientific symbols, musical notes, stockmarket quotations and other business symbols, baseball ratings, athletic scores, statistical measures, tabular arrange-

*The symbol 10*

---

† This, of course, is posited on the assumption that the writer previously has made serious efforts toward careful designation of context of use and clear significance of pattern in the symbolism he has employed.

ments, and all such symbolic devices utilized by civilized man can carry significant meanings only when a responsible effort is made to interpret them in the context of their uses.

**Algebra is symbolic**

The study of algebra is couched in a symbolic language. As a result, many people fail to comprehend much of its significance as an independent body of mathematical thought. A study of the history of algebra will reveal that algebra has attained its full stature as a distinctive mathematical system only after a slow process of evolution characterized by critical analysis and constructive syntheses.

One of the purposes of this chapter is to present a very brief look at the development of algebra from its early beginnings as a sort of symbolic arithmetic to its present-day status as a mathematical system or a collection of such systems. Subsequently a more detailed study of certain fundamental algebraic systems will be made.

## 1-1. THE PRIMITIVE CONCEPT OF ALGEBRA

**Etymology of algebra**

From the Arab al-Khowarizmi (ca. 825) we get at least two words of significance in the modern vocabulary of mathematics.† From a Latin corruption of his name we have the word "algorism," and from the title of one of his mathematical treatises, "Hisâb al-jabr w'al-muqâbalah," we derive our word "algebra." The word "al-jabr" carries the meaning of reunion or consolidation as applied to equations, and "muqâbalah" means opposition or cancellation.‡ Thus we find in the early part of the ninth century a formal identification of algebra with the study of equations. From the time of the Babylonians (ca. 2000 B.C.), to the Egyptians (ca. 1550 B.C.), to Diophantus§ (ca. 275), to Brahmagupta (ca. 628), to al-Khowarizmi, there was a long history of algebra as it evolved from a sort of rhetorical arithmetic into a recognizable theory of equations.

**Three periods in history of algebra**

Nesselman‖ divides the early history of algebra into three periods: (1) the *rhetorical period*, during which the analysis and solution of equations was carried out in full rhetorical style; (2) the *syncopated period*, during which abbreviations were used for the more common and frequently occurring terms; and (3) the *symbolic period*, during which full symbolization was used. While there is no clear-cut pattern

† Howard Eves, "An Introduction to the History of Mathematics," rev. ed., p. 197, Holt, Rinehart and Winston, Inc., New York, 1964.

‡ D. E. Smith, "History of Mathematics," vol. II, pp. 388–389, Ginn and Company, Boston, 1925.

§ Howard Eves states that recent research tends to associate Diophantus with the first century rather than the third (*op. cit.*, p. 158).

‖ G. H. F. Nesselman, "Die Algebra der Griechen," pp. 301–305, G. Reimer, Berlin, 1842.

of dates which identify periods, it is safe to state that the algebra prior to the time of Diophantus was purely rhetorical.† The syncopated period, starting approximately with Diophantus, predominated until about the middle of the seventeenth century, which marks the real beginning of the full use of symbolism.

**Example 1-1.**   As an indication of what the basic differences of the three periods might be, consider this problem:

Find a number such that if 5 times the number is added to its square, the result is 14.

The form used in each period might be illustrated by each of the following patterns:

*Rhetorical:* The square of a number plus five times the number has the value 14.
*Syncopated:* No. sq $\tilde{p}$ 5M no. = 14.
*Symbolic:* $n^2 + 5n = 14$.

It is not pertinent here to enter into a discussion of methods used during the different periods to effect the solution of any given problem. Suffice it to say that the full use of symbolism made it possible to delete all the nonessentials of the problem and to direct attention to the basic relations and information needed.

In spite of the fact that no single date can be said unequivocably to mark the beginning of the symbolic period, it is probably acceptable without much challenge to say that the year 1637 marks the origin of the most efficient patterns for the use of symbolism in mathematics. This is the year in which the French philosopher and mathematician René Descartes (1596–1650) published his book "La méthode." In the third appendix of this book, to which he gave the title "La géométrie," he gave a great deal of emphasis to the extension and generalization of the techniques of the geometric algebra of the Greeks. It was as a consequence of this work, frequently referred to as the arithmetization of geometry, that algebraic symbolism began to take on its full stature. By means of a frame of reference and a system of coordinates, Descartes made available for the study of geometry the techniques of algebra and analysis. These techniques, however, were primarily nothing more than refined techniques for dealing with functions and equations, made possible by the use of symbolism. The subject matter of algebra was still concerned essentially with the theory of equations. Little attention, if any at all, was being given to the basic structure of algebras as distinct

**Descartes**

† Eves, *op. cit.,* p. 158.

mathematical systems. In fact, there still remained approximately two more centuries of evolution of mathematical thought before algebra was to become anything much more than a chest of manipulative tools consisting of rules, formulas, and techniques for the more efficient analysis of equations.

## 1-2.  THE MODERNIZATION OF ALGEBRA

**Congruence**

In 1801 Gauss discovered a new relation between subsets of the set of integers, which he called a *congruence relation* and defined as follows: The integer $a$ is said to be *congruent* to the integer $b$ modulo $m$, written $a \equiv b$ (mod $m$), if and only if $a - b$ is divisible by $m$ or, equivalently, if $a$ and $b$ yield the same remainder upon division by $m$. It was established that this relation is preserved under addition and multiplication; that is, if $a \equiv b$ (mod $m$) and $c \equiv d$ (mod $m$), then $a + c \equiv b + d$ (mod $m$) and $ac \equiv bd$ (mod $m$). Furthermore, congruence was found to possess all the properties of an equivalence relation.

**Equivalence relation**

**Definition 1-1.  A relation R on a set S is said to be an** *equivalence relation* **if and only if it has the following properties:†**

**Reflexivity: a R a for every a $\in$ S.**
**Symmetry: If, for a, b $\in$ S, a R b, then b R a.**
**Transitivity: If, for a, b, c $\in$ S, a R b and b R c, then a R c.**

The concept of congruence provided a basis for abstractions in arithmetic and for analogies between arithmetic and algebra which caused mathematicians to turn interests and efforts from a study of the specifics associated with the use of numbers to an investigation of the generalities which describe the relations between numbers and between sets of numbers. Along with the work of Abel (1802–1829) and Galois (1811–1832) in the theory of algebraic equations, these activities served, during the period from 1830 to 1850, to direct the attention of mathematicians to the investigation of basic algebraic systems.

The first serious look at the foundations of algebra seems to have taken place in England. George Peacock, in works published in 1834 and 1845, made a critical study of the distinctions between "arithmetical algebra" and "symbolic algebra." In the former, for example, the operations of subtraction and division were restricted, and in the latter many such restrictions were removed. Such critical study of the nature of algebra was pursued by other British mathematicians and was later (1867) given wide publicity through the results of a thorough analysis by the German mathematician Hermann Hankel.

† The symbol $a\ R\ b$ is to be read "a is R-related to b."

The real liberation of algebra, however, took place with the denial of the commutative law of multiplication (1843) by Sir William Rowan Hamilton and by the publication (1844) of a work by Hermann Grassmann on classes of algebras of even greater generality than that considered by Hamilton. The rejection of the postulate of commutativity served to open the way for the creation of many different types of algebraic systems. The genius of the seventeenth and nineteenth centuries combined to add still another chapter to the content of modern-day algebra. The concept of symbolic logic as an important portion of mathematical content seems to have originated with Leibniz (1665–1690). It was pursued more intensely by De Morgan and later (1854) refined and added to the domain of algebra by Boole.

**Symbolic logic**

Mathematicians now began to direct their attention to the critical study of mathematical systems, or, more precisely, axiomatic systems. It was then recognized that, fundamentally, any algebraic system is characterized by its set of elements, undefined terms, definitions, postulates, deductive processes, and derived properties.

## EXERCISES

1. List several illustrations of the use of abbreviations as symbols.
2. Construct a tabular presentation of some selected set of data, and discuss how such a table may be construed as a symbol.
3. How may a weather map be considered to be a symbol?
4. How can statistical measures such as arithmetic mean, median, and mode be considered as symbols?
5. Name other types of symbols in common use.
6. The English mathematician Augustus De Morgan, who lived during the nineteenth century, is said to have stated his age in conundrum form as follows:

   In the year $n^2$ I was $n$ years old.

   How old was he at that time?
7. How old would De Morgan have been if he had been living in the twentieth century when he made his statement?
8. Solve the following problems, first only by the techniques of rhetorical algebra (no symbols or abbreviations, only sentences); then by the techniques of the syncopated period (use these abbreviations: no. for number, sq for square, and the operational symbols $+, \times, -, =$); then only by symbolism, as in the symbolic period:

   (a) If 8 is subtracted from 5 times a number, the result is 7. What is the number?

(b) What is the natural number which, added to its own square, gives 6?

9. Which of the following relations applied to real numbers are equivalence relations? Give reasons to support your answer in each case.

(a) =        (d) "is the square root of"
(b) <        (e) "is the cube of"
(c) >        (f) "is the same as"

10. Which of the following relations applied to geometric figures are equivalence relations? Give reasons to support your answer in each case.

(a) "is the same length as"        (d) "is congruent to"
(b) "is shorter than"              (e) "is longer than"
(c) "is similar to"                (f) "has the same area as"

## 1-3. THE NATURE OF A MATHEMATICAL SYSTEM

Almost every day we hear of systems such as traffic-control systems, navigational systems, circulatory systems, and number systems. A *system* is a set of objects, together with all the information that can be obtained about the relationships between the objects.

**Mathematical system**      A *mathematical system* consists of:

1. A set of elements
2. Certain concepts which remain undefined
3. A list of postulates (assumptions) which are to be used to establish relationships between the elements
4. Definitions of additional concepts to be used
5. All the derivable theorems (facts)

The techniques of derivation may even be included as part of the structure of the system. Since, in general, it is not possible to list all the derivable theorems, a system is most frequently identified by one or more sets of elements, together with the undefined concepts and associated postulates.

**Example 1-2.**   The system of natural numbers consists of the set $N = \{1,2,3,4, . . .\}$, two well-defined operations (addition and multiplication), and postulates for carrying out the operations. In any discussion we may refer to this system as "the system $N$ of natural numbers."†

† F. Lynwood Wren, "Basic Mathematical Concepts,"pp. 42–77, McGraw-Hill Book Company, New York, 1965.

In general, the use of one symbol to represent two different concepts should be avoided. However, if no ambiguity can result, it is often convenient to denote a mathematical system by the symbol that indicates its set of elements. Such a practice is indicated by the last sentence of Example 1-2. Also, at times it becomes desirable to consider a subsystem in which the postulates of a given system hold on a proper subset of the system. We may even wish to compare two different systems for which the postulates are the same but the sets are different. On the other hand, we may wish to consider which postulates of a given system hold on a particular subset of the system.

**Example 1-3.** Let $E$ be the set of even natural numbers; that is, $E = \{2,4,6, \ldots\}$. All the postulates for the system $N$ of natural numbers hold except for the existence of a multiplicative identity. However, if we exclude the multiplicative postulates and consider the corresponding systems for the sets $N$ and $E$ with only the postulates for addition, then both $N$ and $E$ satisfy the same postulates. In this case $E \subset N$, and we say that the system $E$ is a subsystem of the system $N$ (with respect to the additive postulates).

**Example 1-4.** Let $O$ be the set of odd natural numbers; that is, $O = \{1,3,5, \ldots\}$. All the postulates for the natural number system hold except for closure with respect to addition (the sum of two odd numbers is an even number). If we restrict our list of postulates to those for multiplication, then, since $O \subset N$, $O$ may be regarded as a subsystem of $N$ (with respect to the multiplicative postulates).

The mathematician's study of a particular system is somewhat like playing a game. With a different set of postulates, the game is different. The game is played by discovering certain facts about the system and then guaranteeing that the system does indeed possess those facts. The guarantee is established by a *proof*, and the "fact" is called a *theorem*. When we learn to play a new game, we learn the basic moves first, and then, through practice, we gradually learn the more subtle strategies and tactics. The same is true in mathematics. We must first become thoroughly familiar with the basic assumptions, fundamental concepts, and pertinent techniques. Only when this has been accomplished is it possible to learn, through the study of examples and the development of proofs, the more sophisticated techniques and procedures.

The fundamental concepts of *term, constant, variable, proposition,* and *propositional form* are essential to the proper understanding of the study undertaken here. A *term* is a symbol or a substantive word or     **Term** phrase which may be used to name or refer to a unique object. Examples of terms are "George Washington," "first President of the United States," "the set of natural numbers," and any number symbol such as 1, 2, 3, $8 + 3$, $6 - 4$, or $7 - 5$. Two terms denoting the same object are said to be *equivalent;* thus the terms 2 and $6 - 4$ are equivalent (they denote the same number), and the terms "George Washington" and "first President of the United States" are equivalent (they denote the same person).

**Equivalent terms**

**Term-replacement Rule**

**Term-replacement rule. In any given statement a term may be replaced by an equivalent term without changing the meaning of the statement.**

For example, in a discussion involving the term $N$, we may, without any change of meaning, replace $N$ by the term $\{1,2,3,4, . . .\}$, since they denote the same set. Similarly, we may replace the term $6 - 4$ by the equivalent term 2 in the term $7 + (6 - 4)$† to obtain an equivalent term $7 + 2$, which in turn may be replaced by the equivalent term 9.

**Constant**

When a special symbol or term is used to denote a particular number, the symbol is called a *constant.* One example of such a symbol is $\pi$, which denotes the ratio of the circumference of a circle to its diameter, since the number it represents remains the same regardless of the size of the circle used. Other examples of constants are numerals such as 1, 2, 3.

It is often desirable to state a property which holds for each element of a set. In such cases we may choose some symbol to represent any arbitrary element of the set and then state the property (which is to hold for each element of the set) in terms of the chosen symbol, called a *vari-*

**Variable**

*able.* A *variable* is a symbol which may be replaced by a term in a statement or an expression. For example, if we say, "let $x$ represent a natural number," then $x$ is a variable which may be replaced by any element of the set $N$ of natural numbers in any subsequent expression involving $x$. Thus in the expression

$$x^2 + 2x + 1 = (x + 1)^2$$

the term $2x$ would be understood to mean the product of 2 and $x$, regardless of which natural number might be used to replace $x$, and similarly, the term $x^2$ would mean the product of $x$ and $x$ for any natural-number replacement.

A lowercase letter is often used as a variable in such expressions as $N = \{x|x \text{ is a natural number}\}$, which is read "$N$ is the set of all $x$ such that $x$ is a natural number." In this case the letter $x$ is called a *dummy variable* and can be replaced by any other symbol without a change in meaning, as for example, $N = \{*|* \text{ is a natural number}\}$. Note that we

† The parentheses are used to identify or set apart the term $6 - 4$.

consider $\{x|x$ is a natural number$\}$ a term, since it denotes a unique set, despite the appearance of a variable in the expression. The set of elements which may be used to replace a variable will be called the *domain*, or *replacement set*, of the variable.

A *simple proposition* is a statement in which two terms are connected by a predicate or verb and which, in a given context, may be judged to be either true or false. Examples of simple propositions are

$2 = 1 + 1$

$N$ denotes the set of natural numbers

George Washington was the first President of the United States

A *proposition* is either a simple proposition or a statement which can be obtained from simple propositions by certain procedures. The *conditional, biconditional,*† *disjunction,* or *conjunction* of two propositions is a proposition. Similarly, the *negation* of a simple proposition is a proposition.

Two propositions connected by the word "then" form a *conditional proposition*. For example,

$1 \in N$, then $1 + 1 \in N$

is a conditional proposition which consists of the two simple propositions:

$1 \in N$

$1 + 1 \in N$

There are several equivalent forms used for writing a conditional proposition. In addition to the one used, some of the more familiar forms are:

If $1 \in N$, then $1 + 1 \in N$

$1 + 1 \in N$ when $1 \in N$

$1 + 1 \in N$ under the condition $1 \in N$

The order in which the two propositions are written depends largely on rhetorical euphony. For this reason a specific order is adopted so that we may establish a symbol to represent a conditional proposition in any discussion. To illustrate, if $p$ is used to represent the conditional clause "1 is a natural number" and $q$ to represent the clause "1 + 1 is a natural number," then the conditional proposition of the example may be written symbolically in either of two forms

$1 \in N \rightarrow 1 + 1 \in N$

$p \rightarrow q$

† The biconditional proposition will be considered in Chap. 2.

**Implication**  The arrow shows the direction in which the *implication* of the proposition reads. The symbol $p \rightarrow q$ is usually read "*p* implies *q*" or "if *p*, then *q*."†

**Disjunction**  The *disjunction* of two propositions is the statement of the two propositions connected by the word "or." Thus

$$2 + 1 = 3 \text{ or } 13 - 3 = 0$$

is the disjunction of the two simple propositions $2 + 1 = 3$ and $13 - 3 = 0$. Note that whether the propositions are true or false is irrelevant.

**Conjunction**  The *conjunction* of two propositions is the statement of the two propositions connected by the word "and." Thus

$$2 + 1 = 3 \text{ and } 13 - 3 = 0$$

is the conjunction of two simple propositions.

**Negation**  The *negation* of a proposition is a statement of denial of the proposition. To obtain this negation the original proposition may be preceded by the word "not" or other equivalent symbolism. For example, we may write the negation of the simple proposition $13 - 3 = 0$ as

$$\text{not-}(13 - 3 = 0)$$

or, equivalently,

$$13 - 3 \neq 0$$

A still more complex type of proposition is

$$2 + 1 = 3 \text{ and } (13 - 3 = 0 \text{ or } 13 - 3 \neq 0)$$

where the parentheses are used only to assist in the identification of the component propositions and to avoid ambiguity. Some writers define an *open proposition* or *open sentence* as a statement which becomes a proposition when an appropriate term is substituted for each of the variables. An example of an open proposition is

$$8 + \# = 12$$

Thus, if #, read "sharp," is replaced by some number, a proposition results. It is immaterial whether the statement is true or false. However, the statement

$$\{x | x \text{ is a natural number}\} = \{1, 2, 3, 4, \ldots\}$$

is a proposition which is not open, since it states the equivalence of two terms, even though a variable *x* occurs in the statement. Full discussion of this is beyond the scope of this book, but we shall avoid the

† Other interpretations of the symbol and further discussion of the logical significance of the conditional proposition are given in Chap. 2.

term "open sentence" and refer to any statement which is not a propo-
sition but appears in the form of a proposition as a *propositional form*.   **Propositional form**
Thus

  x was the first President of the United States

is a propositional form and becomes a proposition when x is replaced
by the name of a person. It becomes a true proposition if x is replaced
by "George Washington" or any equivalent term, but it becomes a
false proposition if x is replaced by the name of anyone who was not
the first President of the United States.

  In mathematics a *definition* is commonly expressed as the equiv-   **Definition**
alence of two terms or the equivalence of two propositions or propositional forms. The equivalence of two terms is usually denoted by an
ordinary equality sign and that of two propositions (or propositional
forms) by the phrase "if and only if" or, at times, simply by the word
"if." There are circumstances which make it desirable to preface a
definition by a statement which identifies symbols used in the definition.

**Example 1-5.**   If $S$ and $T$ are sets, then $S \subseteq T$ if and only if every element of $S$ is an element of $T$.

  In this example the concept being defined is $S \subseteq T$. The preface
indicates that the variables $S$ and $T$ are restricted to sets.

**Example 1-6.**   If $S$ is a set, then $P_S = \{X | X \subseteq S\}$, where $P_S$ is read "P
sub S" and is called the *power set* of S.   **Power set**

  If the variable $S$ is replaced by the symbol $N$, which represents the
set of natural numbers, then $P_N$ is the name of the power set of $N$, which
is just the set of all subsets of $N$. If we let $S = \{a,b,c\}$, then the subsets
of $S$ are $S, S_1 = \{a,b\}, S_2 = \{a,c\}, S_3 = \{b,c\}, S_4 = \{a\}, S_5 = \{b\}, S_6 =$
$\{c\}$ and $\phi$ (the *null* or *empty set*). Then $P_S = \{S,S_1,S_2,S_3,S_4,S_5,S_6,\phi\}$.   **Null set**

  Finally, one of the necessary requisites of any mathematical system
is that its basic set of postulates be consistent. A list of postulates is said
to be *consistent* if there is no statement $p$ such that both $p$ and *not-p* can   **Consistency of postulates**
be derived from the postulates. If to a list of consistent postulates we
add one more assumption $q$, and if we can deduce *not-q* or some other
proposition and its negation, then we say that $q$ is false in the system
and that *not-q* is true in the system. This is the basis for a form of proof
called *indirect proof*, as we shall see later. Whether we are proving a
theorem or solving a problem, we must follow certain logical principles.
In the next chapter we shall consider some of the basic forms of reasoning, the nature of a proof, and the pattern of problem solving.

EXERCISES

In Exercises 1 and 2 identify each expression as a term, a proposition, or neither. For each proposition, determine whether or not it is a simple proposition.

1. (a) {Christopher Columbus, Amerigo Vespucci}
   (b) Alexander the Great
   (c) {Pacific Ocean}
   (d) William Shakespeare was Sir Francis Bacon
   (e) {x|x is a king}
   (f) Julius Caesar lived in Rome
   (g) C. F. Gauss
   (h) C. F. Gauss was the Prince of Mathematicians
   (i) Aristotle preceded Archimedes
   (j) Eudoxus and Thales
   (k) Euler was older than Gauss
   (l) George Washington was a contemporary of Thomas Jefferson
   (m) {x|x is a mathematician}
   (n) George

2. (a) $\{^-1,1\}$          (m) $\{x|x = 2 \text{ or } x = 3\}$
   (b) $^-5$               (n) $x = 5 \text{ or } x = 3$
   (c) $\{13\}$            (o) $N = \{1,2,3,4, \ldots\}$
   (d) $2 + 5 = 7$        (p) $\{1,2,3,4, \ldots\}$
   (e) $\{x|x \text{ is an integer}\}$   (q) $2 + 5 = 7 \text{ and } 3 + 7 = 9$
   (f) $3 = 4$            (r) $2 + 5 = 7 \text{ or } 3 + 7 = 9$
   (g) $3 \neq 4$         (s) $\{x|x = 2\}$
   (h) $2 + 7 = 3 + 6$   (t) $3 \leqslant 4 \text{ or } 4 \leqslant 3$
   (i) $3 < 5$            (u) $5 < 2 \text{ or } 5 = 2 \text{ or } 2 < 5$
   (j) 3 and 4            (v) $\pi$
   (k) $5 \geqslant {}^-2$   (w) $\pi + 5$
   (l) 3 or 7             (x) $\{\ldots, ^-2, ^-1, 0, 1, 2, \ldots\}$

3. If $a$ and $b$ are natural numbers, then the property of commutativity with respect to addition may be stated in symbolic form as $a + b = b + a$.

   (a) State the property of commutativity in the rhetorical form.
   (b) State the property of associativity in both the rhetorical form and the symbolic form.

4. The symbol 2 is normally a constant. Consider the term

   {2|2 was a President of the United States}

   Discuss the advantages or disadvantages of using 2 in this term.

5. Show that the relation "equivalence of terms" satisfies the three properties of an equivalence relation.

In Exercises 7 to 11 follow the example of Exercise 6 and translate each propositional form from its verbal to its symbolic form.

6. If $a$ and $b$ are natural numbers, then $a = b$, $a < b$, or $a > b$.

Symbolic form: $a \in N$ and $b \in N \rightarrow a = b$ or $a < b$ or $a > b$

7. If $a$ and $b$ are natural numbers, then $a + b = b + a$.
8. If $a$ and $b$ are natural numbers, then $ab$ is a natural number.
9. If $a$, $b$, and $c$ are natural numbers such that $a < b$, then $a + c < b + c$.
10. If $a$, $b$, $c$ and $d$ are natural numbers such that $a = b$ and $c = d$, then $ac = bd$.
11. If, $a$, $b$, and $c$ are natural numbers such that $a < b$, then $ac < bc$.
12. Translate each propositional form from its symbolic to verbal form:

   (a) $a \in N$ and $b \in N \rightarrow a + b \in N$
   (b) $a \in N$ and $b \in N$ and $a \nless b \rightarrow a > b$ or $a = b$

## 1-4. ALGEBRA AS A MATHEMATICAL SYSTEM

Mathematicians eventually came to realize that there were certain properties which seemed to characterize the behavior of natural numbers under the familiar operations of addition and multiplication. They further observed that the corresponding uses of integers, rational numbers, real numbers, and complex numbers revealed certain distinct similarities as well as fundamental differences in intrinsic behavior from that of the natural numbers. These facts, combined with the growing emphasis on symbolization and abstraction in arithmetic and algebra, led to the investigation of the possibility of characterizing certain types of number systems by defining an operation, or operations, and postulating, without specific identification, a set of elements which would conform to certain assumed principles under these operations.

The fundamental characteristics of an algebraic system were recognized as consisting of a set, at least one well-defined operation on the set, and one or more governing postulates. One such system, with respect to one operation, was defined as a *group*, and another, with respect to two operations, was defined as a *field*. The great advantage of such generalization is that any valid property derived from the basic postulates of a group or a field will then hold true for any set of elements

**Group and field**

which conforms to these postulates, whether it consists of integers, rational numbers, real numbers, complex numbers, or any other components, either abstract or concrete.†

Further pursuit of the latitude of interpretation, made possible through the use of generalized symbols instead of just numerals, led to modification of the definition of the operations to such patterns as modular addition, modular multiplication, addition and multiplication of polynomials, addition and multiplication of matrices, and the combination of geometric transformations. This made it possible to exercise **Different forms of algebra** a great deal of freedom in specifying the sets of elements to be considered. For example, the definitions of modular arithmetic lend new significance to finite sets of numbers, polynomial arithmetic makes it possible to use polynomials as elements of the set to be studied, rules for combining geometric transformations open up the application of group properties to the study of geometry, and the algebra of matrices is made possible by the extension of the definitions of addition and multiplication. Each of these systems is identified as an algebra, with its individual structure consisting of the specified elements, the defined operations, the postulated properties, and the derived theorems.

The only algebraic systems we have thus far identified by name are those of group and field. They are distinguishable by their defined operations and postulated properties. Modification of the basic postulates may change the structure of any given algebraic system to that of another. Whether a group is *abelian* (commutative) or not depends upon whether the postulate of commutativity is among its basic assumptions. If the postulate which provides the existence of a multiplicative inverse for all nonzero elements is deleted from the basic field properties, the field structure is destroyed, but the remaining postulates serve to characterize another significant algebraic system, known as a *commuta-* **Finite or infinite algebras** *tive ring* with identity. Also, a given postulate set will define a finite or an infinite system, depending to some extent upon whether the set of elements itself is finite or infinite.

Algebra is no longer considered as being restricted to the consideration of the properties and techniques of a symbolized arithmetic, or even to the more elaborate study of the principles and practices for **Algebra a mathematical** solving algebraic equations. Rather, algebra is a formalized mathemati- **system** cal system with its undefined terms, definitions, postulates, deductive processes, and derived properties. In fact, there are many different algebraic systems, each receiving its individual characterization from the basic postulates and the constitution of its particular set of elements.

† The concepts of group and field are developed in Chaps. 3 and 5, respectively.

In Chaps. 3 to 5 we shall discuss some of the algebraic systems of greatest significance to elementary mathematics. The development of subsequent chapters will then be within the prescribed domains of these respective algebras.

## Invitations to Extended Study

**1.** Use the rule of false position† to find values of $x$ and $y$ that satisfy the equations

$$x^2 + y^2 = 208$$
$$2x - 3y = 0$$

**2.** Except for the fraction $\frac{2}{3}$, the Egyptians used only unit fractions (fractions with 1 as the numerator). For example, the fraction $\frac{2}{15}$ would have been written as $\frac{1}{12}\,\frac{1}{20}$, where the juxtaposition means the sum of the two fractions. History does not reveal just how these unit fractions were derived. One formula which was found on an early Greek papyrus is $a/bc = 1/bn + 1/cn$, where $b$ and $c$ are factors of the denominator and $b + c = na$. For example, in the fraction $\frac{2}{15}$, $a = 2$, $b = 3$, $c = 5$, and $n = 4$ since $3 + 5 = 4(2)$. Therefore

$$\frac{2}{15} = \frac{1}{3(4)} + \frac{1}{5(4)} = \frac{1}{12} + \frac{1}{20}$$

Explain why this formula works.

Use the formula to convert each of these fractions into unit fractions:

$$\frac{4}{15} \qquad \frac{8}{15} \qquad \frac{7}{12} \qquad \frac{3}{20} \qquad \frac{6}{35}$$

**3.** The Egyptians used a process of multiplication known as *duplication and mediation*. The multiplicand and multiplier are recorded in separate columns. The multiplicand is doubled and the multiplier is halved, the remainder, if any, being discarded. This process is repeated on each pair of numbers obtained. When the multiplier is odd, the remainder, obtained upon the division by 2, is discarded. When the final quotient in the multiplier column is 1, the desired product is obtained as the sum of the numbers in the multiplicand column which correspond to the odd numbers in the multiplier column. For example, find the product of 25(37):

† Eves, *op. cit.,* p. 41.

| Multiplier | Multiplicand |
|------------|--------------|
| ✔ 25       | 37 ✔         |
| 12         | 74           |
| 6          | 148          |
| ✔ 3        | 296 ✔        |
| ✔ 1        | 592 ✔        |

$592 + 296 + 37 = 925$

Use the symbolism of a binary numeral system to explain why this works.

Use the method of duplication and mediation to find these products.

$$64 \times 26 \qquad 71 \times 98 \qquad 125 \times 37$$

4. The decimal numerals 1 to 15 are written on four cards, as pictured here. Ask someone to select any one of the numerals and indicate the cards on which it is to be found. You can tell what the numeral is by finding the sum of the numerals found in the upper-left corner of the designated cards.

| 1 | 9  | 2 | 10 | 4 | 12 | 8  | 12 |
|---|----|---|----|---|----|----|----|
| 3 | 11 | 3 | 11 | 5 | 13 | 9  | 13 |
| 5 | 13 | 6 | 14 | 6 | 14 | 10 | 14 |
| 7 | 15 | 7 | 15 | 7 | 15 | 11 | 15 |

For example, the numeral 14 is found on the cards with 2, 4, and 8 in the upper-left corner $2 + 4 + 8 = 14$.

Use the symbolism of a binary system to explain why this works.

# CHAPTER 2

# BASIC CONCEPTS OF LOGIC

## Guidelines for Careful Study

Intuition and induction will always be important tools of the student or investigator in any area of mathematical thought, particularly in problem solving and in discovery of concepts and relations. However, deduction is the principal instrument used in any mathematical system to derive the properties implied by logical inference from the basic postulates.

In this book only five of the more fundamental algebraic systems are defined, discussed briefly, and illustrated. No effort is made in any case at exhaustive treatment. Only a few of the basic theorems of each system are derived. For this purpose we need some of the simpler principles of logic. In this chapter we shall present and illustrate the principles needed in subsequent chapters.

The following questions will provide helpful guidelines for the careful study of Chap. 2.

1. What is an equivalence relation?
2. What is a mathematical system?
3. When may a propositional form be used in the same way as a proposition? When may it not be so used?
4. How may conjunction, disjunction, and negation be used to derive propositions?
5. What are some of the basic distinctions between an informal proof and a formal proof?
6. What are equivalent terms? Equivalent propositions?
7. What is meant by term replacement? Proposition replacement?

8. What is meant by the biconditional of propositions $p$ and $q$?
9. What is the Substitution Rule?
10. What is the Simple-inference Rule?
11. What is a conditional proposition?
12. What is the Conditional-biconditional Rule?
13. What is the contrapositive of a given proposition?
14. What is the converse of a given proposition?
15. What is the Contrapositive Rule?
16. What is the Double-negative Rule?
17. What is the Rule of Conjunction?
18. What is the Rule of Disjunction?
19. What are De Morgan's Laws?
20. What are the distinctions among conditions which are necessary, sufficient, and necessary and sufficient?
21. What is a conjecture?
22. What is the context of proof?
23. What is a counterexample?
24. What is a direct proof?
25. What is an indirect proof?
26. What is one of the basic differences between solving a problem and proving a theorem?
27. Into what four major categories may problem-solving difficulties be classified.

## Introduction

In deriving the theorems of any particular algebra the principal concern is whether or not the derivation has been accomplished by means of a valid argument. The *validity* of any argument depends upon the proper use of the rules and concepts of logic. A rigorous discussion of such rules and concepts is beyond the scope of this book. However, careful attention to the basic structure of proofs as they are met will gradually develop some sophistication in the use of these techniques of logic. Whether the argument is presented formally or informally, or whether the techniques are those of direct or indirect proof, does not matter so long as logical inference leads from postulate, or hypothesis, to conclusion.

Solving problems is in many ways similar to proving theorems, but there is one aspect in which there is a great difference. In the proof of a theorem the task is completed when the conclusion has been derived as a necessary consequence of the hypothesis and the logical structure within a given system. Similarly, in a problem situation the data serve as the hypothesis, and a chain of inferences leads from these data to a necessary conclusion. Before a problem can be considered as solved, however, it is essential to test this necessary condition to determine whether or not it is sufficient to meet the demands of the problem. Both in proving theorems and in solving problems, the rules and concepts of logic provide the guidelines for an orderly chain of inferences leading to the results desired.

Among the more familiar properties of significance in deriving proofs and solving problems are those of equivalence and equality. The equivalence relation was defined in Sec. 1-2. As specified in the definition, equivalence expresses only a fundamental relation between pairs of elements of a given set under consideration. There is no property which associates the relation with any operation upon these elements. Equality is an equivalence relation with an additional property or properties that control its use with any operation combining the elements of the given set.

Unless otherwise indicated by specific definition, *equality* is to be interpreted to mean "is the same as." Its use is prescribed by these properties:

Equality relation

**Reflexivity.   a = a.**

Any element is the same as itself.

**Symmetry.   If a = b, then b = a.**

If *a* is the same as *b*, then *b* is the same as *a*.

**Transitivity.   If a = b and b = c, then a = c.**

If *a* is the same as *b* and *b* is the same as *c*, then *a* is the same as *c*.

**Operativity.   If a = b, then a ∘ c = b ∘ c and c ∘ a = c ∘ b.**

If *a* is the same as *b*, then, with a given operation ∘, the result of combining *a* with *c* is the same as the result of combining *b* with *c*.

When applied to the ordinary numbers of arithmetic, the operative property is usually interpreted in the form of these two distinct properties:

**Additive property.   If a = b, then a + c = b + c.**

**Multiplicative property.   If a = b, then ac = bc.**

These properties may seem trivial, and one can easily overlook their significance. They do characterize the relation of equality. There are other relations between numbers which do not conform to these characteristics. Two such relations are exhibited in Examples 2-1 and 2-2.

**Example 2-1.**  The relation "is smaller than," applied to natural numbers, is neither reflexive nor symmetric, but it does satisfy the transitive, additive, and multiplicative properties.

*Reflexivity fails:* No number is smaller than itself.

*Symmetry fails:* 2 is smaller than 3, but it does not follow that 3 is smaller than 2.

*Transitivity:* If 2 is smaller than 3 and 3 is smaller than 4, then 2 is smaller than 4. (List other illustrations.)

*Additive property:* Since 2 is smaller than 3, it is true that 2 + 5 is smaller than 3 + 5. (List other illustrations.)

*Multiplicative property:* Since 2 is smaller than 3, it is true that 2(6) is smaller than 3(6). (List other illustrations.)

**Example 2-2.**  The relation "is the square of," applied to natural numbers, has none of the properties of equality.

*Reflexivity fails:* No number (other than 1) is the square of itself.

*Symmetry fails:* 4 is the square of 2, but 2 is not the square of 4.

*Transitivity fails:* 16 is the square of 4 and 4 is the square of 2, but it does not follow that 16 is the square of 2.

*Addition fails:* 4 is the square of 2, but 4 + 3 is not the square of 2 + 3.

*Multiplication fails:* 4 is the square of 2, but 4(3) is not the square of 2(3).

## EXERCISES

**1.** Why is any relation of equality necessarily an equivalence relation?

**2.** Which of these relations is an equivalence relation? In those cases where the relation is not an equivalence relation, indicate which properties fail.

(a) "Is an integral multiple of" applied to integers

(b) "Lives within a mile of" applied to people

(c) "Has the same area as" applied to geometric figures

(d) "Is tangent to" applied to circles in a plane

(e) "Is identical to" applied to algebraic expressions

(f) "Is the sister of" applied to people

(g) "Is greater than" applied to integers

(h) "Is as tall as" applied to buildings

(i) "Has the same shape as" applied to geometric figures

(j) "Is the same length as" applied to line segments

(k) "Is relatively prime to" applied to positive integers

(*l*) "Is perpendicular to" applied to straight lines in a plane

(*m*) "Is an ancestor of" applied to people

(*n*) "Is congruent to" applied to geometric figures

(*o*) "Represents the same cardinal number as" applied to numerals

(*p*) "Is parallel to" applied to straight lines in a plane

(*q*) "Is shorter than" applied to straight-line segments

(*r*) "Has the same measure as" applied to angles

(*s*) "Is the same age as" applied to people

(*t*) "Disagrees with" applied to people

3. Which of the equivalence relations of Exercise 2 are also equality relations?

4. Give at least two additional nonmathematical examples of equivalence relations which are not equality relations.

5. Give at least two additional mathematical examples of equivalence relations which are not equality relations.

6. Give at least two additional nonmathematical examples of relations which are not equivalent relations.

7. Give at least two additional mathematical examples of relations which are not equivalence relations.

## 2-1. THE NATURE OF PROOF

A mathematical proof is based on certain assumptions and postulates and consists of a finite number of statements arranged in a particular order. The statements may be propositions or propositional forms, and they are often called *lines*, or *steps*, of the proof. A *formal proof* may be displayed in two columns, with the lines of the proof in one column and their justifications (reasons) opposite them in the second column. For convenience, the lines may be numbered. In an *informal proof* the statements may be written in narrative form, with justifications given for only some of the statements; the reader is then expected to supply the missing ones. There is no essential difference in basic structure between an informal proof and a formal proof. The statements of each must carry the same logical support and provide the same valid chain of deductions leading from the initial assumption to the final conclusion. The only real difference is in the format and the manner of writing.

Although the arrangement of the statements in a proof is generally not unique, it does not follow that they may be arranged in random order. They must be arranged according to certain logical rules. Each statement is a proposition or propositional form which must be supported by a definition, a previously assumed or proved statement, or an equivalent statement. Two propositions, or two propositional forms,

**Formal proof**

**Informal proof**

**Equivalent propositions**

are said to be *equivalent* if each follows as a consequence from the other. This is just another way of saying that the two carry exactly the same information. A simple example of two equivalent propositions is

**1.** The numbers 2, 3, and 5 are the prime factors of 30.
**2.** The prime factors of 30 are 2, 3, and 5.

Any two such propositions can be used interchangeably, with no contextual change, in any situation to which they are pertinent. Term replacement and proposition replacement are two important techniques in deriving an equivalent proposition from a given one. Since two terms are equivalent whenever they denote the same object, it follows that if any term in a given proposition is replaced by an equivalent term, the resulting proposition is equivalent to the given one. In this case the second proposition is said to be obtained from the first by *term replacement*. Similarly, if $p$ and $q$ are equivalent propositions, and if $p$ occurs in some given proposition, then the replacement of $p$ by $q$ produces a proposition which is equivalent to the original one, and the second proposition is said to be obtained from the first by *proposition replacement*. It should be obvious that any proposition is equivalent to itself.

**Term replacement**

**Proposition replacement**

**Example 2-3.   Term replacement.** The proposition

$$2 + 7 = 13 - 4$$

is equivalent to the proposition

$$9 = 13 - 4$$

by term replacement, since the term $2 + 7$ is replaced by the equivalent term 9.

**Example 2-4.   Proposition replacement.** The proposition

$$2 + 7 = 13 - 4 \qquad \text{and} \qquad 2 + 2 = 5$$

is equivalent to the proposition

$$9 = 13 - 4 \qquad \text{and} \qquad 2 + 2 = 5$$

by proposition replacement, since, from Example 2-3, the propositions $2 + 7 = 13 - 4$ and $9 = 13 - 4$ are equivalent. Note that whether a proposition is true or false has nothing to do with the replacement rule, although equivalent propositions will have the same truth value.

The statement of equivalence of two propositions is also a proposition. If $p$ and $q$ are two propositions, then we shall denote the statement of their equivalence as $p \leftrightarrow q$, which may be read "$p$ is equivalent to

*q,*" "*p* if and only if *q,*" "*q* if and only if *p,*" "*p* is a necessary and sufficient condition for *q,*" "*q* is a necessary and sufficient condition for
*p,*" or simply "*p* double arrow *q.*" $p \leftrightarrow q$ is called the *biconditional*
of *p* and *q.* An example of an equivalence of two propositions is Example 2-3, where the equivalence may be written as

Biconditional proposition

$$(2 + 7 = 13 - 4) \leftrightarrow (9 = 13 - 4)$$

From the above discussion it follows that for any propositions *p, q,*
and *r*

| | |
|---|---|
| $p \leftrightarrow q$ | reflexive property |
| If $p \leftrightarrow q$, then $q \leftrightarrow p$ | symmetric property |
| If $p \leftrightarrow q$ and $q \leftrightarrow r$, then $p \leftrightarrow r$ | transitive property |

Thus the symbol $\leftrightarrow$ represents a relation which satisfies the reflexive,
symmetric, and transitive properties and hence is an equivalence relation (Definition 1-1).

**Substitution Rule. If a proposition occurs as a line of a proof, then any equiv-
alent proposition may replace it in a subsequent line of the proof.**

Substitution Rule

For any two propositions *p* and *q,* the proposition $p \rightarrow q$ was defined in Sec. 1-3 as a conditional proposition which may be read "if
*p,* then *q*" or "*p* implies *q.*" It also may be read "*p* is a sufficient condition for *q,*" "*q* is a necessary condition for *p,*" "assuming *p,* then
*q,*" "*q* on condition *p,*" "*p* only if *q,*" or simply "*p* arrow *q.*" The
proposition *p* is called the *hypothesis* or *antecedent,* and *q* is called
the *conclusion* or *consequent.* Such a proposition is called a conditional proposition because of its grammatical form. It consists of two
clauses, one of which states a condition, or hypothesis, and the other a
resultant situation, or conclusion. The conditional clause is usually introduced by the conjunction "if" or some such synonymous connective.

Conditional proposition

**Simple-inference Rule. If a proposition p $\rightarrow$ q occurs as a line of a proof and
the proposition p occurs as another line of a proof, then the proposition q may
occur as a subsequent line.**

Simple-inference Rule

Sometimes in somewhat less precise terminology the Simple-
inference Rule is stated

If $p \rightarrow q$ is true and *p* is true, then *q* is true

It would be better to say "if we have $p \rightarrow q$ and *p,* either by assumption
or previous proof, then we may conclude or deduce *q.*" The reason this
second statement is preferable will be better understood when we discuss indirect proof in the next section.

We have stated that the biconditional, $p \leftrightarrow q$, indicates that *p* and *q* are equivalent propositions. If the proposition $p$ is known to hold, then we may deduce $q$. Similarly, given $q$, we may deduce $p$. These facts suggest that if the propositions $p$ and $q$ are equivalent, we may legitimately write as a consequence either $p \rightarrow q$ or $q \rightarrow p$. Similarly, if both $p \rightarrow q$ and $q \rightarrow p$ are known to hold, we may deduce either proposition from the other and write $p \leftrightarrow q$.

**Conditional-biconditional Rule**

**Conditional-biconditional Rule. If the proposition p $\leftrightarrow$ q occurs as a line of a proof, then the propositions p $\rightarrow$ q and q $\rightarrow$ p may occur as subsequent lines. If the proposition p $\rightarrow$ q and the proposition q $\rightarrow$ p occur in separate lines of a proof, then the proposition p $\leftrightarrow$ q may occur in a subsequent line.**

The first part of the rule allows us to deduce the conjunction of the two conditionals from the biconditional, and the second part of the rule allows us to deduce the biconditional from the conjunction of the two conditionals.

**Example 2-5.**   After consultation with his instructor, a student is told that he will pass his course if and only if he passes the final examination. From this he understands

**1.** If I pass the final examination, then I pass the course.
**2.** I pass the course only if I pass the final examination.

In the first case we say that passing the final examination is a sufficient condition for passing the course, and in the second case we say that passing the final examination is a necessary condition for passing the course. Thus passing the final examination is both a necessary and sufficient condition for passing the course. If we let $p$ represent the proposition "I pass the final examination" and $q$ the proposition "I pass the course," then a simple translation of the instructor's advice would be that $p$ is a necessary and sufficient condition for $q$, or, symbolically, $p \leftrightarrow q$. If the sufficient condition is separated from the necessary condition, we may translate the two statements above into, respectively,

**1.** $p \rightarrow q$: $p$ is a sufficient condition for $q$
**2.** $q \rightarrow p$: $p$ is a necessary condition for $q$

In the first statement the arrow goes from $p$ to $q$ and in the second it goes from $q$ to $p$, so that the two statements taken together (in conjunction) may be replaced by a single statement with a double arrow between $p$ and $q$, $p \leftrightarrow q$. This is an example of the Conditional-biconditional Rule.

If the student discovers that he has passed the final examination, then he deduces from the first proposition that he has passed the course.

His reasoning is that, given $p \rightarrow q$ and $p$, then $q$ must follow. This is an example of the Simple-inference Rule.

Let us look again at Proposition 2 of Example 2-5, "I pass the course only if I pass the final examination," or, symbolically, $q \rightarrow p$. This is informing the student that he must pass the final examination in order to pass the course. Another proposition which carries the same information is "if I fail the final examination, then I fail the course." Since $p$ represents the proposition "I pass the final examination," we may use *not-p* to represent its negation, "I fail the final examination." Similarly, not-$q$ may be used to represent the proposition "I fail the course." Thus the two propositions, $q \rightarrow p$ and not-$p \rightarrow$ not-$q$, carry the same information and are consequently equivalent. The second proposition is called the *contrapositive* of the first. Note that to obtain the contra-positive of a given conditional proposition both the hypothesis and conclusion are negated and the two are then interchanged.

**Contrapositive**

One example of the significance of this equivalence of a proposition and its contrapositive is found in the familiar tests for evenness or oddness of integers. For any integer $a$ we have

a is even if and only if 2 is a factor of a

This biconditional statement may be represented symbolically as $p \leftrightarrow q$, where $p$ represents the proposition "a is even" and $q$ represents the proposition "2 is a factor of a."

By the Conditional-biconditional Rule, we have

$p \rightarrow q$: If a is even, then 2 is a factor of a
$q \rightarrow p$: If 2 is a factor of a, then a is even

The contrapositives of each of these statements are:

not-$q \rightarrow$ not-$p$: If 2 is not a factor of a, then a is not even
not-$p \rightarrow$ not-$q$: If a is not even, then 2 is not a factor of a

Recalling that an integer is odd if and only if it is not even, these two contrapositive statements may be reworded as

If 2 is not a factor of a, then a is odd
If a is odd, then 2 is not a factor of a

The Conditional-biconditional Rule now yields

a is odd if and only if 2 is not a factor of a

From the fact that a proposition and its contrapositive are always equivalent, the Contrapositive Rule follows:

**Contrapositive Rule**

**Contrapositive Rule. If a proposition p → q occurs as one line of a proof and the proposition not-q occurs as another line, then the proposition not-p may occur as a subsequent line.**

**Example 2-6.** Suppose we must determine whether 162,347 is divisible by 9. A test for determining whether or not an integer is divisible by 9 is

If an integer is divisible by 9, then the sum of its digits is divisible by 9

This test applied to the given number becomes

If 162,347 is divisible by 9, then $1 + 6 + 2 + 3 + 4 + 7$ is divisible by 9

Since $1 + 6 + 2 + 3 + 4 + 7 = 23$ and 23 is *not* divisible by 9, it follows by the Contrapositive Rule that 162,347 is *not* divisible by 9.

**Converse**

If $p$ and $q$ are two propositions, then the statement $q \to p$ is called the *converse* of the statement $p \to q$. Note that the conclusion of the given proposition is the hypothesis of its converse, and the hypothesis of the given proposition is the conclusion of its converse. An error frequently made in deductive arguments is the assumption that because a certain proposition is true, its converse is also true. One simple example is sufficient to show that this is not necessarily the case.

If a number is divisible by 8, it is an even number

is evidently a true proposition, since 2 is a factor of 8. The converse statement is

If a number is an even number, it is divisible by 8

This is evidently not true, since the numbers 2, 4, and 6, among others, are even numbers no one of which is divisible by 8.

The proposition $p \leftrightarrow q$ is equivalent to the conjunction of a conditional and its converse; that is, $p \leftrightarrow q$ is equivalent to the conjunction

$$p \to q \quad \text{and} \quad q \to p$$

In the definition of an even integer (page 27) there are essentially two statements involving the variable $a$. These two statements are the propositional forms:

**1.** The integer $a$ is even only if 2 is a factor of $a$.
**2.** If 2 is a factor of the integer $a$, then $a$ is even.

We treated these propositional forms as if they were propositions. Unless a propositional form is preceded by such quantifying statements as "for all," "for every," "for each," "for some," or "there exists," the propositional forms usually can be treated in deductive arguments like propositions. In other words, we may think of the variable as representing some specific (although unknown) name or term.

**Example 2-7.** One property which holds on the set $N$ of natural numbers is stated in the following propositional form:

$a = b$ if and only if $a + c = b + c$

This may be written symbolically as

$a = b \leftrightarrow a + c = b + c$

By the Conditional-biconditional Rule, we may deduce

$a + c = b + c \rightarrow a = b$

If each of the variables $a$, $b$, and $c$ of this propositional form is replaced by a natural number, the resulting proposition will hold. This property is called the *Cancellation Law* with respect to addition.

Also by the Conditional-biconditional Rule, we may deduce the propositional form

$a = b \rightarrow a + c = b + c$

This property is often referred to as the *additive property of equality*.

If $p$ is a proposition, then *not-(not-p)* is a proposition called the *double negative of p*. A basic property of logic is that a proposition is equivalent to its double negative.

**Double-negative Rule. p ↔ not-(not-p).**

**Example 2-8.** From the definition of an even number we have the true theorem:

If the integer $n$ is divisible by 2, then $n$ is not odd

Let $p$ be the proposition "the integer $n$ is divisible by 2," and $q$ be the proposition "the integer $n$ is odd." With this notation the theorem may be written as

$p \rightarrow \text{not-}q$

The contrapositive of the theorem may then be written in the symbolic form

$\text{not-(not-}q) \rightarrow \text{not-}p$

Cancellation Law

Double-negative Rule

By the Double-negative Rule and the rule of proposition replacement, we now have

$q \rightarrow$ not-$p$

This symbolic statement is recognized as the true theorem

If the integer $n$ is odd, then $n$ is not divisible by 2

Inference rules are rules which, within the framework of a logical system, allow us to deduce valid propositions from one or more given propositions. When the given propositions are lines of a proof, the deduced proposition occurs on a subsequent line. The Simple-inference Rule was stated in terms of lines of a proof. It could have been stated as

From propositions $p$ and $p \rightarrow q$ we may deduce the proposition $q$

**Argument**

A sequence of propositions which, by inference rules, follow logically from an assumed list of propositions may be called an *argument* from that list. The proof of a theorem, for example, usually consists of a list of postulates selected from the system, together with the hypothesis of the theorem, followed by an argument which results in the proposition which is the conclusion of the theorem.

Of course, a complete list of all rules of inference is impractical, and in reading a mathematical proof we must always be alert to recognize when a rule of inference is being used. This is especially true for informal proofs in which statements are listed with few or no reasons. Some of the subtleties of inference will be pointed out as they occur in subsequent proofs. However, there are some rules which are used often enough to justify consideration.

In the discussion of the equivalence of a biconditional proposition with the conjunction of two conditional propositions we used, without specific mention, the *Rule of Conjunction*.

**Rule of Conjunction**

**Rule of Conjunction. From the conjunction of two propositions we may deduce either proposition. From two given propositions we may deduce their conjunction.**

Another important rule is that of disjunction.

**Rule of Disjunction**

**Rule of Disjunction. From the disjunction of two propositions and the negation of one of them we may deduce the other proposition.**

**Example 2-9.** From the definition of the union of two sets $A$ and $B$ we have the propositional form

If $x \in A \cup B$, then $x \in A$ or $x \in B$

If we are given that $x \in A \cup B$, we may write, by the Simple-inference Rule,

$x \in A$ or $x \in B$

which is the disjunction of two propositional forms. Now, if we know from other considerations that $x \notin B$, then, by the Rule of Disjunction, we may conclude that $x \in A$. Similarly, if we know that $x \notin A$, we may conclude that $x \in B$.

In the above example the word "or" used in the disjunction is interpreted in the *inclusive* sense, meaning that an element may be in either or both of the two sets. Logically we always allow the "inclusive or" interpretation, even though we may know from other considerations that the exclusive sense is intended, that is, that either proposition may be true, but not both.

**Example 2-10.** A well-known property of integers is stated in the theorem

If $a$, $b$, and $c$ are distinct integers, then $ac \neq bc$ or $c = 0$

The conclusion of this theorem is the disjunction of two propositional forms. If $c \neq 0$, then we may conclude, by the Rule of Disjunction, that $ac \neq bc$. On the other hand, if $c = 0$, then by utilizing the multiplicative properties of 0 we know that $ac = bc$. Thus the assumption of $c = 0$ precludes the other proposition as a logical consequence.

Two rules which are very useful in taking care of the negation of a conjunction and the negation of a disjunction are sometimes called the *De Morgan Laws*, in honor of A. De Morgan (1806–1871), who did a great deal of work in the foundations of mathematics.

**De Morgan Laws. If p and q are two propositions, then**          De Morgan Laws

   1. **Not-(p and q) ↔ (not-p or not-q)**
   2. **Not-(p or q) ↔ (not-p and not-q)**

**Example 2-11.** For integers $a$, $b$, and $c$ the Cancellation Law for multiplication is

If $ac = bc$ and $c \neq 0$, then $a = b$

The contrapositive of this law is

If $a \neq b$, then not-($ac = bc$ and $c \neq 0$)

By the first of the De Morgan Laws, this may be written as

If $a \neq b$, then $ac \neq bc$, or $c = 0$

Now let us assume that, in a problem situation, it has been established that $2c = 5c$. What conclusion can be drawn about $c$? Since $2 \neq 5$, it follows that either $2c \neq 5c$ or $c = 0$. It has been established that $2c = 5c$. Therefore, by the Rule of Disjunction, we have $c = 0$.

The fundamental pattern of deductive reasoning begins with certain basic assumptions and proceeds by verified logical procedures to a conclusion which is implied. In mathematics we may have, in addition to the logical rules, the properties of some mathematical system which may also be assumed. It must be remembered that the validity of the argument and of the conclusion need not be related to the truth of the assumption. For a proof to be valid each step must be justified by some assumed or established property of the system. When this has been accomplished, we say that the hypothesis, the basic assumption, *implies* the conclusion. Symbolically, if $p$ represents the hypothesis and $q$ represents the conclusion, then we may say that $p \rightarrow q$ holds in the system.

It is of interest here to examine three arguments, one based on a true assumption and the other two based on the same false assumption. We shall assume the properties of the natural number system, which include the properties of the equality relation.

**Case 1.** Let us state as the basic assumption the true proposition $1 = 1$. From the additive property of equality we have

If $1 = 1$, then $1 + 2 = 1 + 2$

It then follows from the basic assumption and the Simple-inference Rule that $1 + 2 = 1 + 2$, or $3 = 3$. Thus, starting with a true assumption, we have used a valid argument to arrive at a true conclusion. If we use $p$ to represent the proposition $1 = 1$ and $q$ to represent the proposition $3 = 3$, we may state

$p \rightarrow q$, where $p$ is true and $q$ is true

**Case 2.** Let us state as the basic assumption the false proposition $2 = 3$, which we agree to use independently of whether it is true or false. From the additive property of equality, we have

If $2 = 3$, then $2 + 2 = 2 + 3$

It then follows from the basic assumption and the Simple-inference

Rule that $2 + 2 = 2 + 3$, or $4 = 5$. Here, starting with a false assumption, we have used a valid argument to arrive at a false conclusion. If we use $p$ to represent the proposition $2 = 3$ and $q$ to represent the proposition $4 = 5$ we may state

$p \rightarrow q$, where $p$ is false and $q$ is false

**Case 3.** Again let us state as the basic assumption the false proposition $2 = 3$. This time we shall make use of the symmetric property of equality and also one of the theorems proved in the system of natural numbers. Using the symmetric property of equality, we have

If $2 = 3$, then $3 = 2$

With an application of the Simple-inference Rule followed by the Rule of Conjunction, we now deduce

$2 = 3$ and $3 = 2$

The theorem we shall use from the natural number system is

If $a = b$, and $c = d$, then $a + c = b + d$

Using this theorem, with $a = d = 2$ and $b = c = 3$, we have

If $2 = 3$ and $3 = 2$, then $2 + 3 = 3 + 2$

From this, together with the conjunction and Simple-inference Rule, we have $2 + 3 = 3 + 2$, or $5 = 5$. This time, starting with a false assumption, we have used a valid argument to arrive at a true conclusion. If we use $p$ to represent the proposition $2 = 3$ and $q$ to represent $5 = 5$ we may state

$p \rightarrow q$, where $p$ is false and $q$ is true

These three cases represent the only three possible outcomes from a valid argument involving a conditional statement. From a false assumption a valid argument may produce a false conclusion (case 2) or a true conclusion (case 3). If we start with a true assumption, the only conclusion that can be derived as the result of a valid argument is a true conclusion (case 1). There is no possible way for a valid argument to lead from a true assumption to a false conclusion. When the statement is made that $p$ implies $q$ ($p \rightarrow q$), this means that there is no way that $q$ can be false if $p$ is true. From this fact and the fact that a proposition and its negation cannot both hold, we see that the negation of the conditional $p \rightarrow q$ is the conjunction of the two propositions $p$ and not-$q$. Symbolically, we may write this rule as follows:

**Negative-conditional Rule.** Not-($p \rightarrow q$) $\leftrightarrow$ ($p$ and not-$q$).          Negative-conditional Rule

Example 2-12 illustrates how the Negative-conditional Rule can be used to derive from a propositional form, implied by the definition of the intersection of two sets, a very useful equivalent propositional form.

**Example 2-12.**  From the definition of the intersection of two sets we have the propositional form

$(x \in A \cap B) \rightarrow (x \in A \text{ and } x \in B)$

Since, by the Double-negative Rule,

$x \in B \leftrightarrow \text{not-}(x \notin B)$

We may now use the Substitution Rule to write

$(x \in A \cap B) \rightarrow [x \in A \text{ and not-}(x \notin B)]$

By the Contrapositive Rule, we derive

$\text{not-}[x \in A \text{ and not-}(x \notin B)] \rightarrow \text{not-}(x \in A \cap B)$

Using the Negative-conditional Rule, we can obtain

$[x \in A \text{ and not-}(x \notin B)] \leftrightarrow \text{not-}[(x \in A) \rightarrow (x \notin B)]$

We may now use the Substitution Rule and the Double-negative Rule to derive

$[(x \in A) \rightarrow (x \notin B)] \rightarrow x \notin A \cap B$

Thus we have that if the fact that x is an element of set A implies that it is not an element of the set B, it then follows that x is not an element of the intersection of sets A and B.

To establish that this conclusion is equivalent to the propositional form used as the hypothesis for the argument it is still necessary to prove the converse of the theorem just proved. (See Exercise 9.)

To study properly the types of mathematical proofs in the next section, one should try to understand each of the inference rules and laws given in this section. To this end it is recommended that this section be thoroughly reviewed, the rules and laws summarized on one sheet of paper (for reference), and additional examples be constructed to illustrate each of these rules.

## EXERCISES

In the following exercises the letters a, b, c, and d represent integers, and propositional forms using these letters may be considered as propositions.

**1.** Express each of the following statements in rhetorical form:

(a) $a = b$ or $a < b$ or $a > b$
(b) $a = b \rightarrow ac = bc$
(c) $(a = b$ and $c = d) \rightarrow ac = bd$
(d) $a < b \rightarrow a + c < b + c$

**2.** Express each of the following statements in symbolic form:

(a) If $a$ is smaller than $b$ and $b$ is smaller than $c$, then $a$ is smaller than $c$.
(b) If $a$ and $b$ are equal, then so are $a + c$ and $b + c$.
(c) If $a$ is greater than $b$, then $ac + ad$ is greater than $bc + bd$.
(d) If $a$ is smaller than $b$ and both are positive, then $b^2$ is larger than $a^2$.

**3.** Assume the listed propositions or propositional forms as the hypotheses. Write the conclusion immediately deducible from the laws or rules stated:

(a) not-$(ab \neq 0)$      (Double-negative Rule)
(b) $2 + 2 = 5$; $a = 2 + 2$      (Substitution Rule)
(c) If $a = b$, then $ac = bc$; $a = b$      (Simple-inference Rule)
(d) If $a + c = b + c$, then $a = b$; $a \neq b$      (Contrapositive Rule)
(e) If $a = b$, then $a + c = b + c$; if $a + c = b + c$, then $a = b$
   (Conditional-biconditional Rule)
(f) $a + c = b + c$ and $b < c$; $a = b$ if and only if $a + c = b + c$
   (Substitution Rule)
(g) $a \leqslant b$ or $b \leqslant a$; not-$(a \leqslant b)$      (Rule of Disjunction)
(h) not-$(a \leqslant b$ and $b \leqslant a)$      (De Morgan's Law)
(i) not-$(a = b$ or $b = a)$      (De Morgan's Law)
(j) not-$(ac = bc \rightarrow a = b)$      (Negative-conditional Rule)
(k) $ac = bc$ and $c \neq 0$      (Negative-conditional Rule)

**4.** Follow the pattern of Exercise 3 to write a conclusion, if any, immediately deducible from the listed propositional forms, and state the law or rule used:

(a) not-$[$not-$(b < a)]$
(b) If $a < b$, then not-$(b < a)$; not-$[$not-$(b < a)]$
(c) If $a|b$, then $a|bc$; $a|b$    ($a|b$ is read "$a$ divides $b$" and means that $a$ is an integral factor of the integer $b$)
(d) If $a|bc$, then $a|b$ or $a|c$; if $a|b$ or $a|c$, then $a|bc$
(e) not-$(a = b$ and $a = c)$
(f) $a \neq b$ and $a \neq c$
(g) not-$(a = b$ or $a < b)$

(h) $a = b$ or $a < c$; $a \neq b$

(i) $ab = b$ if and only if $a = 1$; if $ab = b$, then $a + b = 1 + b$

**5.** Write a conclusion which can be deduced from all the propositional forms in each part:

(a) $a < b$; $b < c$; if $a < b$ and $b < c$, then $a < c$

(b) If $ab = ac$ and $a \neq 0$, then $b = c$; $b \neq c$; $a \neq 0$

(c) $a + c = b + c$ if and only if $a = b$; $a + c = b + c$

(d) $0 < a$; $a < b$; if $0 < a < b$, then $a^2 < b^2$ (*Hint:* $0 < a < b$ is an abbreviation for the conjunction of two propositional forms.)

(e) If $c < 0$, then $\sqrt{c^2} = -c$; $\sqrt{c^2} \neq -c$

(f) $c = 5$ or $c = 6$; $c \neq 5$

(g) not-($a = 2$ and $a \neq 5$); $a = 2$

(h) If $a \neq 0$ and $b \neq 0$, then $ab \neq 0$; $ab = 0$

(i) If $a|b$ and $a|c$, then $a|bc$; $a|b$; $a|c$

**6.** Write a conclusion which can be deduced from the propositional forms in each part:

(a) $\sqrt{c^2} = c$; $c = 5$

(b) If $\sqrt{a^2} = a$, then $a \geq 0$; $a < 0$

(c) $\sqrt{ab} = \sqrt{a} \cdot \sqrt{b}$ for $a, b > 0$; $a = 25$; $b = 16$

(d) $a < 5$ or $a > 5$ or $a = 5$; $a \neq 5$
    *Hint:* $[p$ or $q$ or $r] \leftrightarrow [(p$ or $q)$ or $r]$

(e) $b = 3a^2 + 2a$; $b = 2a + 3$

(f) $ac = bc$ and $c \neq 0$; not-($ac = bc \rightarrow c = 0$) $\rightarrow a = b$

(g) $a \in B$; $a \notin C$; not-($a \in B \rightarrow a \in C$) $\rightarrow a \notin B \cap C$

**7.** Before returning a set of examination papers, a teacher remarked, "All students with A papers are sitting in the front row."

(a) If Sally is in the front row, can she conclude that she made an A on the examination?

(b) Write the teacher's remark as a conditional-propositional form.

(c) In this situation what is a sufficient condition for a student to sit in the front row?

(d) In this situation what is the necessary condition for a student to have an A paper?

**8.** Let $L = \{x | x$ was a person who lived before 1900$\}$ and $P = \{x | x$ was a president of the United States$\}$.

(a) Write a biconditional propositional form expressing the necessary and sufficient conditions for an element $x$ to be in the set $L$.

(b) Write a propositional form expressing a necessary condition for an element $x$ to be the set $P$.

(c) Write a propositional form expressing a necessary condition for an element $x$ to be in the set $L \cup P$.

**9.** Prove the conditional proposition $p \to q$ where:

$p$: $[(x \in A) \to (x \notin B)] \to (x \notin A \cap B)$
$q$: $(x \in A \cap B) \to (x \in A$ and $x \in B)$

**10.** Consider the statement

   If $x$ and $y$ are odd integers, then $x + y$ is an even integer.

(a) Write the converse of the statement.
(b) Write the contrapositive of the statement.

In each of Exercises 11 to 15 one proposition is labeled "condition" and a second is labeled "situation." First determine whether the condition is necessary but not sufficient, sufficient but not necessary, or necessary and sufficient for the situation. Finally, use "if and only if," "only if," or "if" to combine the two propositions in one sentence.

**11.** *Condition:* The number $n$ is divisible by 6
   *Situation:* The number $n$ is divisible by 3

**12.** *Condition:* The integer $a$ is odd
   *Situation:* 2 is not a factor of the integer $a$

**13.** *Condition:* The binomial $x^n - y^n$ is divisible by $x + y$
   *Situation:* The exponent $n$ is a positive even integer

**14.** *Condition:* I have $5
   *Situation:* I can make a $10 purchase

**15.** *Condition:* The sum of the digits in the integer $n$ is a multiple of 3
   *Situation:* The integer $n$ is divisible by 3

**16.** Which of these relations between propositions are equivalence relations?

(a) "Is implied by"
(b) "Is the converse of"
(c) "Is the contrapositive of"
(d) "Is the negation of"
(e) "Is a necessary and sufficient condition for"
(f) "Is a sufficient condition for"

To augment the logical rules listed in the text, additional inference rules are indicated in Exercise 17.

**17.** If any propositional form in the left column occurs as a line in a proof, then the propositional form opposite it in the second column may occur as a valid deduction on a subsequent line. In each replace the variables $p$ and $q$ with propositions to given an example of a valid inference.

(a) $p$ and $q$            $p$
(b) $p$ and $q$            $q$
(c) $p$ and $q$            $q$ and $p$
(d) $p$ or $q$             $q$ or $p$
(e) $p$ or $q$             not-$p \rightarrow q$
(f) not-$p \rightarrow q$   $p$ or $q$
(g) $p$                    $p$ or $q$
(h) $p \leftrightarrow q$   $q \leftrightarrow p$

## 2-2. TYPES OF PROOF

As a preliminary step in constructing a proof one should have a clear statement of what is to be proved. He also should know what assumptions, theorems, and definitions, may be used to prove that statement. Any proposition or propositional form which is to be proved or dis-

**Conjecture**  proved is called a *conjecture*. The *context of proof* is the mathematical
**Context of proof**  system in which we are working, or the array of postulates, other assumptions, proved theorems, and accepted definitions which may be
**Theorem**  used to construct a proof. A *theorem* is any conjecture for which there exists a proof. Certain theorems play special roles and may be given names which suggest their role in the development of a mathematical
**Corollary**  system. A *corollary* is a theorem which follows readily (has a brief, simple proof) from another theorem or from a definition or postulate; a
**Lemma**  *lemma* is a theorem whose principal use is in the proof of another, and often more important, theorem.

It is significant to recognize the context of proof, for a conjecture may have a proof in one context but be false in another. For example, if the context of proof includes only natural numbers, then $ac = bc \rightarrow a = b$ is a true statement. It is, in fact, the Cancellation Law for multiplication in the natural-number system.[†] However, if the context includes the properties of integers, the statement may be false. Since it can be proved that $a(0) = 0$ for any integer $a$,[‡] if $a = 7$ and $b = 3$, $7(0) = 0 = 3(0)$. In this case $7(0) = 3(0)$, but $7 \neq 3$. The context of proof is usually clear from the system under discussion or from the statement of the conjecture.

The first type of proof we shall consider is a proof by counterexample, or, more suggestively, a disproof. Given a conjecture, if we can

† F. Lynwood Wren, "Basic Mathematical Concepts," p. 70, McGraw-Hill Book Company, New York, 1965.

‡ *Ibid.*, p. 85.

find a case which demonstrates, within the context of proof, that the conjecture cannot hold, then the example is called a *counterexample*, and we say that the conjecture is proved false by counterexample, within that context.

**Counterexample**

### Example 2-13

*Conjecture:* The square of every real number is positive

In this conjecture the system of real numbers is obviously the context of proof. Frequently it is helpful to consider several examples before attempting a proof. If we use the real numbers 3, $^-4$, 16, and $^-2.5$ as examples, we see that their squares are, respectively, 9, 16, 256, and 6.25, all of which are positive real numbers. The situation for negative real numbers utilizes the property that the product of two negative numbers is a positive number, and this clue should lead us to check whether such a theorem has already been established. If so, then something of this property should be used in the proof. The examples, however, will not constitute a proof unless we consider *all possible* real numbers. Since there are infinitely many real numbers, and the checking of all cases is then impossible, where do we begin in attempting to discover a proof?

In the examples we noted that there were two kinds of numbers, positive and negative. By the trichotomy property of real numbers, we know that every real number must be positive, negative, or zero. A check of the square of zero gives an example of a number whose square is not positive, so the conjecture is proved false by counterexample.

### Example 2-14.  The closure property of multiplication for the set $N$ of natural numbers states

If $a \in N$ and $b \in N$, then $ab \in N$

We state the converse as a conjecture:

If $ab \in N$, then $a \in N$ and $b \in N$

The context of proof for the converse is not clearly stated. If our context is restricted to natural numbers, then the conjecture follows trivially, since only natural numbers are considered for the elements $a$ and $b$. However, if we allow $a$ and $b$ to be any two real numbers, not necessarily distinct, then we may let $a = b = \sqrt{2}$. Clearly, $ab = 2 \in N$, but neither $a$ nor $b$ are natural numbers. Hence, in the context of the real number system, the conjecture is false. The values given to $a$ and $b$ constitute a counterexample, and we say that the conjecture is proved false by counterexample.

**Direct proof**

Two basic classifications of proofs are the direct and the indirect proof. A *direct proof* proceeds from the basic assumptions to the conclusion by the principles of logic and those properties which are known or can be deduced from the context. If a conjecture is of the form $p \rightarrow q$, where $p$ and $q$ are propositions, then we may write as a line of the proof the proposition $p$. If, by the rules of inference and the properties of the given system, we can deduce the proposition $q$, then we say we have proved $q$ under the assumption $p$, which is logically equivalent to proving the conjecture $p \rightarrow q$. Example 2-15 illustrates a direct proof of a conditional proposition.

**Example 2-15.   Direct proof.** For convenience, we use the following form, stating the conjecture as a theorem, since a proof follows:

*Theorem:* If $a$, $b$, and $c$ are integers and $a = b$, then $a + c = b + c$
*Hypothesis:* $a = b$; $a$, $b$, and $c$ are integers
*Conclusion:* $a + c = b + c$
*Context of proof:* Algebra of integers

**Proof:**

| *Statement* | *Reason* |
| --- | --- |
| 1. $a$, $b$, and $c$ are integers | 1. Hypothesis |
| 2. $a + c$ and $b + c$ are integers | 2. 1; closure property |
| 3. $a = b$ | 3. Hypothesis |
| 4. $a + c = a + c$ | 4. Reflexivity of equality |
| 5. $a + c = b + c$ | 5. 3, 4; term replacement |

**Remark.**   The proof is complete. Under the assumption of the hypothesis we have deduced the conclusion which, by the direct proof technique, proves the theorem. Note that in deducing step 5 only one replacement of $a$ by $b$ was necessary to comply with the Term-replacement Rule.

**Indirect proof**

An *indirect proof* proceeds from the basic assumptions and the additional assumption of the negation of the conclusion. A proof is said to have been accomplished when some two propositions have been deduced in which one is the negation of the other. In this case we say that the two propositions are contradictory and cannot hold within the system. The negation of the conclusion is therefore untenable, and consequently, the conclusion of the theorem is said to hold. Thus, if a conjecture is of the form $p \rightarrow q$, we assume its negation, not-$(p \rightarrow q)$. By the Negative-conditional Rule, we may write, equivalently, $p$ and not-$q$. If by the assumption $p$ and the assumption not-$q$ we can deduce some proposition $r$ and its negation not-$r$, or some proposition $s$, the negative of a proposition which has been assumed or is known to hold in the system, then we say we have reached a contradiction. In this case the original assumption, not-$(p \rightarrow q)$, cannot hold; hence $p \rightarrow q$ must hold. Example 2-16 illustrates an indirect proof of a conditional proposition.

### Example 2-16.   Indirect proof

*Theorem:* If $a$ and $b$ are integers and $a \neq 0$ and $b \neq 0$, then $ab \neq 0$
*Hypothesis:* $a$ and $b$ are integers and $a \neq 0$ and $b \neq 0$
*Conclusion:* $ab \neq 0$
*Context of proof:* Algebra of integers

### Proof:

| Statement | Reason |
|---|---|
| 1. $a$ and $b$ are integers | 1. Hypothesis |
| 2. $ab$ is an integer | 2. 1; closure property |
| 3. $a \neq 0$ | 3. Hypothesis |
| 4. $b \neq 0$ | 4. Hypothesis |
| 5. $ab = 0$ | 5. Assumption |
| 6. $a(0) = 0$ | 6. Multiplicative property of zero |
| 7. $ab = a(0)$ | 7. 5, 6; Substitution Rule |
| 8. $b = 0$ | 8. 3, 7; Cancellation Law of integers |
| 9. $ab \neq 0$ | 9. 4, 8; contradiction of assumption in 5 |

**Remark.**   The proof is complete. Under the assumption of the negation of the conclusion (line 5) we have obtained a statement (line 4) and its negation (line 8) which, by the indirect-proof technique, proves the theorem. Of course the reasons given for lines 6 and 8 involve postulates or theorems which must have been given or proved previously in the system. One other comment is in order regarding lines 1, 3, and 4 of the proof: the hypothesis of the theorem is the conjunction of three propositional forms; an extension of the Rule of Conjunction justifies the writing of each as a separate hypothesis.

A word of caution is in order here. One method which involves a direct proof somewhat resembles an indirect proof. To prove the proposition $p \rightarrow q$ we may first prove the equivalent contrapositive proposition not-$q \rightarrow$ not-$p$. In this case we assume not-$q$ and proceed directly to deduce not-$p$. When this is done, we say we have proved not-$p$ under the assumption not-$q$, which is equivalent to not-$q \rightarrow$ not-$p$.

By the Contrapositive Rule, it follows that $p \rightarrow q$. Note that an indirect proof of a conditional or of its contrapositive involves equivalent assumptions (what are they?).

From this discussion we see that a conditional proposition $p \rightarrow q$ may be proved by any one of the following procedures:

**1.** Assume $p$ and proceed directly to deduce $q$.
**2.** Assume not-$q$ and proceed directly to deduce not-$p$.
**3.** Assume $p$ and not-$q$ and proceed to deduce two contradictory propositions or a proposition which contradicts a proposition which has been assumed or is known to hold in the system.

At times it is desirable to state a theorem as the equivalence of two propositions $p$ and $q$. In this case we see such statements as "$p$ if and only if $q$," "$p$ when and only when $q$," "$q$ is a necessary and sufficient condition for $p$," or, symbolically, $p \leftrightarrow q$. The proof may consist of proving the two propositions

$q$ is a necessary condition for $p$, or $p$ only if $q$ $(p \rightarrow q)$
$q$ is a sufficient condition for $p$, or if $q$, then $p$ $(q \rightarrow p)$

When this has been done we may deduce $p \leftrightarrow q$ by the Conditional-biconditional Rule. It is also possible that a third proposition $r$ is equivalent both to $p$ and to $q$. Symbolically, $p \leftrightarrow r$ and $r \leftrightarrow q$. When this is the case we may use substitution to deduce $p \leftrightarrow q$. More generally, we may be able to establish the equivalence of two propositions through a chain of equivalent propositions. This technique is particularly useful in establishing the equivalence of two equations or of two inequalities (see Example 6-13 and the discussion immediately following Example 9-13).

**Universal property**

Any property which holds, or is conjectured to hold, for each element of a set, as in Example 2-13, is called a *universal property* for that set. Phrases such as "for each," "for every," and "for all" are indications of a universal property. As in the example, we need only show that the property fails for one element to prove that the conjecture is false. However, to prove that a conjecture is true, or that a universal property holds, we may let a variable represent an arbitrary element of the set and show that the property holds for that element, using the postulates and any other theorems which have been proved. A property which holds for one or a select number of elements of a set is called a

**Local property**

*local property* for that set. Phrases such as "for some" and "there exists" are indications of a local property. Postulating a property, however, does not guarantee that it holds. Once a system has been defined, at least one example or model must be produced that satisfies the listed postulates; otherwise the deductions are only exercises in logic and are without mathematical content.

At this point it is desirable to become acquainted with informal proofs. To this end we shall consider an example involving odd and even integers. An *odd integer* is an integer of the form $2n + 1$, where $n$ is an integer. Thus, if $x$ is an odd integer, then there exists an integer $n$ such that $x = 2n + 1$. If $y$ is an *even integer*, then there exists an integer $m$ such that $y = 2m$.

**Odd integer**

**Even integer**

### Example 2-17.  Informal proof

> *Theorem:* The sum of two odd integers is an even integer
> *Restatement:* If $x$ is an odd integer and $y$ is an odd integer, then $x + y$ is an even integer

**Proof.**  By hypothesis, $x = 2m + 1$ and $y = 2n + 1$ for some integers $m$ and $n$. Consequently, $x + y = (2m + 1) + (2n + 1)$. From the associative, commutative, and distributive laws, it follows that $x + y = 2(m + n + 1)$, which is even.

In this example several steps were left to the reader. For example, if $m$ is an integer and $n$ is an integer, then $m + n$ is an integer (by closure), and since 1 is an integer, then (again, by closure) $(m + n) + 1$ is an integer. It will be instructive to construct a formal proof, using this informal proof as an outline.

One very useful technique in proving a conditional proposition in which the hypothesis is the disjunction of two propositions is a *proof by cases*. If $p$, $q$, and $r$ are propositions and it is desired to prove a proposition of the form

**Proof by cases**

$$(p \text{ or } q) \rightarrow r$$

we first prove $p \rightarrow r$ and then prove $q \rightarrow r$. The proof of these two cases guarantees the proof of the original proposition. The following example will illustrate an informal proof by cases.

### Example 2-18

> *Theorem:* The square of every nonzero real number is positive

**Proof.**  Let $x$ be any nonzero real number. By the trichotomy property, either $x$ is positive or $x$ is negative. If $x$ is positive, then $x^2 = xx$, the product of two positive numbers, which is positive. If $x$ is negative, then $x^2$ is the product of two negative numbers, which is positive. Hence, if $x \neq 0$, $x^2$ is positive.

**Remark.**   It should be noted which theorems in the real number system were used. It is suggested that this proof be made into a formal proof.

The proofs we have considered thus far have been simple and rather short. Some proofs require a long and somewhat involved logical structure in conjunction with mathematical facts. Suppose, for example, we were proving a proposition of the form $p \rightarrow q$. We should assume $p$. Now suppose in the process we were able to derive the disjunction of two propositions, $r$ or $s$. At this point we may need to prove $(r$ or $s) \rightarrow q$, and to do this we introduce a line of argument which we might call a lemma. That is, we show first that $r \rightarrow q$ and then that $s \rightarrow q$, and by "cases" we deduce the proposition $q$. Similarly, the proof of a theorem may depend on several lemmas which involve direct and indirect arguments.

Each time a new proof is encountered, whether it is formal or informal, it should be examined to see if any new logical techniques are used. Better understanding can be acquired by attempting to formalize informal proofs and to make informal any formal proofs encountered. In the latter case there is a danger that some essential steps might be omitted. It is difficult to define what is essential, but analysis of the proofs encountered will soon show which steps are the crucial ones for the informal argument.

## EXERCISES

1. Show by counterexample that each of the following conjectures is false:

   (a) If $a$ and $b$ are negative numbers, then $ab$ is a negative number
   (b) If $a$ and $b$ are negative numbers, then $a - b$ is a negative number
   (c) If $a$ and $b$ are negative numbers, then $a \div b$ is a negative number
   (d) If $a$ and $b$ are irrational numbers, then $a + b$ is an irrational number
   (e) If $a$ and $b$ are irrational numbers, then $ab$ is an irrational number
   (f) If $a$ and $b$ are irrational numbers, then $a \div b$ is an irrational number

2. The closure property of the set $N$ of natural numbers with respect to addition is given as

   If $a \in N$ and $b \in N$, then $a + b \in N$

(a) State the converse as a conjecture.

(b) Disprove the conjecture if the context of proof includes (1) the set of integers, (2) the set of rational numbers, (3) the set of real numbers.

3. Consider the conjecture

If $a$ and $b$ are real numbers, then $\sqrt{ab} = \sqrt{a}\,\sqrt{b}$

Show by counterexample that the conjecture is false, and rewrite the conjecture to form a true statement.

In Exercises 4 to 6 fill in the missing reasons and identify the proof as direct or indirect. Note that in some cases the proof is abbreviated. Fill in additional steps as necessary. $Z$ represents the set of integers.

4. *Theorem:* If $a, b \in Z$, then $(a + b) + {}^-b = a$
   *Hypothesis:* $a \in Z$ and $b \in Z$
   *Conclusion:* $(a + b) + {}^-b = a$
   *Context:* Algebra of integers

**Proof:**

| *Statement* | *Reason* |
|---|---|
| 1. $a \in Z$ | 1. Hypothesis |
| 2. $b \in Z$ | 2. |
| 3. $a + b \in Z$ | 3. Closure property |
| 4. ${}^-b \in Z$ | 4. Additive inverse of $b$ |
| 5. $(a + b) + {}^-b \in Z$ | 5. |
| 6. $(a + b) + {}^-b = a + (b + {}^-b)$ | 6. Associative property |
| 7. $b + {}^-b = 0$ | 7. Definition of additive inverse |
| 8. $(a + b) + {}^-b = a + 0$ | 8. |
| 9. $a + 0 = a$ | 9. Definition of additive identity |
| 10. $(a + b) + {}^-b = a$ | 10. |

5. *Theorem:* If $a$ and $b$ are integers and $a = b$, then $a^2 = b^2$
   *Hypothesis:* $a$ and $b$ are integers and $a = b$
   *Conclusion:* $a^2 = b^2$
   *Context:* Algebra of integers

**Proof:**

| *Statement* | *Reason* |
|---|---|
| 1. $a = b$ | 1. |
| 2. $aa = a^2$ | 2. Definition |

3. $aa = ab$    3.
4. $a^2 = ab$    4.
5. $ab = bb$    5.
6. $b^2 = bb$    6.
7. $ab = b^2$    7.
8. $a^2 = b^2$    8.

**6.** *Theorem:* If $a, b \in Z$ and $a + 1 \neq b + 1$, then $a \neq b$
*Hypothesis:* $a, b \in Z$ and $a + 1 \neq b + 1$
*Conclusion:* $a \neq b$
*Context:* Algebra of integers

**Proof:**

| Statement | Reason |
|---|---|
| 1. $a + 1 \neq b + 1$ | 1. |
| 2. $a = b$ | 2. Assumption |
| 3. $a + 1 = b + 1$ | 3. |
| 4. $a \neq b$ | 4. |

In Exercises 7 to 12 prove or disprove the conjectures.

**7.** If $a$ and $b$ are integers and $a + b = 0$, then $a = {}^-b$.
**8.** If $a$ and $b$ are real numbers, then $ab(1/b) = a$.
**9.** The sum of an odd and an even integer is odd.
**10.** The sum of two even integers is even.
**11.** There exists a natural number $x$ such that $a + x = a$ for every natural number $a$.
**12.** If $a$ and $b$ are integers, then there exists an integer $c$ such that $b + c = a$.
**13.** Prove this theorem:

For the integers $a, b, c$, and $m$, if $a \equiv b \pmod{m}$ and $c \equiv d \pmod{m}$, then $a + c \equiv b + d \pmod{m}$

**14.** Prove this theorem:

For the integers $a, b, c$, and $m$, if $a \equiv b \pmod{m}$ and $c \equiv d \pmod{m}$, then $ac \equiv bd \pmod{m}$

## 2-3. THE NATURE OF PROBLEM SOLVING

A problem to be solved differs materially from a theorem to be proved, but there are many aspects of basic similarity. We have seen that in simplest form a theorem always contains two statements, expressed either in words or in symbols. One of these statements is the hypothesis which is either known or assumed to be true and is thus accepted as the foundation upon which a logical structure is to be built.

The purpose and design of this procedure is to exhibit a chain of valid implications which establish the fact that the second statement, the conclusion, follows as a necessary consequence of acceptance of the hypothesis. In a problem the concern is somewhat different. In place of the two statements of a theorem, there is usually one statement and a question. The statement contains data which only partially describe a desired situation. The question not only asks what consequences are necessarily implied by the known data, but also calls for a determination of which of these, if any, are sufficient to complete the description of the desired situation. The procedure for seeking a solution may, and usually does, follow techniques for the discovery of necessary conditions which are analogous to those used in the process of proving a theorem. The basic difference in the two situations lies in the fact that a theorem has been proved and the work is finished when the desired conclusion has been established as a necessary consequence implied by the acceptance of the hypothesis. In solving a problem, however, when the conditions necessary to secure the situation have been discovered, there still remains the task of determining which, if any, are the desired sufficient conditions.

Compare the following two examples:

**Example 2-19.**   Prove this theorem:

If $r$ is a real number, then $r(0) = 0$

*Hypothesis:* $r$ is a real number
*Conclusion:* $r(0) = 0$
*Context:* Algebra of real numbers

**Proof:**

| *Statement* | *Reason* |
|---|---|
| 1. $r$ is a real number | 1. Hypothesis |
| 2. $r + 0 = r$ | 2. Additive identity |
| 3. $r(r + 0) = rr$ | 3. Multiplicative property of equality |
| 4. $rr + r(0) = rr$ | 4. Distributive property and substitution |
| 5. $rr = rr + 0$ | 5. Additive identity |
| 6. $rr + r(0) = rr + 0$ | 6. Transitive property of equality |
| 7. $r(0) = 0$ | 7. Cancellation property for addition |

**Example 2-20.**   Solve this problem:

What is the real number $r$ such that $\sqrt{r + 1} = \sqrt{r - 4} - 5$?

*Hypothesis:* There exists a real number $r$ such that $\sqrt{r + 1} = \sqrt{r - 4} - 5$
*Question:* What is the real number $r$?

The phraseology of the problem implies the existence of a real number $r$ which satisfies the specified equation. The attack procedure is to accept this as a true assumption and use valid properties and relations of the field of real numbers to see if we can determine what this real number must be. Once we have done this, we shall still have to test to see whether the assumption is really true. If it is, we have found the solution to the problem. If the assumption is found to be false, we have discovered that the problem has no solution.

**Procedure:**

| Statement | Reason |
|---|---|
| 1. $\sqrt{r+1} = \sqrt{r-4} - 5$ | 1. Hypothesis |
| 2. $r + 1 = (\sqrt{r-4} - 5)^2$ | 2. Squaring |
| 3. $r + 1 = (r - 4) - 10\sqrt{r-4} + 25$ | 3. Simplifying |
| 4. $r + 1 = r + 21 - 10\sqrt{r-4}$ | 4. Associative and commutative properties of addition |
| 5. $10\sqrt{r-4} = 20$ | 5. Additive property of equality |
| 6. $\sqrt{r-4} = 2$ | 6. Cancellation law for multiplication |
| 7. $r - 4 = 4$ | 7. Squaring |
| 8. $r = 8$ | 8. Additive property of equality |

At this point it is well to note that in both the proof of the theorem and the solution of the problem a conclusion was derived. In the case of the theorem we were able to establish a predetermined statement, $r(0) = 0$, as a necessary consequence implied by the accepted hypothesis, and our work was finished. In the problem, however, all that can be said is that we have discovered the only conclusion we can draw from the hypothesis, that $r$ must be 8. In fact, all that has been accomplished is to discover the statement which can be used as the conclusion in a theorem whose hypothesis is that of the problem. In other words, we have proved the theorem

If there exists a real number $r$ such that $\sqrt{r+1} = \sqrt{r-4} - 5$, then $r = 8$

The argument used in the discovery of the conclusion constitutes the proof of this theorem. There still remains the significant task of determining whether or not this possibility of a value for $r$ is sufficient to give the relation assumed in the hypothesis. Substitution in the assumed equality gives on the left $\sqrt{8+1} = 3$, while substitution on the right gives $\sqrt{8-4} - 5 = {}^-3$. Since $3 \neq {}^-3$, it follows that the equality assumed in the hypothesis is not a true equality. Consequently, there exists no solution of the equation. In other words, the condition $r = 8$ is a necessary but not a sufficient condition for $\sqrt{r+1} = \sqrt{r-4} - 5$.

Note that if the assumed equation were $\sqrt{r+1} = 5 - \sqrt{r-4}$, then an analogous argument would establish $r = 8$ as both a necessary and a sufficient condition for the assumed equality to exist. This, of course, is saying that $r = 8$ is a solution of the equation $\sqrt{r+1} = 5 - \sqrt{r-4}$.

Examples 2-19 and Example 2-20 were developed specifically to point out a basic distinction between proving a theorem and solving a problem. They serve, however, to illustrate very effectively another important aspect not only of problem solving, but also of mathematical thinking in general. Why is it that a necessary condition arrived at through a chain of valid reasoning is not automatically a sufficient condition? What characteristic in the chain of reasoning will guarantee that it can be or cannot be sufficient? Applied to this particular example, these questions become the single question:

If $r = 8$ is a necessary condition that $\sqrt{r+1} = \sqrt{r-4} - 5$, how can it be that it is not also a sufficient condition?

The last paragraph of the example contains a strong hint as to what the answer is to this particular question.

In solving the problem the equation of step 2 was obtained by squaring both sides of the given equation. If the equation of the last paragraph of the example also is squared, we get $r + 1 = (5 - \sqrt{r-4})^2$. The same reasoning as that used in seeking a solution to the equation will establish that $r = 8$ is also a necessary condition for each of the equations obtained by squaring to have a solution. Notice that the expression in parentheses in step 2 of the example is the negative of the expression within the parentheses of this last equation:

$$\sqrt{r-4} - 5 = {}^-(5 - \sqrt{r-4})$$

By substitution, we can establish that $r = 8$ satisfies each of the equations

$$r + 1 = (\sqrt{r-4} - 5)^2 \qquad \text{and} \qquad r + 1 = (5 - \sqrt{r-4})^2$$
$$9 = (\sqrt{8-4} - 5)^2 \qquad\qquad\qquad 9 = (5 - \sqrt{8-4})^2$$
$$9 = ({}^-3)^2 \qquad\qquad\qquad\qquad 9 = ({}^+3)^2$$
$$9 = 9 \qquad\qquad\qquad\qquad\qquad 9 = 9$$

The necessary condition ($r = 8$) that each of these equations have a root is also a sufficient condition. In fact, 8 is the root of each equation.

The reason $r = 8$ is not a sufficient condition for the given equation of Example 2-20 but is sufficient for the equation obtained by squaring the equation of the example lies in the fact that the operation of squaring is *not reversible*. Whether we square a positive real number or a negative real number, the result is a unique real number which is positive. In extracting the square root of a positive real number it is possible to get two real numbers, one positive and the other negative. The square root of 9 is either $^+3$ or $^-3$. By using the symbol $\sqrt{r+1}$, the given equation of Example 2-20 called for the *positive* square root of whatever value $r + 1$ might have. It follows, therefore, that if $r + 1 = 9$, then $\sqrt{r+1} = 3$. It is impossible for any value of $r$ to give $\sqrt{r+1} = ^-3$. A positive number cannot equal a negative number. This demonstrates why $r = 8$ is a sufficient condition for $\sqrt{r+1} = 5 - \sqrt{r-4}$ to have a root, but is not a sufficient condition for $\sqrt{r+1} = \sqrt{r-4} - 5$ to have a root.

In any problem situation, what, then, is the critical test of whether a chain of equations will lead to a necessary condition which is also sufficient? The question to be asked at each step is whether or not the procedure used in deriving a new equation from an old equation is *reversible*. If it is, the two equations will be said to be *equivalent equations,* since they will have the same solution set. If at any step a nonreversible procedure, such as squaring, is used, then the new equation may not be equivalent to the old one. In this case the new equation may have a solution, or solutions, which will not satisfy the old equation. Example 2-21 will illustrate this further by the parallel development of two simple equation situations.

**Equivalent equations**

**Example 2-21.**  Find the solution of each of these equations:

$$\frac{2x}{x-1} - 6 = \frac{2}{x-1} \quad \text{and} \quad \frac{2x}{x-2} - 6 = \frac{8}{x-2}$$

Multiply by $x - 1$:       Multiply by $x - 2$:

$$2x - 6(x - 1) = 2 \qquad\qquad 2x - 6(x - 2) = 8$$

Simplify

$$2x - 6x + 6 = 2 \qquad\qquad 2x - 6x + 12 = 8$$
$$2x - 6x = 2 - 6 \qquad\qquad 2x - 6x = 8 - 12$$
$$^-4x = ^-4 \qquad\qquad\qquad ^-4x = ^-4$$

Divide by $^-4$:

$$x = 1 \qquad\qquad\qquad\qquad x = 1$$

In each case we have the conclusion that $x = 1$ is a necessary condition for each equation to have a solution. In other words, if either equation has a solution, then it has to be $x = 1$.

If $x = 1$, then $x - 1 = 0$, so $x = 1$ cannot be a root of this equation, since we cannot have division by zero. What step in the solution process is not reversible?

If $x = 1$ is substituted in this equation, we get

$$\frac{2(1)}{1 - 2} - 6 = \frac{8}{1 - 2}$$

or

$$^-2 - 6 = {}^-8$$

and $x = 1$ is a solution. Why are all steps reversible?

To get answers to these questions let us start with the assumption that $x = 1$ and see if we can derive each of the given equations.

$x = 1$                  $x = 1$

Multiply by $^-4$:

$$^-4x = {}^-4 \qquad\qquad {}^-4x = {}^-4$$
$$2x - 6x = 2 - 6 \qquad\qquad 2x - 6x = 8 - 12$$
$$2x - 6x + 6 = 2 \qquad\qquad 2x - 6x + 12 = 8$$
$$2x - 6(x - 1) = 2 \qquad\qquad 2x - 6(x - 2) = 8$$

To get the original equation it now is necessary to divide by $x - 1$. Since $x = 1$ and $x - 1 = 0$, we could multiply by $x - 1$, but we cannot divide by $x - 1$. This is the step which is not reversible.

To get the original equation it now is necessary to divide by $x - 2$. Since $x = 1$ and $x - 2 \neq 0$, this is possible. All steps are reversible, and the equations are all equivalent equations.

In attacking any verbal problem the first major difficulty is that of *comprehension*. This entails not only understanding the words and language in the context in which the problem is stated, but also analyzing the problem situation to determine what significant data are given; what unknown element is to be determined; what basic relationships exist both between the data and between data and unknown; what hidden questions and relations exist; what pertinent diagram, if any, might be drawn and used as an aid in the analysis of the problem; and what area of previously established knowledge seems to provide the most promising framework within which to attempt shaping a solution. Critical evaluation of the data should determine not only the essential data, but also the nonessentials and any need for additional data. Such an analysis will perforce raise such questions as: What relations exist between the data? What relations tie the known to the unknown? What formulas express these relations? What information would be sufficient to draw the desired conclusion? Are there any hidden implications

**Comprehension difficulty**

which are important? Is there a context of previously established information which is pertinent to the problem? What relations between data and unknown are necessary consequences of the data prescriptions?

**Example 2-22.**  The Byrds have $2,500 which they plan to spend in improving their property. Their house is on a corner lot formed by two streets which intersect at right angles. The lot dimensions are 120 ft along one street, 60 ft along the other street, 75 ft (see Fig. 2-1) and 75

**FIG. 2-1**

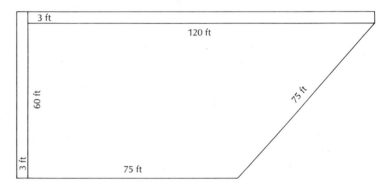

ft. As part of their improvement program they plan to put a concrete walk, 3 ft wide, along the two street sides of their lot. How much of the $2,500 will this part of their improvement program use?

> *Data:* $2,500 to spend
> *Dimensions of lot:* 120 ft, 60 ft, 75 ft, 75 ft
> *Width of sidewalk:* 3 ft
> *Question:* How much of the $2,500 will this part of their improvement program use?

The walk is to be only on the street sides of the lot. Complete realization of this fact points out that the two dimensions of 75 ft each are nonessential data, since they make no contribution to the problem situation. A diagram helps to show that the area to be covered consists of two rectangles, one 3 by 63 ft and the other 3 by 120 ft. This brings to mind the formula for finding the area of a rectangle, $A = lw$. The total area to be covered is 189 sq ft + 360 sq ft = 549 sq ft. It now becomes evident that more information is needed before a solution can be reached. It is not possible to determine the cost of the project until material and labor costs are known.

**Structure difficulty**    The second major difficulty in any problem situation is that of *structuring* the solution process. It is here that intuition and induction can make significant contributions to the essentially deductive process of problem solving.

Intuitive reasoning is primarily a thought process based on following hunches and making guesses. Generally speaking, the more informed one is in a given area of knowledge, the more likely intuition is to be of significance as an aid in problem solving. Such reasoning can never produce conclusive results, but it can suggest possible results, pertinent procedures, helpful diagrams, analogous problems of simpler structure, or other forms of concrete models of abstract problem situations.

**Intuitive reasoning**

**Example 2-23.**   Find the solution set of this system of simultaneous linear equations:

$$u + 3v + 5w + 4t = 91$$
$$3u + 5v + 4w + t = 91$$
$$4u + v + 3w + 5t = 91$$
$$5u + 4v + w + 3t = 91$$

A bit of careful consideration of this system of equations brings out the fact that there is a unique pattern of coefficients. The numerals 1, 3, 4, and 5 appear as coefficients in each of the four equations, and each variable appears once and only once, with each numeral as a coefficient; also, the equations express a sum which remains constant. Observing these facts, intuition might suggest that the variables must have the same value. At least, this seems a good guess to make. If it is assumed that $u = v = w = t$, then each of the equations can be replaced by one equation in any one of the variables, say $t$, namely, $13t = 91$. From this equation it follows that $t = 7$. The substitution of the values $u = 7$, $v = 7$, $w = 7$, and $t = 7$ in each of the four original equations verifies the fact that they constitute the solution of the system.

In the example intuitive reasoning reduced the fairly formidable task of finding the solution set of a system of four linear equations in four variables to a very simple one of finding the solution set of one equation involving one variable. The rewards of intuition are not always so profitable. One of the contributions made by Euclid (ca. 300 B.C.) to number theory was the proof of a theorem which states that there are infinitely many prime numbers. A simple application of the sieve of Eratosthenes will reveal that the primes less than 100 are 2, 3, 5, 7, 11, 13, 17, 19, 23, 29, 31, 37, 41, 43, 47, 53, 59, 61, 67, 71, 73, 79, 83, 89, 97. In this list of primes there are certain pairs which differ by 2. They are called *prime pairs*. The prime pairs less than 100 are 3, 5; 5, 7; 11, 13; 17, 19; 29, 31; 41, 43; 59, 61; and 71, 73. If the list

**Prime pairs**

is extended, it will be discovered that there are 35 prime pairs less than 1,000 and 26 between 1,000 and 2,000. Further extensions are possible; in fact, the largest known prime pair seems to be 1,000,000,009,649 and 1,000,000,009,651.† In the context of such evidence and the knowledge that there are infinitely many primes, it seems intuitively acceptable to surmise that there must be an infinite number of prime pairs. Over the years considerable effort has been expended by mathematicians in the attempt to prove or disprove the conjecture that there are infinitely many prime pairs. However, it still remains as one of the unsolved problems in mathematics.

Fundamentally, induction is a pattern of reasoning which leads from the particular to the general. This means that general conclusions are drawn on the basis of the outcome of a finite number (usually rather small) of events. These outcomes may be the result of some forms of experimentation, judgments which seem intuitively reasonable, or conclusions deduced from restricted data. The effort is made to arrive at the benefits of generalization through the technique of seeking support in analogous argument or confirmation by special cases. The conclusions drawn as a result of such a pattern of reasoning should never be stated as actualities. They can never be accepted as any more than mere possibilities, probably worthy of further investigation.

**Example 2-24.**   The table presents three columns of facts. Examine each column to see if you can detect a pattern.

| A | B | C |
|---|---|---|
| $1^2 - 1 + 11 = \ 11$ | $1^2 - 1 = \ \ \ 0$ | $4 = 2 + 2$ |
| $2^2 - 2 + 11 = \ 13$ | $3^2 - 1 = \ \ \ 8$ | $6 = 3 + 3$ |
| $3^2 - 3 + 11 = \ 17$ | $5^2 - 1 = \ \ 24$ | $8 = 3 + 5$ |
| $4^2 - 4 + 11 = \ 23$ | $7^2 - 1 = \ \ 48$ | $10 = 3 + 7 = 5 + 5$ |
| $5^2 - 5 + 11 = \ 31$ | $9^2 - 1 = \ \ 80$ | $12 = 5 + 7$ |
| $6^2 - 6 + 11 = \ 41$ | $11^2 - 1 = 120$ | $14 = 3 + 11 = 7 + 7$ |
| $7^2 - 7 + 11 = \ 53$ | $13^2 - 1 = 168$ | $16 = 3 + 13 = 5 + 11$ |
| $8^2 - 8 + 11 = \ 67$ | $15^2 - 1 = 224$ | $18 = 5 + 13 = 7 + 11$ |
| $9^2 - 9 + 11 = \ 83$ | $17^2 - 1 = 288$ | $20 = 3 + 17 = 7 + 13$ |
| $10^2 - 10 + 11 = 101$ | $19^2 - 1 = 360$ | $22 = 3 + 19 = 5 + 17$ |
| | | $= 11 + 11$ |

**Column A.**   This column provides evidence to support the statement that the formula $n^2 - n + 11$ yields a prime number for each positive

† Ross A. Beaumont and Richard S. Pierce, "The Algebraic Foundations of Mathematics," p. 161, Addison-Wesley Publishing Company, Inc., Reading, Mass., 1963.

integer from $n = 1$ to $n = 10$. Similar results can be obtained for still other positive integers. For example, for $n = 18$ we have $18^2 - 18 + 11 = 317$, and for $n = 31$ we have $31^2 - 31 + 11 = 941$. The integers 317 and 941 are primes. Here are 12 cases where *the formula $n^2 - n + 11$ yields a prime for $n$ a positive integer.* One might be tempted to conclude from the induction that this statement is true for all positive integers $n$. However, a counterexample, to disprove such a generalization is the fact that for $n = 11$ the formula becomes $11^2 - 11 + 11 = 11^2$, and $11^2$ is not a prime. Although other counterexamples can be given, this one is sufficient to prevent the general conclusion suggested. Similar formulas are $n^2 - n + 41$, which yields primes for $n = 1$ to $n = 40$, and $n^2 - 79n + 1601$, which yields primes for $n = 1$ to $n = 79$. The counterexamples are $n = 41$ in the first case and $n = 80$ in the second.

Of greater historical significance is the conjecture (ca. 1640) made by Fermat (1601–1665) that *the formula $2^{2^n} + 1$ yields a prime for all nonnegative integers $n$.* This statement was based on the fact that the formula produces the primes 3, 5, 17, 257, and 65,537 for the respective values $n = 0, 1, 2, 3, 4$. It was not until approximately 100 years later that it was demonstrated that for $n = 5$ the formula yields a composite number. At present it is known that the statement is false for at least 28 values of $n$.†

These illustrations establish the fact that no matter how many specific cases exist to offer support to an inductive generalization, one counterexample is sufficient to disprove it.

**Column B.**    In this column, 1 is subtracted from the square of each of the first 10 positive odd integers. The result of this operation in each case is an integer which is divisible by 8. Since the odd integer is squared, its sign is immaterial. These observations might well lead us to conclude by induction that to subtract 1 from the square of an odd integer yields an integer which is divisible by 8.

To investigate this generalization it is pertinent to observe that the formula $2n - 1$ represents an odd integer for all integral values of $n$. The formula suggested by column B, then, might be written as $(2n - 1)^2 - 1 = 8k$, where $n$ and $k$ are integers. For example, for $n = 3$, $(2n - 1)^2 - 1 = [2(3) - 1]^2 - 1 = (6 - 1)^2 - 1 = 5^2 - 1 = 24 = 8(3)$, and $k = 3$. The general formula $(2n - 1)^2 - 1$ may be simplified in the following manner:

$$(2n - 1)^2 - 1 = (4n^2 - 4n + 1) - 1$$
$$= 4n^2 - 4n$$
$$= 4n(n - 1)$$

† *Ibid.,* p. 162.

In the last equation, for any integral value of $n$ either $n$ or $n - 1$ is an even number. Thus the integer $4n(n - 1)$ has 8 as one of its factors. It then follows that $(2n - 1)^2 - 1 = 8k$, where $n$ and $k$ are integers. In this case the induction is supported by a pattern of deductive reasoning which provides a valid proof of the generalization.

**Column C.**   Here the first 10 consecutive even numbers greater than 2 follow a pattern which suggests the generalization that every even number greater than 2 can be expressed as the sum of two primes. This is known as *Goldbach's* (1690–1764) *conjecture* and is another of the unsolved problems in mathematics. No one has yet been able either to present a counterexample to disprove the statement or to construct a valid argument to prove it.

One of the three induced generalizations of the example could be disproved by counterexample, another could be firmly established by deductive argument, and the third has remained in the limbo of un-solved problems for more than two centuries.† These illustrations pro-vide three-way support for the statement that no generalization based on inductive reasoning can be accepted as anything more than a promising possibility for further investigation.

**Operation difficulty**

Even when a problem has been structured carefully, there is still the threat of *operational* difficulty. Are the fundamental characteristics of the operational processes understood? Is there ability to use the vari-ous algorisms proficiently? Is one well-versed in the procedures es-sential to the most efficient use of formulas, equations, and graphs? Questions such as these are very personal, but they call for strong affirm-ative answers before one can expect to perform, with any degree of proficiency, the sometimes elusive task of problem solving. It is well to add at this point that one very important practice to be ob-

† Attention is called to the basic distinction between an *unsolved* problem and an *un-solvable* problem. There are many problems, such as Goldbach's conjecture and the conjec-ture on page 54 concerning the existence of an infinite number of prime pairs, for which mathematicians have not been able to find a solution. This *does not mean* that their solution is impossible. It simply means that if a solution exists, no one has been able to discover it. On the other hand, there are problems for which the impossibility of solution has been clearly established. For example, there are valid algebraic arguments which definitely prove that it is impossible, with *only* a compass and an unmarked straightedge, to trisect an arbitrary angle, to construct a circle equal in area to the area of a given square, or to construct a cube whose volume is twice the volume of a given cube. These three problems are at times referred to as the three unsolvable problems of antiquity. It is definitely known that it is impossible to solve any one of them within the euclidean restrictions of drawing *only* straight lines and circles. If other curves or a marked straightedge are allowed, then the problems become solvable. It is possible, however, to trisect certain angles, for example, a right angle, within the speci-fied restrictions.

served, in the interest of reducing operational difficulties to a minimum, is that of being neat, orderly, and careful in carrying out the various operational processes. Carelessness with details and messy, disorderly arrangement of work can be extremely costly in any type of problem solving.

As has been pointed out previously, no problem is solved until the conclusions implied by the data have been tested to see if they are sufficient to provide a solution to the problem. The problem solver is thus confronted with a final type of difficulty which might be classified as one of *judgment*. It now becomes necessary to decide if the discovered necessary conditions are in reality sufficient, whether the discovered data constitute a solution to the problem, and what constitutes a valid check. No problem-solving procedure is complete until considerations such as these have been resolved satisfactorily.

Judgment difficulty

The following suggestions may be used as a guide to improving problem-solving techniques.

Guidelines in problem solving

1. Read the problem carefully and consider all the elements, either expressed or implied. Assign letters or symbols to represent all elements which are unknown.
2. If possible, make a diagrammatic sketch representing the elements and the relationships in the problem.
3. Try to find some element which remains quantitatively unchanged throughout the problem or for which two separate expressions can be obtained to make a basic equation.
4. Write the basic equation in words.
5. Translate the basic equation into algebraic symbolism, using the data given or implied in the statement of the problem. It will probably be helpful in this connection to tabulate the pertinent data.
6. Solve the equation.
7. Check your solution *in the original problem.*
8. Be patient and painstaking. Do not become discouraged.
9. Use particular care to make your written work neat and orderly.
10. In problem situations that are not too involved, it is frequently desirable to make rough estimates of the answers before attempting to solve the problem.†

**Example 2-25.** The distance by rail from Los Angeles to Chicago is 2,225 miles. Train A leaves Los Angeles for Chicago and travels at an overall average speed of 54 mph. Train B leaves Chicago for Los Angeles $6\frac{1}{2}$ hr later and travels at an overall average speed of 56 mph. At what

† Charles H. Butler and F. Lynwood Wren, "The Teaching of Secondary Mathematics," 4th ed., pp. 381–382, McGraw-Hill Book Company, New York, 1965.

distance from Los Angeles will the trains pass each other? Express your answer correct to the nearest mile.

1. *Given elements of problem:*

Total distance from Los Angeles to Chicago is 2,225 miles.

Train A's average speed is 54 mph.

Train B's average speed is 56 mph.

Train B's starting time is $6\frac{1}{2}$ hr after train A starts.

*Implied relation:*

Distance = rate × time

*Unknowns:*

The distance of the passing point from Los Angeles

The time necessary for each train to reach the passing point

Let

$d$ = unknown distance from Los Angeles to passing point

$t$ = time necessary for Train A to reach passing point

$t - 6\frac{1}{2}$ = time necessary for train B to reach passing point

FIG. 2-2

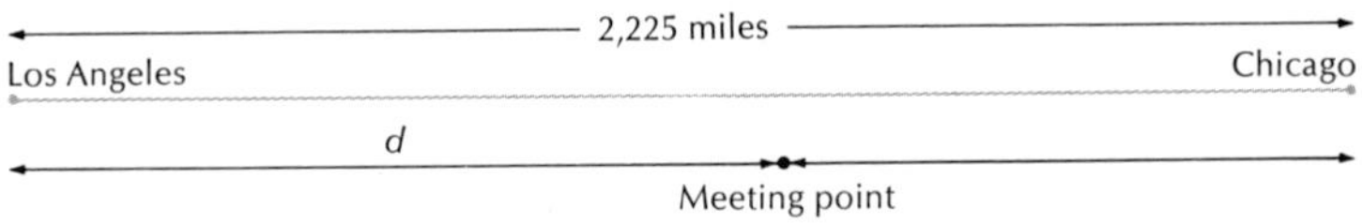

2. Since train A will have been traveling $6\frac{1}{2}$ hr longer than train B, the meeting point should be a bit farther from Los Angeles than the midway point. An estimate might be approximately 1,200 miles from Los Angeles (this is the rough estimate suggested in step 10).

3. The distance between the two cities remains fixed.

4. The distance train A travels plus the distance train B travels is equal to the total distance from Chicago to Los Angeles.

5. $56(t - 6\frac{1}{2}) + 54t = 2,225$

6. $56t - 364 + 54t = 2,225$

$$110t = 2,589$$

$$t = 23.5 \text{ hr (approximately)}$$

$$d = 54(23.5) = 1,269 \text{ miles (approximately)}$$

The trains will pass at a point approximately 1,269 miles from Los Angeles. This is a very satisfactory check with the rough estimate made previously.

7. $t - 6.5 = 23.5 - 6.5 = 17$ hr

$17(56) = 952$ miles

$952 + 1269 = 2,221$ miles

This is a very satisfactory check against the facts of the stated problem. The difference of 4 miles is a very small error due to the necessary rounding.

## EXERCISES

1. The airline distance between Los Angeles, California, and Atlanta, Georgia, is 1,936 miles. A morning jetliner flight leaves Los Angeles at 8:45 A.M. (P.S.T.) and arrives in Atlanta at 3:30 P.M. (E.S.T.). An afternoon flight leaves Los Angeles at 2:50 P.M. (P.S.T.) and arrives in Atlanta at 9:30 P.M. (E.S.T.). What is the average speed on each flight? Give your answers correct to the nearest mile per hour.

2. A triangle and a square are to be constructed such that they will have the same area. If the altitude of the triangle is to be one-half the length of the base, what must be the ratio of the base of the triangle to the side of the square?

3. A circle is to be constructed such that it will have an area equal to the surface area of a sphere of known radius. What must be the ratio of the radius of the circle to the radius of the sphere?

4. The total cost for 1 month's telephone service was $38.50. This includes a Federal Tax of 10 percent. Seventy-six percent of the net bill was for long-distance calls. What was the amount of the net bill, and what was the long-distance toll?

5. The total bill for water and light for 1 month was $20.70. If the ratio of the cost of electricity to the cost of water was 3:2, what was the cost of each utility service?

6. The record total receipts for a baseball World Series was $2,626,-973. Fifty-one percent of this amount was the players' pool, of which 30 percent was divided among the second, third, and fourth teams of the two leagues. The balance was divided so that the winning team received 60 percent. After assigning partial shares and other small portions, the team divided the balance among the players. How much did each player receive?

The following data pertain to Exercises 7 to 10.

The total expenditure for building construction in the United States during a recent year was $22,466,500,000. Of this amount, 54.2 percent was for new nonresidential units, 38.3 percent for new residential units, and the balance for repairs. Fifty percent of the total cost of new residential construction was for materials, distributed as follows: 22.5 percent for plumbing and air conditioning; 3.5 percent for electrical equipment; 8.2 percent for decoration; and 65.8 percent for all other construction costs.

7. During the year for which the data are given, how much was spent on new residential units? Give your answer correct to the nearest $100,000.

8. During this same year, how much money was spent on repairs? Give your answer to the nearest $100,000.

**9.** It is estimated that 65 percent of the total cost for plumbing and air conditioning in new residential construction is for air conditioning. How much money was spent for air conditioning new residences during the year for which the data are given? Give your answer correct to nearest $100,000.

**10.** If the total cost for the construction of a particular residence is estimated to be $18,600, approximately how much must be allowed for plumbing and air conditioning, for electric equipment, for decorations, and for all other construction costs? Give your answer correct to the nearest $100.

## Invitations to Extended Study

**1.** Let $S = \{1,2\}$ and consider the possible operations between all pairs of elements of $S$. Each of these operations could be given by a kind of multiplication table. For example, the following table determines the operation $*$, where $a * b = 2$ for every $a, b \in S$.

| * | 1 | 2 |
|---|---|---|
| 1 | 2 | 2 |
| 2 | 2 | 2 |

In this case an abstract system is determined in which the operation $*$ satisfies the properties of closure, commutativity, and associativity. There are 16 possible tables, each of which determines an operation on $S$ which satisfies the closure property; i.e., the "product" of any two elements of $S$ is an element of $S$. Construct the other 15 tables, and determine which of these abstract systems satisfy the commutative property and which satisfy the associative property.

**2.** Suppose in a particular system we associate with a proposition $p$ the number 1 if $p$ is true and the number 0 if $p$ is false in the system. We may use the following table to summarize the relationships between $p$ and not-$p$:

| $p$ | 0 | 1 |
|---|---|---|
| not-$p$ | 1 | 0 |

Thus, if $p$ is true, $p$ takes on the value 1. But if $p$ is true, then not-$p$ is false, and not-$p$ takes the corresponding value of 0. This is represented in the last column in the table. Complete the following table which represents the conjunction of p and q, where

p and q is true if and only if both p and q are true

| p | 0 | 0 | 1 | 1 |
|---|---|---|---|---|
| q | 0 | 1 | 0 | 1 |
| p and q | | | | |

3. Complete a table similar to that in Exercise 2 for the disjunction of the propositions p and q, where

p or q is false if and only if both p and q are false

4. Complete a table similar to that in Exercise 2 for the conditional of p and q, where

p → q is false if and only if p is true and q is false

5. The tables in Exercises 2 to 4 are called *truth tables* for the proposi- **Truth tables**
tions not-p, p and q, p or q, and p → q, respectively. Truth tables are sometimes helpful in discovering inference rules. Consider the truth table for the proposition p → (q → p):

| p | 0 | 0 | 1 | 1 |
|---|---|---|---|---|
| q | 0 | 1 | 0 | 1 |
| q → p | 1 | 0 | 1 | 1 |
| p → (q → p) | 1 | 1 | 1 | 1 |

The proposition p → (q → p) takes the value 1 for every possible value of 0 and 1 that the propositions p and q may have. When this situation occurs, we say that the proposition is a *tautology*. Show **Tautology** that the proposition (p and q) → p is a tautology. Find other examples of tautologies.

# CHAPTER 3

# THE CONCEPT OF A GROUP

## Guidelines for Careful Study

In Chap. 1, the concept of an algebraic system was discussed in general terms. In this chapter we shall investigate the properties of one of the most important and fundamental of algebraic systems, the *group*. A group is defined by four postulates, and any system which satisfies these four postulates is a group, even though it may satisfy many other postulates as well. The following questions will serve as helpful quidelines for the careful study of Chap. 3.

1. What is meant by a well-defined operation?
2. What is the definition of a group? An abelian group?
3. What is the order of a group?
4. What are finite and infinite groups?
5. What is meant by groups of congruences?
6. What is meant by a model of a group?
7. What is a mapping? A permutation?
8. What is a group of rotations? Of symmetries?
9. What is a group of permutations?
10. What is the symmetric group?
11. What is a subgroup?
12. What are the properties of the equality relation?

## Introduction

A mathematical system consists of a set of elements and at least one well-defined operation. A *binary operation* is one which assigns to each ordered pair† of elements of a set a distinct third element. For such an operation to be *well-defined*, the third element, whether or not it is an element of the given set, must be uniquely determined by the two given elements. If the element thus determined is also an element of the set, then the set is said to be *closed* with respect to that operation. For example, consider the set of all odd integers with the ordinary operation of addition. The sum of any two odd integers is a unique number which is an even integer. The operation of addition is well-defined, but the sum of two odd integers is not an element of the given set. Next consider the ordinary operation of multiplication with the set of all odd integers. The product of two odd integers is a unique odd integer, so that in this case the operation is well-defined, and the element representing the product is an element of the same set.

Suppose * (star) denotes a binary operation defined on a set $G$. If $a$ and $b$ are elements of $G$ which, together with *, determine a third element $c$, then we may write $c = a * b$, read "$c$ is equal to $a$ star $b$." The expression $a * b$ is frequently called the product of $a$ and $b$, although the usual operation of multiplication between numbers is not necessarily intended.

**Binary operation**

**Well-defined**

**Closure**

## 3-1. DEFINITION OF A GROUP

As you read a definition, it can be helpful in clarifying the concept to construct examples or models which have the prescribed properties, and at the same time consider examples or models which do not have all the properties listed in the definition. In reading the following definition, consider as an example the elements of the set of even integers and the binary operation of ordinary addition. For the first two postulates, observe that the operation of addition between the elements holds; for the second two postulates, try to find elements whose existence is postulated.

**Definition 3-1.** A group is an algebraic system consisting of a nonempty set $G$ and a well-defined binary operation * such that the elements of the set satisfy the following postulates with respect to the given operation:

**Group**

G-1   Closure: If $a, b \in G$, then $a * b \in G$.
G-2   Associativity: If $a, b, c \in G$, then $a * (b * c) = (a * b) * c$.

---

† An *ordered pair* is a set of two elements in which it is possible to distinguish a first element and a second element. In the ordered pair $(a,b)$ $a$ is the first element and $b$ is the second element.

**Ordered pair**

G-3   Identity: There exists an element in G, denoted by e, such that for every element a in G, e $*$ a = a $*$ e = a.

G-4   Inverse: For each element a in G there exists an element a′ in G such that a′ $*$ a = a $*$ a′ = e.

**Identity and inverse elements**

The element e is called an *identity element* or *identity,* and the element a′ is called an *inverse element* or *inverse* of the element a.

It is common to denote the group, as defined, by $<G,*>$. More generally, if S is a set and $*$ is a binary operation on S, then $<S,*>$ may denote the system determined by S, $*$, the listed postulates, and the equality relation.

**Example 3-1.**   Let G be the set of integers and $*$ the operation of ordinary addition. Since the sum of two integers is an integer, the property of closure is satisfied. The associative property is a well-known property of the integers.† There exists an additive identity, namely, the number 0. If a denotes any integer, then its additive inverse is $^-a$, since $^-a + a = a + {^-a} = 0$. Therefore the set of integers together with the operation $+$ is a group.

**Example 3-2.**   Let G = {a,b,c} and $*$ be the operation defined by the table

| $*$ | a | b | c |
|---|---|---|---|
| a | a | b | c |
| b | b | a | a |
| c | c | a | b |

in which, for example, the product a $*$ b of a and b is found by entering the table in the row preceded by a and the column headed by b. The element b is in both that row and column and represents the product of a and b; thus a $*$ b = b. We can see immediately from the table that property G-1 holds, since the only elements in the table are elements of G (is the operation well-defined?). The element a is an identity, since a $*$ a = a, a $*$ b = b $*$ a = b, and a $*$ c = c $*$ a = c. Since a $*$ a = a, a is an inverse of a. Since c $*$ b = b $*$ c = a, b is an inverse of c, and c is an inverse of b. Consequently, for each element of G there exists an inverse element. To determine whether the associative property holds,

† F. Lynwood Wren, "Basic Mathematical Concepts," p. 95, McGraw-Hill Book Company, New York, 1965.

we must check all possible ways that three elements (allowing for repetition) may be associated. If any one fails, the associative property fails to hold. Consider the following:

$$b * (b * c) = b * a = b$$
$$(b * b) * c = a * c = c$$

If $b$ and $c$ are distinct elements, then $b \neq c$, and consequently, $b * (b * c) \neq (b * b) * c$; the associative property fails to hold, and the system is proved, by counterexample, not to be a group.

You may have noticed in the preceding example that the element $b$ is also its own inverse. In some systems an element may have more than one inverse element. It will be proved later that in a group, for each element there exists exactly one inverse, and in this case we say that each element has a *unique inverse*. It will also be shown that in a group there is exactly one identity element, and we say that a group possesses a *unique identity element*. In the following example we define an operation on the set $G = \{a,b,c\}$ different from that defined in Example 3-2.

**Example 3-3.**  Let $G = \{a,b,c\}$ and ∘ (circle) be the operation defined by the table

| ∘ | a | b | c |
|---|---|---|---|
| a | a | b | c |
| b | b | c | a |
| c | c | a | b |

From an examination of the table it should be clear that the closure property holds. The identity element is $a$, and $a$ is its own inverse. As in Example 3-2, $b$ is an inverse of $c$, and $c$ is an inverse of $b$. The property of associativity can be seen to hold by an examination of all 54 products of three elements (allowing repetition). For example, $a \circ (a \circ a) = (a \circ a) \circ a$, and $a \circ (a \circ b) = (a \circ a) \circ b$. This system, $<G,\circ>$, is a group.

Following the convention discussed in Sec. 1-3, we may refer to any given group $<G,*>$ as a group $G$. Using this convention, we may say "let $a$ be an element of a group $G$," instead of the more precise "let $a$

be an element of the set G of a group." If the operation of the group is clear from the context, we may also adopt the convention of juxtaposition to represent the products; for example, we may write $ab$ for the product $a * b$. With this convention, the property of associativity $a * (b * c) = (a * b) * c$ may be expressed by the formula $a(bc) = (ab)c$. When this property holds, we may write the product as $a * b * c$ or $abc$, without parentheses. We shall use these conventions except where there might be ambiguity or when it is necessary to emphasize the group operation.

If in an algebraic system the commutative property holds with respect to an operation, then the operation is called a commutative operation. In the set of integers the operations of both addition and multiplication are commutative operations; however the operation of subtraction is not. In fact, if we consider the set of integers with the operation of subtraction, the only group postulate which holds is that of closure (check this).

**Abelian group**

**Definition 3-2. A group G is an abelian† group if it satisfies the commutative postulate:**

  **C   Commutativity: If a, b ∈ G, then ab = ba.**

**Nonabelian group**

Sometimes it is desirable to emphasize the fact that the group operation is not commutative. In this case the group is said to be *nonabelian*.

The groups in Examples 3-1 and 3-3 are examples of abelian groups. Let us now consider an example of a nonabelian group.

**Example 3-4.**   Let $G = \{r,s,t,u,v,w\}$ and $*$ be the operation defined by the following table:

| * | r | s | t | u | v | w |
|---|---|---|---|---|---|---|
| r | r | s | t | u | v | w |
| s | s | r | v | w | t | u |
| t | t | w | r | v | u | s |
| u | u | v | w | r | s | t |
| v | v | u | s | t | w | r |
| w | w | t | u | s | r | v |

† In honor of the Norwegian mathematician N. H. Abel (1802–1829).

The closure property clearly holds (why?), and $r$ is the identity element. Since the identity $r$ occurs exactly once in each row and in each column, each element has an inverse which is unique. It can be shown that the associative property holds. It then follows that $G$ is a group.

For $G$ to be an abelian group the commutative property must hold; i.e., for every pair of elements $a$ and $b$, $a * b = b * a$. If for any pair of elements the property does not hold, then the group is a nonabelian group. The elements of $G$ are assumed to be distinct. Consider the pair of elements $t$ and $s$ in $G$. $s * t = v$, and $t * s = w$; since $v \neq w$, we have $s * t \neq t * s$. Thus $G$ is a nonabelian group.

**Definition 3-3. If G is a group, then the order of G is the number of elements in the set G. If the number of elements is finite, then G is called a finite group; otherwise G is called an infinite group.**

Order of group

The groups discussed in Examples 3-3 and 3-4 are finite groups of orders 3 and 6, respectively. The group in Example 3-1 is an infinite group.

Postulate G-3 states that in a group there exists an identity element. Note that this statement says nothing about whether or not there might be more than one such element. Theorem 3-1 guarantees that there is exactly one identity element in a group. To establish the theorem it is necessary to show that any two identity elements must be the same element; that is, if $e$ and $f$ are any two identities, it must be shown that the group properties imply that $e = f$. The identity element in a group is therefore unique.

**Theorem 3-1. If e and f are identity elements of a group, then e = f.**

*Hypothesis:* e and f are identity elements
*Conclusion:* e = f
*Context:* Group

**Proof:**

| *Statement* | *Reason* |
|---|---|
| 1. $e$ is an identity | 1. Hypothesis |
| 2. $f$ is an identity | 2. Why? |
| 3. $e = fe$ | 3. 2; postulate G-3 |
| 4. $fe = f$ | 4. 1; postulate G-3 |
| 5. $e = f$ | 5. 3,4; transitivity of equality |

Theorem 3-2 states that the inverse element is unique. The proof is similar to that of Theorem 3-1.

**Theorem 3-2.** If y and z are inverses of an element x in a group, then $y = z$.

*Hypothesis:* y and z are inverses of x
*Conclusion:* $y = z$
*Context:* Group

**Proof:**   Let e be the identity of the group.

| Statement | Reason |
|---|---|
| 1. $yx = e$ | 1. Postulate G-4 |
| 2. $xz = e$ | 2. Why? |
| 3. $y = ye$ | 3. Why? |
| 4. $ye = y(xz)$ | 4. Why? |
| 5. $y(xz) = (yx)z$ | 5. Why? |
| 6. $(yx)z = ez$ | 6. Why? |
| 7. $ez = z$ | 7. Why? |
| 8. $y = z$ | 8. Why? |

In the preceding proof step 8 is justified by a multiple use of the transitive property of equality. For example, from steps 3 and 4 we may deduce by transitivity that $y = y(xz)$. This, together with step 5, implies that $y = (yx)z$. Continuing this process, we may deduce step 8. To avoid unnecessary repetition in writing such a sequence of related equalities, the left side of some statements of equality may be left blank. Thus steps 3 to 7 may be written as

$3'$. $y = ye$
$4'$. $= y(xz)$
$5'$. $= (yx)z$
$6'$. $= ez$
$7'$. $= z$

In general, this convention will be used in subsequent proofs.

Because of Theorem 3-1, we shall refer to an identity of a group as *the* identity; by Theorem 3-2, the inverse of an element is unique, and we shall henceforth refer to an inverse of a given element as *the* inverse of that element. If a is any element of a group and a′ is its inverse, then the inverse of a′ is a. The proof of this fact is left as an exercise (Exercise 14). Other symbols which are commonly used for the inverse of an element a are $^-a$, if the operation is addition, and $a^{-1}$, if the operation is multiplication.

Thus far only some simple consequences of the definition of a group have been demonstrated. Ample opportunity to explore other basic properties will be given in the exercises before we investigate various situations in which the group concept arises.

## EXERCISES

In Exercises 1 to 7 let $G = \{a,b,c\}$ and $*$ be a binary operation defined by the indicated table.

1. In Table 3-1: (a) What is an identity for this system? (b) Is it unique? (c) Does every element have an inverse? (d) Are inverses unique? (e) Is $*$ a commutative operation? (f) Given that the system is not a group, which group postulate fails to hold?

TABLE 3-1

| $*$ | $a$ | $b$ | $c$ |
|-----|-----|-----|-----|
| $a$ | $a$ | $c$ | $a$ |
| $b$ | $c$ | $a$ | $b$ |
| $c$ | $a$ | $b$ | $c$ |

2. In Table 3-2: (a) Given that $*$ is an associative operation, is the system a group? (b) Is it an abelian group?

TABLE 3-2

| $*$ | $a$ | $b$ | $c$ |
|-----|-----|-----|-----|
| $a$ | $a$ | $b$ | $c$ |
| $b$ | $b$ | $c$ | $a$ |
| $c$ | $c$ | $a$ | $b$ |

3. In Table 3-3: (a) Is $*$ a well-defined operation? (b) Which of postulates G-1, G-3, and G-4 hold in this system? (c) Give a counterexample for each postulate that fails to hold.

TABLE 3-3

| $*$ | $a$ | $b$ | $c$ |
|-----|-----|-----|-----|
| $a$ | $a$ | $b$ | $c$ |
| $b$ | $b$ | $d$ | $c$ |
| $c$ | $c$ | $b$ | $a$ |

**4.** In Table 3-4: (a) Prove or disprove that ∗ is an associative operation. (b) Is G an abelian group?

**TABLE 3-4**

| ∗ | a | b | c |
|---|---|---|---|
| a | a | b | c |
| b | b | a | c |
| c | a | b | c |

**5.** In Table 3-5: (a) Is ∗ a commutative operation? (b) Does postulate G-1 hold? G-3? G-4? (c) Give a counterexample in each case where a postulate does not hold.

**TABLE 3-5**

| ∗ | a | b | c |
|---|---|---|---|
| a | a | c | b |
| b | b | a | c |
| c | c | b | a |

**6.** In Table 3-6: (a) Given that the system is associative, which of the other group postulates hold? (b) Is ∗ a commutative operation?

**TABLE 3-6**

| ∗ | a | b | c |
|---|---|---|---|
| a | c | a | b |
| b | a | b | c |
| c | b | c | a |

**7.** In Table 3-7, prove or disprove that the system is an abelian group.

**TABLE 3-7**

| ∗ | a | b | c |
|---|---|---|---|
| a | a | b | c |
| b | b | a | b |
| c | c | b | a |

8. Let $G = \{a,b,c,d\}$ and $*$ be the operation defined in Table 3-8. Given that the system satisfies postulate G-2, is it a group? An abelian group? What is its order? Suppose we let $b^1 = b$, $b^2 = bb^1$ $b^3 = bb^2$, and $b^4 = bb^3$. Find the elements corresponding to each of the products $b$, $b^2$, $b^3$, and $b^4$ and note that every element of $G$ can be represented by $b^n$ for some positive integer $n$. The element $b$ is said to *generate* $G$. Find another generator of $G$.

Generator of a group

**TABLE 3-8**

| $*$ | $a$ | $b$ | $c$ | $d$ |
|-----|-----|-----|-----|-----|
| $a$ | $a$ | $b$ | $c$ | $d$ |
| $b$ | $b$ | $c$ | $d$ | $a$ |
| $c$ | $c$ | $d$ | $a$ | $b$ |
| $d$ | $d$ | $a$ | $b$ | $c$ |

9. Let $G = \{a,b,c,d\}$ and $*$ be the operation defined by Table 3-9. Given that the operation is associative, is the system a group? An abelian group? What is its order? Does the system have a generator (see Exercise 8)?

**TABLE 3-9**

| $*$ | $a$ | $b$ | $c$ | $d$ |
|-----|-----|-----|-----|-----|
| $a$ | $a$ | $b$ | $c$ | $d$ |
| $b$ | $b$ | $a$ | $d$ | $c$ |
| $c$ | $c$ | $d$ | $a$ | $b$ |
| $d$ | $d$ | $c$ | $b$ | $a$ |

10. Use the pattern of Exercise 8 to construct a table which represents a group of order 5. Is it abelian?

11. For each of the sets listed below let the binary operation be that of ordinary addition. Which are groups? Abelian groups? Finite groups? Infinite groups?

   (a) The set of positive integers.
   (b) The set of negative integers
   (c) The set of integers
   (d) The set of even integers

(e) The set of odd integers

(f) The set of all integral multiples of 3

**12.** Repeat Exercise 11 with the binary operation that of ordinary multiplication.

**13.** (a) In Example 3-4 find two elements $a$ and $b$ such that $(ab)' \neq a'b'$. For these two elements note that $(ab)' = b'a'$.

(b) Prove that if $a$ and $b$ are any two elements of a group $G$, then $(ab)' = b'a'$.

(c) Prove that if $G$ is an abelian group and $a, b \in G$, then $(ab)' = a'b'$.

**14.** Prove that if $a$ is an element of a group, then

(a) $a = a''$    where $a'' = (a')'$

(b) $a' = a'''$

**15.** Prove the following Cancellation Law for groups:

If $a$, $b$, and $c$ are elements of a group and $ac = bc$, then $a = b$

**16.** Let $G$ be the group in Example 3-3. Find an element $x$ such that

(a) $ax = a$      (c) $bx = a$

(b) $ax = b$      (d) $bx = b$

**17.** Let $G$ be the group in Example 3-4. Find an element $x$ such that

(a) $tx = v$        (d) $t = xv$

(b) $xt = v$        (e) $x = tv$

(c)  $t = vx$       (f) $x = vt$

**18.** (a) Show that the set of even integers is a group with respect to the operation of ordinary addition.

(b) Is it a group with respect to the operation of ordinary multiplication?

## 3-2. GROUPS FROM GEOMETRY

The concept of congruence of two geometric figures is usually developed rather early in the study of geometry. Two plane figures are considered to be congruent if one can be brought into coincidence with the other by a movement which does not change its size or shape, **Rigid motion**    otherwise known as a *rigid motion*. To visualize the relation of congruence it is sometimes helpful to construct cardboard models. A practical application of the congruence relation is the jigsaw puzzle. For example, Fig. 3-1 represents a puzzle which is complete except for one piece. The missing piece, as shown, must be turned over and rotated

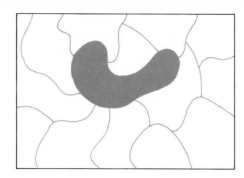

FIG. 3-1

to such a position that it will fit the shaded region. In this case the missing piece will fit in one and only one position. If it were symmetrically shaped, then there might be several positions in which it might fit, and each such position would represent a congruent position.

The movements themselves can be regarded as the elements of a set which, together with a well-defined operation, form groups called *groups of congruences* or groups associated with congruences. For example, consider a simplified form of a jigsaw puzzle which consists of a base, or frame, with one region which can be filled with a symmetrical diamond-shaped piece as represented in Fig. 3-2. The diamond, on

**Groups of congruences**

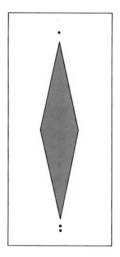

FIG. 3-2

the right, is to be placed in the shaded region of the base. For identification, the upper and lower corners of the diamond are marked with one and two dots, respectively, and the upper and lower corners of the shaded region of the base are similarly marked. Without turning the diamond over, we may fit it into the shaded region in two ways: (1) the corners with the same number of dots together (position 1 of Fig. 3-3),

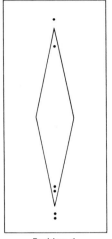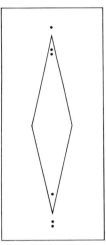

FIG. 3-3

Position 1          Position 2

and (2) the corners with different numbers of dots together (position 2 of Fig. 3-3).

Suppose now that the diamond is affixed to the base in such a way that it may be rotated over the shaded region and moved to either of the two congruent positions (Fig. 3-4). Whatever the initial congruent

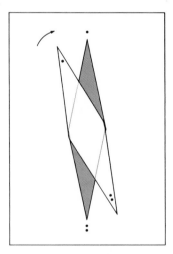

FIG. 3-4

position of the diamond, a clockwise rotation through 180° will move it to a new congruent position, and a clockwise rotation of 360° will return it to its original position. Thus, if the diamond is in position 1 of Fig. 3-3, then a rotation through 180° will move it to position 2. Two successive rotations through 180° will be equivalent to a single rotation through 360° as far as the position of the diamond is concerned; a rotation through 0°, or no rotation at all, will be equivalent to a rotation through 360°.

Consider all clockwise rotations of the diamond through angles which are multiples of 180°, namely, 0°, 180°, 360°, 540°, . . . . We form two sets as follows: $O$ consists of all the even multiples of 180° and $I$ of all the odd multiples of 180°; that is,

$$O = \{0°, 360°, 720°, . . .\}$$
$$I = \{180°, 540°, 900°, . . .\}$$

The sum of any two elements of $O$ is again an element of $O$, the sum of any two elements of $I$ is an element of $O$, and the sum of an element of $O$ with an element of $I$ is an element of $I$ (why?). This suggests an operation which may be defined on the set $\{O, I\}$, and we let # (sharp) represent this operation, defined as follows:

$$O \# O = O \qquad \text{read "}O \text{ sharp } O \text{ equals } O\text{"}$$
$$O \# I = I$$
$$I \# O = I$$
$$I \# I = O$$

The operation # may be interpreted as "followed by" in the sense that a rotation through an angle listed in one set followed by a rotation listed in either of the sets results in a rotation which is again listed in one of the two sets. These definitions may be summarized as follows:

| # | $O$ | $I$ |
|---|-----|-----|
| $O$ | $O$ | $I$ |
| $I$ | $I$ | $O$ |

The set $\{O, I\}$, together with the operation #, satisfies the properties of an abelian group of order 2 (check this statement), and it is called the *group of rotations of the diamond*. The element $O$ is the identity of this group and is called the *identity rotation*.

**Group of rotations**

**Identity rotation**

The group of rotations of the diamond is a special instance of a group of congruences. In each case the points of one diamond are made to correspond to the points of the other, so that the outline of the first matches the outline of the second. If we have two "identical" cardboard models of the diamond, we may place one on top of the other in a congruent position; then, if we stick a pin through either the top or the bottom figure, it will designate a corresponding point on the other. By this procedure we may say that the points on the top diamond match, or correspond to, the points on the bottom diamond. Suppose, for example, the diamonds were given identifying dots, as in Fig. 3-2, and were matched by the identity rotation; a pin piercing the single dot on the top diamond would pierce the corresponding dot on the bottom diamond. If the top diamond were rotated 180°, then the pin through the corner identified by the single dot on the top diamond would pierce the bottom diamond in the corner identified by the two dots. The two figures would again be in a congruent position, but the correspondence between them would be different. Notice that in either case, to each point on the top there is one and only one point corresponding on the bottom figure. This correspondence is called a *mapping.*

**Mapping**

**Definition 3-4. A mapping from one geometric figure to another is a correspondence between the points of the two figures such that to each point of the first there corresponds one and only one point of the second.**

Example 3-5 illustrates the fact that the definition of a mapping does not exclude the possibility that more than one point of one figure may correspond to a single point of a second.

**Example 3-5**   Consider a circle with a fixed diameter $\overline{AB}$. Let C be the set of points of the circle and D be the set of points of the line segment $\overline{AB}$ (see Fig. 3-5). By means of lines perpendicular to $\overline{AB}$, each point of

**FIG. 3-5**

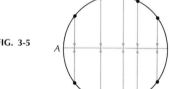

the set C can be made to correspond to one and only one point of the set D. Except for the points A and B, which correspond to themselves, two points of the circle correspond to a single point of the diameter.

If S is the set of points of a semicircle AKB, then under the same correspondence each point of the set S corresponds to one and only one point of the set D. Furthermore, in this case, exactly one point of S corresponds to a single point of D.

If in a mapping, such as that of the correspondence of the set S to the set D in the example, it is true that to each point of one figure there corresponds one and only one point of the second figure, and conversely, to each point of the second figure there corresponds one and only one point of the first, then the mapping is said to be a *one-to-one mapping*. The mapping of set $C$ to set $D$ is a *many-to-one mapping*.

Many-to-one and one-to-one mappings

Since each element of the group of rotations of the diamond determines a one-to-one mapping, we shall use these rotations to develop a notation which will enable us to describe one-to-one mappings more conveniently. Suppose the two diamonds of Fig. 3-4 have, instead of dots, the numbers 1 and 2 as identifying marks. If we place one diamond above the other in a congruent position corresponding to the identity rotation, the identifying marks will be so arranged that 1 is above 1 and 2 is above 2. With this notation it is convenient to denote the mapping $O$ by the symbol

$$O = \begin{pmatrix} 1 & 2 \\ 1 & 2 \end{pmatrix}$$

where the top numbers refer to points on the top diamond and the bottom ones refer to the corresponding points on the bottom diamond. By this notation we mean a mapping which carries 1 into 1 and 2 into 2. Any mapping on a set which carries each element into itself is called an *identity mapping*. The mapping $O$ is an identity mapping on the set $\{1,2\}$.

Identity mapping

The rotation $I$ may be denoted similarly by the symbol

$$I = \begin{pmatrix} 1 & 2 \\ 2 & 1 \end{pmatrix}$$

which indicates that 1 maps into 2 and 2 maps into 1. This notation is convenient, for it describes completely the mapping under consideration. Once the two identifying points on one diamond are lined up with the identifying points of the other, the two figures will be congruent, and the correspondence between all pairs of points of the two figures will be automatically determined. If the two figures are initially in position 1 of Fig. 3-3, then after a rotation $I$, the point 1 corresponds to, or maps into, the point 2. If we follow with another rotation $I$, the point 2 will be mapped back into 1. The net result of $I$ followed by $I$ is the mapping of 1 into 1. Similarly, under $I \# I$ the point 2 maps into 1, under the first rotation, followed by a mapping into 2 by the second; the result is that 2 is mapped into 2. Thus $I \# I$ may be represented by

$$\begin{pmatrix} 1 & 2 \\ 1 & 2 \end{pmatrix}$$

or the rotation $O$. The operation $\#$ between mappings is called the *composition of mappings*.

Composition of mappings

Let us use this new notation to describe the rotations of an equilateral triangle about its centroid.† We shall denote the vertices of the equilateral triangle by the numbers 1, 2, and 3 and the centroid by $C$, as in Fig. 3-6. As in the case of the diamonds, let us regard two triangles, one superimposed on the other. Let $V$ represent counterclockwise rota-

**FIG. 3-6**

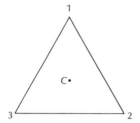

tion of 120°, $W$ the counterclockwise rotation through 240°, and $R$ the identity rotation, or a rotation through 0°. Using # to denote composition of mappings, we have V # $V = W$ and W # $W = V$. Now a rotation counterclockwise through 120° moves the point 1 into 3, 3 into 2, and 2 into 1. Thus we may write the mapping $V$ as

$$V = \begin{pmatrix} 1 & 2 & 3 \\ 3 & 1 & 2 \end{pmatrix}$$

and in a similar way we may write

$$W = \begin{pmatrix} 1 & 2 & 3 \\ 2 & 3 & 1 \end{pmatrix}$$

To find the mapping V # W we shall find the images of the three points under $V$ and then under $W$. Under $V$ the point 1 goes into 3, and under $W$ the point 3 goes into 1; the net result is that 1 maps into 1. Similarly, under $V$ the point 2 goes into 1, and under $W$ the point 1 maps into 2, so that the result of $V$ followed by $W$ is that 2 maps into itself. Again, under V # W the point 3 maps into 2 and then into 3, so that the result is that 3 maps into 3. Summarizing this procedure, we have

$$\begin{pmatrix} 1 & 2 & 3 \\ 3 & 1 & 2 \end{pmatrix} \# \begin{pmatrix} 1 & 2 & 3 \\ 2 & 3 & 1 \end{pmatrix} = \begin{pmatrix} 1 & 2 & 3 \\ 1 & 2 & 3 \end{pmatrix}$$

or just the rotation R. Thus V # W = R.

We may similarly compute all possible products of pairs of elements in the set $\{R,V,W\}$ with respect to the operation #. The results may be summarized in the table

† The centroid of a triangle is the point of intersection of the medians of the triangle. A median is a line drawn from a vertex to the midpoint of the opposite side.

| # | R | V | W |
|---|---|---|---|
| R | R | V | W |
| V | V | W | R |
| W | W | R | V |

which represents an abelian group of order 3 (first check each of the products in the table, and then show that the postulates for an abelian group hold). This group is called the *group of rotations of the equilateral triangle* and is another example of a group of congruences. **Group of rotations**

Using this notation, we might be curious to know what kind of mapping occurs on the equilateral triangle if we take the first row as 1, 2, 3 and arbitrarily make the second row, say, 1, 3, 2. We define such a mapping by

$$S = \begin{pmatrix} 1 & 2 & 3 \\ 1 & 3 & 2 \end{pmatrix}$$

First of all, we note $S \mathbin{\#} S = R$ (why?). We can see that geometrically the mapping $S$ corresponds to fixing the vertex 1 and interchanging the vertices 2 and 3. The result of the mapping $S$ can be described as turning over the triangle so that the top side becomes the bottom side. The turning is done about an axis which is the median from the vertex 1 to the opposite side. This mapping is called a *reflection in the median*. **Reflection**

The mappings $R$ and $S$ form an abelian group of order 2 with table

| # | R | S |
|---|---|---|
| R | R | S |
| S | S | R |

(check this.) Let us define the reflection in each of the other two medians as

$$T = \begin{pmatrix} 1 & 2 & 3 \\ 3 & 2 & 1 \end{pmatrix} \quad \text{and} \quad U = \begin{pmatrix} 1 & 2 & 3 \\ 2 & 1 & 3 \end{pmatrix}$$

Each of these, together with $R$, forms an abelian group of order 2.

For the equilateral triangle we now have six mappings, each of which maps the triangle onto itself. Consider one more composition, a rotation with a nonrotation, say $V \# U$:

$$\begin{pmatrix} 1 & 2 & 3 \\ 3 & 1 & 2 \end{pmatrix} \# \begin{pmatrix} 1 & 2 & 3 \\ 2 & 1 & 3 \end{pmatrix} = \begin{pmatrix} 1 & 2 & 3 \\ 3 & 2 & 1 \end{pmatrix}$$

Thus $V \# U = T$. By considering all possible compositions of mappings from the set $A = \{R,S,T,U,V,W\}$, we obtain the following table:

| # | R | S | T | U | V | W |
|---|---|---|---|---|---|---|
| R | R | S | T | U | V | W |
| S | S | R | V | W | T | U |
| T | T | W | R | V | U | S |
| U | U | V | W | R | S | T |
| V | V | U | S | T | W | R |
| W | W | T | U | S | R | V |

From the table we can easily verify that postulates G-1, G-3 (the identity element is $R$), and G-4 hold. The associative property also holds, as will be shown in general for mappings in the next section. Assuming that this has been shown, we see that the set $A$ with the operation $\#$ **Group of symmetries** forms a group. This group is called the *group of symmetries of the equilateral triangle*. It is an example of a nonabelian group (compare with Example 3-4).

The set $B = \{R,S\}$ is a subset of $A$, and, with respect to the same operation $\#$, it forms a group, called a subgroup of $A$.

**Subgroup** **Definition 3-5. If G is a group and S is a subset of G, then S is a subgroup of G if S is a group with respect to the same operation as that of G.**

Every group is automatically a subgroup of itself, and the set consisting of just the identity element is also a subgroup. In the group of symmetries of the equilateral triangle, the set of rotations $\{R,V,W\}$ is a subgroup of order 3. An opportunity to find all the subgroups of the group $A$ will be afforded in the exercises.

It is of more than passing interest to compare the table of group $A$ with that of group $G$ in Example 3-4. The two tables are identical, except that for $G$ the elements are represented by lower case letters and for $A$ the elements are represented by capital letters. If we regard the tables as geometric figures and the letters as representing points in the tables, then we could justify the consideration of mapping from the table of $A$ to that of $G$ which would, in our new notation, be of the form

$$\begin{pmatrix} R & S & T & U & V & W \\ r & s & t & u & v & w \end{pmatrix}$$

and this mapping would be one to one. Such a mapping of one group to another is of considerable interest in the study of algebra, since such a mapping preserves the algebraic structure and thus enables us to study distinct types of groups.

## EXERCISES

1. Find all the subgroups of the group of symmetries of the equilateral triangle.
2. Let the vertices of a square be denoted by 1, 2, 3, and 4, as in Fig. 3-7. Let $A$, $B$, $C$, and $D$ represent the clockwise rotations of the

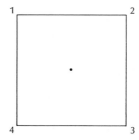

FIG. 3-7

square about its center (the point of intersection of the diagonals) through 0, 90, 180, and 270°, respectively.

(a) Construct a table representing the composition of pairs of all clockwise rotations.
(b) Show that this table is that of an abelian group (associativity may be assumed).
(c) Use the symbolism introduced in the discussion of the symmetries of the equilateral triangle to represent each of the clockwise rotations and to verify the table. Find the products of mappings, using this notation, and check the results found in part (a).
(d) Find all of the subgroups of the group $\{A,B,C,D\}$.

In Exercises 3 to 10 the notation of Exercise 2 is to be used.

3. Let $E$ represent the mapping of the square which keeps the vertices

1 and 3 fixed and interchanges the vertices 2 and 4. Is it a rotation? If so, through what angle? Is it a reflection? If so, in what line as an axis? Show that the set $\{A,E\}$ is an abelian group of order 2.

4. Let $F$ represent the mapping in which the vertices 2 and 4 remain fixed and vertices 1 and 3 are interchanged. Show that $\{A,F\}$ is an abelian group of order 2.

5. Let $G$ represent the mapping in which the vertices 1 and 2 are interchanged and also vertices 3 and 4 are interchanged. Show that $\{A,G\}$ is an abelian group of order 2.

6. Let $H$ represent the mapping in which the vertices 1 and 4 are interchanged and also 2 and 3 are interchanged. Show that $\{A,H\}$ is an abelian group of order 2.

7. Write a symbol to represent each of the mappings $E$, $F$, $G$, and $H$.

8. Show that $\{E,F,G,H\}$ does not constitute a group under composition of pairs of mappings.

9. Let $S$ represent the set $\{A,B,C,D,E,F,G,H\}$. Find all compositions of pairs of mappings from $S$ and summarize them in a table. Show that the system is a group of order 8. Is it abelian? This group is called the *group of symmetries of a square*. Find all subgroups of $S$.

10. (a) Show that if $x$, $y \in S$ (Exercise 9), in general, $(x \# y)' \neq x' \# y'$.
    (b) Show that if $x$, $y \in \{A,B,C,D\}$, then $(x \# y)' = x' \# y'$.
    (c) Account for the difference in results of (a) and (b).

11. Consider the set of all clockwise rotations of a circular disk. Show that this set forms an abelian group. *Hint:* The composition of two rotations through angles with measures $r$ and $s$ is the same as a single rotation through an angle with measure $r + s$. In an angle of $30°$, the measure of the angle is said to be the real number 30.

12. Let $I$ be the identity rotation of a circle and $J$ the reflection of the circle in a fixed diameter, that is, a movement which turns the circle about the diameter so that the top and bottom side of the circle are interchanged. Does the set $\{I,J\}$ form a group?

13. In Sec. 3-2 the group of rotations of the diamond was found. Find the group of symmetries of the diamond.

14. Find the group of symmetries of a rectangle which is not a square. What is its order? How many subgroups does it have?

## 3-3. MAPPINGS AND PERMUTATION GROUPS

In this section we shall be interested primarily in mappings of the elements of finite sets. Some of the more general properties of mappings will be discussed. One-to-one mappings on finite sets are called *permutations*, and groups whose elements are permutations are called *permutation groups.*

**Permutation groups**

Suppose $L$ and $M$ are two sets and $\phi$ (phi) represents a mapping from the set $L$ to the set $M$. Then for every element $x$ in $L$ there corresponds one and only one element $y$ in $M$. We call $y$ the *image of x under the mapping $\phi$* and write $y = x\phi$,† which may be read "y equals x phi."

In a set consisting of exactly two points we may list all the possible ways in which the set can be mapped onto itself. Let $S = \{a,b\}$. With the notation of Sec. 3-2, the only two possible mappings which are one to one may be expressed as

$$\phi = \begin{pmatrix} a & b \\ a & b \end{pmatrix} \quad \text{and} \quad \psi = \begin{pmatrix} a & b \\ b & a \end{pmatrix}$$

where $\phi$ is the identity mapping and $\psi$ (psi) is called the inversion mapping on the set. Using the operation of composition (represented by #), we can find all possible "products" of these two mappings and list them in a table:

| # | $\phi$ | $\psi$ |
|---|--------|--------|
| $\phi$ | $\phi$ | $\psi$ |
| $\psi$ | $\psi$ | $\phi$ |

The system thus determined is an abelian group of order 2 (compare this table with that of the group of rotations of the diamond). Since the set $\{a,b\}$ is finite and the mappings $\phi$ and $\psi$ are one to one, they are called permutations. The set $\{\phi,\psi\}$ constitutes a group which is a permutation group of order 2.

The question of whether, in general, the composition of two mappings on a set is also a mapping must be more carefully considered. Let $\alpha$ (alpha) and $\beta$ (beta) be two arbitrary mappings on a set $A$. For each arbitrary element $x$ of $A$, $x$ has a unique image, say $y$, in $A$ under the mapping $\alpha$: $y = x\alpha$. Since $y$ is an element of $A$, it has a unique image, say $z$, in $A$ under the mapping $\beta$: $z = y\beta$. Thus $z = y\beta = (x\alpha)\beta$. The image, then, of $x$ under the composition $\alpha$ # $\beta$ is a unique element $z$ in the set $A$. In general, the composition $\gamma$ (gamma) of two mappings $\alpha$ and $\beta$ on $A$ is that mapping such that for every $x$ in $A$

$$x\gamma = x(\alpha \text{ # } \beta) = (x\alpha)\beta$$

Note that the mapping $\gamma = \alpha$ # $\beta$ is accomplished by first determining

† The notation $y = \phi(x)$ is also used and will be introduced in Chap. 5. The widespread use of both notations justifies the introduction of both.

the effect of the mapping $\alpha$ on the original configuration and then carrying out the dictates of $\beta$ on this resultant figure.

**Example 3-6.** Let $L$ be a straight-line segment and $\alpha$ and $\beta$ be mappings on $L$. Draw three copies of $L$, as in Fig. 3-8. To find the image

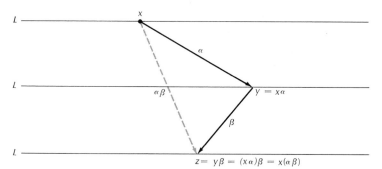

**FIG. 3-8**

under $\alpha \,\#\, \beta$ of a point $x$ on $L$, first locate $x$ on the first copy of $L$. If $y = x\alpha$, then locate the point $y$ on the second copy. If $z = y\beta$, locate the point $z$ on the third copy. The point $z$ is the image, then, of the mapping $\alpha \,\#\beta$; that is, $z = x(\alpha \,\#\, \beta)$.

Let $A$ be a set consisting of three elements, say $a$, $b$, and $c$. Using the notation of Sec. 3-2, we write these three elements in a fixed order in the first row and in any arrangement in the second row. To each such arrangement there corresponds a mapping or permutation. For example, one such mapping is represented by

$$\begin{pmatrix} a & b & c \\ c & a & b \end{pmatrix}$$

Since there are $3!\dagger$ possible arrangements, six different permutations are determined on the set $A$. It is sometimes desirable to list the elements of a finite set as numbers and express the permutations in this symbolic form with the first row consisting of the integers $1, 2, 3, \ldots, n$, where $n$ represents the number of elements in the given set. Each of the possible arrangements can be then used as a second row in the symbol. Since there are $n!$ possible arrangements, there are $n!$ possible mappings on a set of $n$ elements. Essentially, this technique was used to find all the mappings of the group of symmetries of the equilateral triangle in the discussion of Sec. 3-2. In that case each mapping of the vertices onto themselves corresponded to a congruence or rigid motion. Al-

---

$\dagger$ If $n$ is a positive integer, then $n!$, read "$n$ factorial," is the product of all of the positive integers between 1 and $n$, inclusive. Thus $3! = 1(2)(3) = 6$.

though not every permutation corresponds to a rigid motion, it is possible that the composition of two such permutations does correspond to a rigid motion.

**Example 3-7.** Suppose four chairs are placed in such a way that they form the vertices of a square. Let the chairs be numbered 1, 2, 3, and 4, as in Fig. 3-9, and let four people, similarly numbered, sit in the chairs

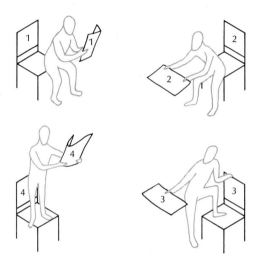

FIG. 3-9

which match their numbers. If the persons in chairs 2 and 3 interchange their positions, we can represent this interchange by

$$\alpha = \begin{pmatrix} 1 & 2 & 3 & 4 \\ 1 & 3 & 2 & 4 \end{pmatrix}$$

If this were to represent a mapping of a square onto itself, it could not represent a rigid motion; since one side (including the vertices 1 and 4) must remain fixed and the opposite side is, in effect, turned over, the square would experience a twisting movement, not a rigid motion.

Again consider the people seated in the chairs in their original position. If the people in chairs 1 and 4 interchange their positions, we could represent this movement by

$$\beta = \begin{pmatrix} 1 & 2 & 3 & 4 \\ 4 & 2 & 3 & 1 \end{pmatrix}$$

As before, this permutation could not represent a rigid motion. In the composition $\alpha \# \beta$ the element 1 goes into 1 under $\alpha$ and subsequently into 4 under $\beta$. In our notation we may write

$$1(\alpha \# \beta) = (1\alpha)\beta = 1\beta = 4$$

and similarly, for each of the other elements,

$$2(\alpha \mathbin{\#} \beta) = (2\alpha)\beta = 3\beta = 3$$
$$3(\alpha \mathbin{\#} \beta) = (3\alpha)\beta = 2\beta = 2$$
$$4(\alpha \mathbin{\#} \beta) = (4\alpha)\beta = 4\beta = 1$$

The composition of these two mappings is given, therefore, by

$$\alpha \mathbin{\#} \beta = \begin{pmatrix} 1 & 2 & 3 & 4 \\ 4 & 3 & 2 & 1 \end{pmatrix}$$

The composition of $\alpha$ and $\beta$ may be seen to represent a rigid motion in which the square is reflected in a line through the center of the square parallel to the side connecting the verticles 1 and 2.

In general, the associative property for an algebraic system is not easy to determine. However, if the elements of a system are mappings and the operation is that of composition, we may always assume associativity. To prove this we must first define what is meant by two mappings being equivalent. If $A$ is a set and $\alpha$ and $\beta$ are mappings on $A$, then **Equivalent mappings** we say that $\alpha$ and $\beta$ are *equivalent* if for every $x$ in $A$, $x\alpha = x\beta$. We may now prove that the operation of composition of mappings satisfies property G-2 of the group postulates.

**Theorem 3-3. If $\alpha$, $\beta$, and $\gamma$ are mappings on a set A, then $(\alpha \mathbin{\#} \beta) \mathbin{\#} \gamma = \alpha \mathbin{\#} (\beta \mathbin{\#} \gamma)$.**

*Hypothesis: $\alpha$, $\beta$, and $\gamma$ are mappings on $A$*
*Conclusion: $(\alpha \mathbin{\#} \beta) \mathbin{\#} \gamma = \alpha \mathbin{\#} (\beta \mathbin{\#} \gamma)$*

**Proof:** Let $\delta = \alpha \mathbin{\#} \beta$, $\epsilon = \beta \mathbin{\#} \gamma$. Let $x$ be an arbitrary element of $A$, and let $y = x\alpha$.

| Statement | Reason |
|---|---|
| 1. $x\delta = x(\alpha \mathbin{\#} \beta)$ | 1. Why? |
| 2. $x\delta = (x\alpha)\beta$ | 2. Definition |
| 3. $x\delta = y\beta$ | 3. Why? |
| 4. $x(\delta \mathbin{\#} \gamma) = (x\delta)\gamma$ | 4. Why? |
| 5. $\qquad = (y\beta)\gamma$ | 5. Why? |
| 6. $\qquad = y(\beta \mathbin{\#} \gamma)$ | 6. Why? |
| 7. $\qquad = y\epsilon$ | 7. Why? |
| 8. $\qquad = (x\alpha)\epsilon$ | 8. Why? |
| 9. $\qquad = x(\alpha \mathbin{\#} \epsilon)$ | 9. Why? |
| 10. $\delta \mathbin{\#} \gamma = \alpha \mathbin{\#} \epsilon$ | 10. By definition, since $x$ is arbitrary |
| 11. $(\alpha \mathbin{\#} \beta) \mathbin{\#} \gamma = \alpha \mathbin{\#} (\beta \mathbin{\#} \gamma)$ | 11. Why? |

By the proof of this theorem we have justified the assumption of associativity for the group of symmetries of the equilateral triangle. Henceforth, for any set of permutations on a given set we may assume that the operation of composition is associative.

Let $S$ be the set of all permutations on a finite set $A$. Then, with respect to composition, postulates G-1 and G-2 will be satisfied. Let $\phi$ be the identity permutation on $A$, that is, the mapping which corresponds every element of $A$ to itself; then $\phi \in S$ (why?). We shall show that, with respect to composition, $\phi$ is an identity element of the set $S$ and satisfies postulate G-3.† Let $\alpha$ be an arbitrary element of $S$ and $x$ an arbitrary element of $A$; then

$$x(\phi \ \# \ \alpha) = (x\phi)\alpha = x\alpha$$

and by the definition which states the conditions for two mappings to be equal, we have $\phi \ \# \ \alpha = \alpha$. Similarly, $\alpha \ \# \ \phi = \alpha$, and hence $\phi$ is an identity element for the set $S$.

The set $S$ will satisfy postulate G-4 and hence is a group. To prove this we must show that every element has an inverse. Thus, if $\alpha$ is any arbitrary element in $S$, we must find an element $\beta$ in $S$ such that $\alpha \ \# \ \beta = \beta \ \# \ \alpha = \phi$, the identity element. A proof of this statement in the general case will be left as an exercise; however, we shall show by example how to find the inverse of a given permutation. Suppose, for example, we are required to find the inverse of

$$\alpha = \begin{pmatrix} 1 & 2 & 3 & 4 \\ 3 & 1 & 4 & 2 \end{pmatrix}$$

The inverse of this permutation can be found merely by interchanging the first row with the second row. When this is done, however, the numbers in the first row of the resulting symbol may not be in their natural order. This can be remedied by interchanging columns so that the natural sequence is obtained. For example, interchanging the two rows in $\alpha$ yields

$$\beta = \begin{pmatrix} 3 & 1 & 4 & 2 \\ 1 & 2 & 3 & 4 \end{pmatrix}$$

The columns of $\beta$ can be interchanged to obtain the more conventional form

$$\beta = \begin{pmatrix} 1 & 2 & 3 & 4 \\ 2 & 4 & 1 & 3 \end{pmatrix}$$

† The concept of an *identity permutation*, which is a mapping, should not be confused with that of an *identity element*, which may or may not be a mapping. In general, an identity mapping maps every element into itself, and the identity permutation is such a mapping. However, an identity element is defined in terms of an algebraic structure (see postulate G-3).

Simple computation shows that $\beta$ is the inverse of $\alpha$; that is, $\alpha \# \beta = \beta \# \alpha = \phi$. The inverse of any permutation can be found similarly. The inverse is, of course, a permutation and will be in the set $S$ of all permutations. Thus $S$ is a group and, in fact, a permutation group, and we have proved informally the following theorem:

**Theorem 3-4. The set of all permutations on a finite set is a permutation group.**

**Symmetric group**

If $A$ is a finite set with $n$ elements, then the set $S_n$ which consists of all permutations on $A$ is a group called the *symmetric group* on $n$ objects. $S_n$ will have $n!$ elements, and so the symmetric group on $n$ objects is a permutation group of order $n!$ The group of symmetries of the equilateral triangle is essentially the symmetric group on three objects and is of order 6. The group of symmetries of the square (see Exercises 2 to 9 of Sec. 3-2) is a permutation group of order 8 and is a subgroup of $S_4$, which is of order $4! = 24$. As can be seen from Sec. 3-2, $S_3$ is not abelian. However, $S_2$, which is essentially the group of rotations of the diamond, is an abelian group. Further study of permutation groups is afforded in the exercises.

## EXERCISES

**1.** Find all the subgroups of $S_3$.

**2.** Use the notation of Sec. 3-2 to write each of the permutations in $S_4$.

**3.** What is the inverse of each element in $S_3$? Of each element in $S_2$?

**4.** Find the inverse of each element of $S_4$.

**5.** Find the inverse of each of the following permutations:

(a) $\begin{pmatrix} 1 & 2 & 3 & 4 & 5 \\ 1 & 3 & 2 & 5 & 4 \end{pmatrix}$

(b) $\begin{pmatrix} 1 & 2 & 3 & 4 & 5 & 6 \\ 6 & 5 & 4 & 3 & 2 & 1 \end{pmatrix}$

(c) $\begin{pmatrix} 1 & 2 & 3 & 4 & 5 & 6 & 7 \\ 7 & 5 & 3 & 1 & 2 & 4 & 6 \end{pmatrix}$

(d) $\begin{pmatrix} 1 & 2 & 3 & 4 & 5 \\ 2 & 4 & 3 & 5 & 1 \end{pmatrix}$

(e) $\begin{pmatrix} 1 & 2 & 3 & 4 & 5 & 6 \\ 2 & 4 & 6 & 1 & 3 & 5 \end{pmatrix}$

(f) $\begin{pmatrix} 1 & 2 & 3 & 4 & 5 & 6 & 7 \\ 1 & 7 & 2 & 6 & 3 & 5 & 4 \end{pmatrix}$

6. Let $A$ be the set of all elements of $S_4$ in which the number 1 remains fixed, that is, those elements of $S_4$ which map 1 into 1. List all the elements of $A$, and determine whether or not $A$ is a group.

7. Let $B$ be the set of all elements of $S_4$ in which the numbers 1 and 4 remain fixed. List the elements of $B$, and determine whether or not $B$ is a group.

8. Let $C$ be the set of all elements of $S_6$ in which the numbers 1, 2, and 3 remain fixed. List all the elements of $C$, and determine whether or not $C$ is a group.

9. Show that an arbitrary element of $S_n$ has an inverse.

## Invitations to Extended Study

1. Let $G$ be a group with operation $*$. If $S$ is a subset of $G$, show that a necessary and sufficient condition for $S$ to be a subgroup of $G$ is that postulates G-1 and G-4 be satisfied.

2. Let $G$ be a group and $S$ a finite subset of $G$. Show that a necessary and sufficient condition for $S$ to be a subgroup of $G$ is that $S$ be closed with respect to the group operation.

3. If $G$ is a group with operation $*$, and if $g \in G$, then we define $g^1 = g$ and $g^n = g * g^{n-1}$, where $n = 2, 3, 4, \ldots$ . The element $g^n$ is called the $n$th power of $g$. Show that for positive integers $m$ and $n$, $g^m * g^n = g^{m+n}$.

4. A group is called *cyclic* if there is an element $g \in G$ such that every element of $G$ can be expressed as some power of $g$; the element $g$ is said to generate $G$. Show that the group of rotations of an equilateral triangle is a cyclic group.  **Cyclic group**

5. Show that the group of rotations of a square is a cyclic group.

6. Show that a cyclic group is abelian.

7. Show that if $G$ is a finite group, then the powers of any element of $G$ generate a subgroup of $G$.

8. A *semigroup* is a system $\langle S, * \rangle$ which satisfies postulates G-1 and G-2. Consider the systems indicated by the tables in Exercise 1 of the Invitations to Extended Study of Chap. 2. Which of these systems are semigroups?  **Semigroup**

# CHAPTER 4

# THE CONCEPTS OF RING AND INTEGRAL DOMAIN

### Guidelines for Careful Study

In Chap. 3 we investigated some of the properties of one of the most basic algebraic systems, the group. In this chapter we shall see how a group may be used to construct two algebraic systems which are of fundamental importance in the study of algebra, the *ring* and the *integral domain*. Many of the concepts studied are familiar but may have been considered in a different context. The following questions will provide helpful guidelines for the careful study of Chap. 4.

1. How is a group used as a basic building block for other algebraic systems?
2. What is a ring? How does it differ from a group?
3. What is a zero?
4. What is meant by zero divisors?
5. What is a matrix?
6. How is the sum of two matrices defined? The product?
7. What is a ring of matrices?
8. What is the Cancellation Law?
9. What ring properties are used to prove that the Cancellation Law is equivalent to the property of having no zero divisors?
10. What is an integral domain? How does it differ from a ring?
11. What is meant by the ring of integers reduced, modulo $m$?
12. Why is the congruence relation an equivalence relation?

## Introduction

In Chap. 3 we considered algebraic systems which consist of one set and one well-defined binary operation on that set which satisfies one or more of the postulates for a group. In this chapter we shall consider systems in which more than one operation is defined between pairs of elements of a given set. Each of the operations will satisfy one or more of the postulates for an abelian group. Furthermore, it is desirable that some relationship be established between the two operations in order to unify the system. One such relationship is the distributive property:

**Definition 4-1. If S is a set on which two operations $*$ and $\circ$ are defined, then the operation $\circ$ is said to be distributive with respect to the operation $*$ if it satisfies the following postulate:**     Distributive property

D   **Distributivity: For every three elements a, b, c $\in$ S, a $\circ$ (b $*$ c) = (a $\circ$ b) $*$ (a $\circ$ c) and (b $*$ c) $\circ$ a = (b $\circ$ a) $*$ (c $\circ$ a).**

Instead of saying that $\circ$ distributes with respect to $*$, we sometimes say that $\circ$ distributes over $*$. It should be noted that the property stated holds for every three elements, and there is no requirement that a, b, and c be distinct. Thus a, b, and c may each denote the same element of S. We shall now consider some examples of the distributive property.

**Example 4-1.**   If the elements of a given set are themselves sets, then we may consider intersection and union as operations on pairs of sets. Thus if A, B, and C are any three sets, then it is well known that

$$A \cap (B \cup C) = (A \cap B) \cup (A \cap C)$$

and

$$(B \cup C) \cap A = (B \cap A) \cup (C \cap A)$$

Therefore the operation $\cap$ is distributive with respect to $\cup$. Similarly,

$$A \cup (B \cap C) = (A \cup B) \cap (A \cup C)$$

and

$$(B \cap C) \cup A = (B \cup A) \cap (C \cup A)$$

and the operation $\cup$ distributes over $\cap$ (see Fig. 4-1). Thus each of the operations is distributive with respect to the other.

**Example 4-2.**   Let $N$ be the set of natural numbers with the two operations of ordinary addition and multiplication. The operation of multiplication is distributive with respect to addition, but the reverse does not

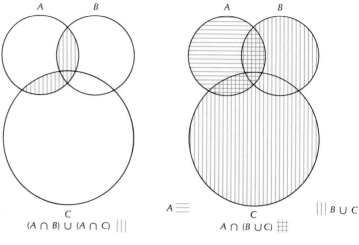

**FIG. 4-1**

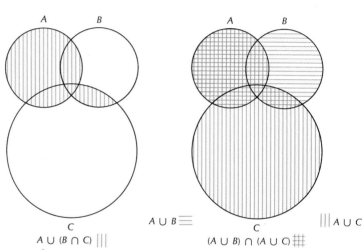

hold. Thus, if $a, b, c \in N$, then

$$a(b + c) = ab + ac$$

and

$$(b + c)a = ba + ca$$

so that multiplication distributes over addition.

The statement of distributivity of addition over multiplication would be

$$a + (bc) = (a + b)(a + c)$$

and

$$(bc) + a = (b + a)(c + a)$$

This property does not hold for every natural number $a$, $b$, and $c$. For example, let $a$, $b$, and $c$ be the numbers 1, 2, and 3, respectively. Then $1 + 2(3) = 1 + 6 = 7$, whereas $(1 + 2)(1 + 3) = 3(4) = 12$. This contradicts the first of the two statements of the distributive property and is sufficient to serve as a counterexample. In contrast to Example 4-1, only one operation is distributive with respect to the other.

## 4-1. DEFINITION OF A RING

We may now define an algebraic system with two operations. In the following definition one of the operations must satisfy the postulates for an abelian group, whereas the other operation may not. It must be carefully observed which operation is distributive with respect to the other.

**Definition 4-2. Let R be a set on which two operations, $*$ and $\circ$, are defined. Then R is a ring if**                                                                      Ring

1. **R is an abelian group with respect to the operation $*$**
2. **R satisfies the properties of closure and associativity with respect to the operation $\circ$**
3. **$\circ$ distributes over $*$**

The operation in property 1 will be called the *first operation,* and the operation in property 2 will be called the *second operation.* The distributive property states that in a ring the second operation is distributive with respect to the first (although it does not rule out the possibility that the first may distribute over the second). Thus property 1 guarantees that, with respect to the first operation, the elements of a ring must satisfy postulates G-1, G-2, G-3, G-4, and C; property 2 guarantees that, with respect to the second operation, the elements must satisfy postulates G-1 and G-2, although they may satisfy additional ones; property 3 establishes the distributive relationship between the two operations. It is important to note that theorems proved for groups and abelian groups hold for the group $\langle R, * \rangle$ of a ring. This is an indication of why mathematical systems are categorized—to enable us to utilize the properties of one system in an "enlarged" system.

Given an algebraic system with two operations, knowing whether the distributive property holds furnishes us with a technique for determining whether the ring postulates are satisfied. It was found (Example 4-2) that in the set of natural numbers multiplication distributes with respect to addition, but the reverse does not hold. Consequently, if this set is to be a ring, addition must be considered as the first operation. With respect to this operation, however, there is no identity element. It therefore follows that with respect to addition the set of natural numbers is not a group and hence cannot be a ring. We shall now consider an example of a ring.

**Example 4-3.**   Let $Z$ be the set of integers with the operations those of ordinary addition and multiplication. The set of integers is a group with respect to addition (see Example 3-1); that it is an abelian group follows from the commutativity of addition. $Z$ is closed with respect to multiplication (that is, postulate G-1 is satisfied), and the properties of associativity (G-2) and distributivity (D) are well established.† It follows, therefore, that the integers form a ring. More explicitly, the system $<Z, +, \cdot>$ is a ring.

In the definition of a ring we refer to ∗ (the first operation) as the additive operation and to ∘ (the second operation) as the multiplicative operation. It should be noted that the ring of integers satisfies additional properties. For example, the multiplicative operation is commutative, and the number 1 serves as a multiplicative identity. If, in any ring, the multiplicative operation ∘ satisfies the commutative property (C), then it is called a *commutative ring*. If there exists an identity with respect to the second operation, then the ring is called a *ring with identity*. The ring of integers, therefore, is a commutative ring with identity.

**Commutative ring**
**Ring with identity**

Let $R$ be a ring, and let 0 be the additive identity of $R$. Then 0 has an interesting property:

$$0 \circ a = a \circ 0 = 0 \qquad \text{for every } a \in R$$

The proof that this property holds follows from the distributive property, as shown in the following informal proof.

Let $a$ be any element of a ring and 0 be the additive identity; then

$$0 * a = a \qquad \text{why?}$$
$$(0 * a) \circ a = a \circ a \qquad \text{operative property of equality}$$
$$(0 \circ a) * (a \circ a) = a \circ a \qquad \text{distributivity}$$

Since the additive identity is unique (Theorem 3-1), it follows that

$$0 \circ a = 0$$

In a similar way it can be shown that $a \circ 0 = 0$ for every element $a$ in a ring, even though the operation ∘ may not be a commutative operation. Because of this property, the additive identity of a ring is frequently

† F. Lynwood Wren, "Basic Mathematical Concepts," p. 95, McGraw-Hill Book Company, New York, 1965.

called a *zero* or an *annihilator element.* The proof that it is unique can    **Zero**
be patterned after that of Theorem 3-1. Using the notation x' for the
additive inverse of an element x in a ring, we can prove a variation of
the distributive property.

**Theorem 4-1. If a, b, and c are any three elements of a ring, then**

$(a \circ c) * (b \circ c)' = (a * b') \circ c$

*Hypothesis;* a, b, and c are arbitrary elements of a ring
*Conclusion:* $(a \circ c) * (b \circ c)' = (a * b') \circ c$
*Context:* Ring

**Proof:**

| *Statement* | *Reason* |
|---|---|
| 1. $(b' \circ c) * (b \circ c) = (b' * b) \circ c$ | 1. Distributivity of $\circ$ over $*$ |
| 2. $\qquad\qquad\quad = 0 \circ c$ | 2. Why? |
| 3. $\qquad\qquad\quad = 0$ | 3. Why? |
| 4. $(b \circ c)' = b' \circ c$ | 4. 3; additive inverse is unique |
| 5. $(a \circ c) * (b \circ c)' = (a \circ c) * (b' \circ c)$ | 5. Why? |
| 6. $(a \circ c) * (b \circ c)' = (a * b') \circ c$ | 6. Why? |

The study of rings leads to some interesting properties which are
not encountered in the ordinary arithmetic of the integers. For example,
it may happen that the product of two nonzero elements is zero, and
in this case we say that the ring has *divisors* of *zero.*

**Definition 4-3. In a commutative ring two nonzero elements a and b whose**    **Divisors of zero**
**product a $\circ$ b = 0 are called divisors of zero.**

**Example 4-4.**   Let $S = \{0,1,2,3,4,5\}$ with operations $*$ and $\circ$ as defined in Table 4-1 (page 96). It can be seen that this system satisfies
the postulates for a commutative ring with identity (see Exercise 3).
It can also be seen from Table 4-1b, which represents the multiplicative operation, that $2 \circ 3 = 0$, so that 2 and 3 are divisors of zero. Use
the table to cite another example.

In the next section we shall consider an important example of rings,
a ring of matrices.

EXERCISES

**1.** Show that in a ring with additive identity 0 and multiplicative operation $\circ$, $a \circ 0 = 0$ for every element a in the ring.

**TABLE 4-1**

| * | 0 | 1 | 2 | 3 | 4 | 5 |
|---|---|---|---|---|---|---|
| 0 | 0 | 1 | 2 | 3 | 4 | 5 |
| 1 | 1 | 2 | 3 | 4 | 5 | 0 |
| 2 | 2 | 3 | 4 | 5 | 0 | 1 |
| 3 | 3 | 4 | 5 | 0 | 1 | 2 |
| 4 | 4 | 5 | 0 | 1 | 2 | 3 |
| 5 | 5 | 0 | 1 | 2 | 3 | 4 |

(a)

| ∘ | 0 | 1 | 2 | 3 | 4 | 5 |
|---|---|---|---|---|---|---|
| 0 | 0 | 0 | 0 | 0 | 0 | 0 |
| 1 | 0 | 1 | 2 | 3 | 4 | 5 |
| 2 | 0 | 2 | 4 | 0 | 2 | 4 |
| 3 | 0 | 3 | 0 | 3 | 0 | 3 |
| 4 | 0 | 4 | 2 | 0 | 4 | 2 |
| 5 | 0 | 5 | 4 | 3 | 2 | 1 |

(b)

2. Show that in a ring the zero element is unique.
3. In Example 4-4 assume both operations are associative.
   (a) Show that $S$ is an abelian group with respect to the operation $*$.
   (b) Illustrate that the operation $\circ$ is distributive with respect to $*$.
   (c) Show that the operation $\circ$ is commutative.
   (d) Find all divisors of zero.

## 4-2  CONCEPT OF A MATRIX

In Sec. 3-2 and 3-3 matrices were used to represent mappings, and in this representation a matrix consisted of two rows and a finite number of columns. Matrices may be used to represent linear transformations (in linear algebra), or they may be used to solve systems of equations (Chap. 8). Indeed, there are many situations in which matrices are elements of significant mathematical structures. Matrices are primarily a notational device, and they may consist of any finite number of rows and columns.

Matrix **Definition 4-4. A matrix is a rectangular array of symbols which consists of a finite number of rows and columns.**

A matrix may be used merely to display information. For example, the matrix

$$\begin{pmatrix} R & V & W \\ V & W & R \\ W & R & V \end{pmatrix}$$

may be used to represent the group table for the set of rotations of an equilateral triangle (see Sec. 3-2). Or a matrix may be used to represent the number of ships leaving Boston in the years 1768 to 1772 with destinations Great Britain, Ireland, and Europe. In this case the matrix is of the form

$$
\begin{array}{l}
\text{Great Britain} \\
\text{Ireland} \\
\text{Europe}
\end{array}
\begin{pmatrix}
67 & 66 & 56 & 55 & 57 \\
2 & 1 & 0 & 0 & 1 \\
22 & 20 & 15 & 22 & 11
\end{pmatrix}
$$
$$
\quad\quad 1768 \quad 1769 \quad 1770 \quad 1771 \quad 1772
$$

where the columns represent the years and the rows represent the destinations.† The labels bordering the matrix are not part of the matrix, but are provided for identification. For example, the number in the third row and second column gives the information that 20 ships left Boston in 1769 bound for Europe.

If $m$ and $n$ are positive integers, then a matrix which has $m$ rows and $n$ columns is called an $m \times n$ (read "$m$-by-$n$") matrix; if $m = n$, then the matrix is also called a *square* matrix. The first matrix in the preceding paragraph has three rows and three columns and is a $3 \times 3$ matrix, or a square matrix. The second matrix has three rows and five columns.

*m × n matrix*
*Square matrix*

An element of a matrix is called an *entry*, and if the elements in a matrix are elements of a ring, then we say that the matrix is defined *over the ring*. Each element may be located by an ordered pair of positive integers, the first denoting the row and the second denoting the column in which the given element may be found. For example, the pair $(3,2)$ may denote that element in the third row and the second column. It is more convenient, however, to let an ordered pair of positive integers index a variable, so that we may use the symbol $a_{32}$, read "a three two," to denote that element of a matrix which occurs in the third row and the second column. Indexing variables this way, we shall denote an $m \times n$ matrix by the symbol $(a_{ij})$ for $i = 1, 2, \ldots, m$ and $j = 1, 2, \ldots, n$. Thus a $3 \times 3$ matrix may be represented either by the symbol

*Entry*

$$(a_{ij}) \quad\quad i = 1,2,3; j = 1,2,3$$

or by the matrix

$$
\begin{pmatrix}
a_{11} & a_{12} & a_{13} \\
a_{21} & a_{22} & a_{23} \\
a_{31} & a_{32} & a_{33}
\end{pmatrix}
$$

When there is no possible ambiguity, the range of values of the indices $i$ and $j$ may be inferred from the context of the discussion. Note that $(a_{ij})$ represents the matrix of which $a_{ij}$ is a representative element.

† U.S. Bureau of the Census, "Historical Statistics of the United States, Colonial Times to 1957," p. 759, 1960.

**Equal matrices**     Two matrices $(a_{ij})$ and $(b_{ij})$ are said to be equal,

$$(a_{ij}) \ominus (b_{ij})$$

if for each $i = 1, 2, \ldots, m$ and each $j = 1, 2, \ldots, n$

$$a_{ij} = b_{ij}$$

**Sum of two matrices**     Let $(a_{ij})$ and $(b_{ij})$ be two $m \times n$ matrices over a ring. We define the sum of these two matrices (using the symbol $\oplus$) as that matrix $(c_{ij})$ in which each element $c_{ij} = a_{ij} + b_{ij}$ for $i = 1, 2, \ldots, m$ and $j = 1, 2, \ldots, n$. Thus we may write $(a_{ij}) \oplus (b_{ij}) \ominus (c_{ij})$, or $(a_{ij}) \oplus (b_{ij}) \ominus (a_{ij} + b_{ij})$. If the matrices are each $2 \times 3$ matrices, we may denote their sum by

$$\begin{pmatrix} a_{11} & a_{12} & a_{13} \\ a_{21} & a_{22} & a_{23} \end{pmatrix} \oplus \begin{pmatrix} b_{11} & b_{12} & b_{13} \\ b_{21} & b_{22} & b_{23} \end{pmatrix}$$

$$\ominus \begin{pmatrix} a_{11} + b_{11} & a_{12} + b_{12} & a_{13} + b_{13} \\ a_{21} + b_{21} & a_{22} + b_{22} & a_{23} + b_{23} \end{pmatrix}$$

**Example 4-5.**  Let

$$A = \begin{pmatrix} 3 & {}^{-}2 \\ 0 & 4 \end{pmatrix} \quad \text{and} \quad B = \begin{pmatrix} 1 & 2 \\ 7 & {}^{-}6 \end{pmatrix}$$

In each of these matrices the entries are elements of the ring $Z$ of integers, and both $A$ and $B$ are $2 \times 2$ matrices defined over $Z$. Using the notation $(a_{ij})$ for $A$, $(b_{ij})$ for $B$, and $(c_{ij})$ for $C = A \oplus B$, we have

| | | |
|---|---|---|
| $a_{11} = 3$ | $b_{11} = 1$ | $c_{11} = 4$ |
| $a_{12} = {}^{-}2$ | $b_{12} = 2$ | $c_{12} = 0$ |
| $a_{21} = 0$ | $b_{21} = 7$ | $c_{21} = 7$ |
| $a_{22} = 4$ | $b_{22} = {}^{-}6$ | $c_{22} = {}^{-}2$ |

Consequently,

$$A \oplus B \ominus C = \begin{pmatrix} 4 & 0 \\ 7 & {}^{-}2 \end{pmatrix}$$

Note that $A \oplus B$ is also a $2 \times 2$ matrix defined over $Z$.

From the definition and the preceding example it is clear that the sum of two $m \times n$ matrices defined over a ring is again an $m \times n$ matrix defined over that same ring, so that the set of all $m \times n$ matrices satisfies the closure postulate G-1. A matrix in which each entry is 0 is **Zero matrix**     called a *zero matrix* and will be denoted by $(0)$. Thus

$$(0) = (z_{ij}) \qquad i = 1, 2, \ldots, m; j = 1, 2, \ldots, n$$

where $z_{ij} = 0$ for each $i$ and $j$. If $A = (a_{ij})$ is also an $m \times n$ matrix, then

$(0) \oplus A \ominus A$ and $A \oplus (0) \ominus A$, for

$$(0) \oplus (a_{ij}) \ominus (z_{ij}) \oplus (a_{ij})$$
$$\ominus (z_{ij} + a_{ij})$$
$$\ominus (0 + a_{ij})$$
$$\ominus (a_{ij})$$

and

$$(a_{ij}) \oplus (0) \ominus (a_{ij}) \oplus (z_{ij})$$
$$\ominus (a_{ij} + z_{ij})$$
$$\ominus (a_{ij} + 0)$$
$$\ominus (a_{ij})$$

The zero matrix is therefore the identity with respect to the addition operation $\oplus$. The matrix $^-A = (^-a_{ij})$ is the additive inverse of the matrix $A$, since

$$^-A \oplus A \ominus (^-a_{ij}) \oplus (a_{ij})$$
$$\ominus (^-a_{ij} + a_{ij})$$
$$\ominus (0)$$

and

$$A \oplus {}^-A \ominus (a_{ij}) \oplus (^-a_{ij})$$
$$\ominus (a_{ij} + {}^-a_{ij})$$
$$\ominus (0)$$

**Example 4-6.** Let

$$A = \begin{pmatrix} 3 & ^-2 \\ 0 & 4 \end{pmatrix}$$

which is a $2 \times 2$ matrix defined over $Z$. We write the entries of $A$, together with their additive inverses, with respect to the ring $Z$ as

$$
\begin{aligned}
a_{11} &= 3 & ^-a_{11} &= ^-3 \\
a_{12} &= ^-2 & ^-a_{12} &= 2 \\
a_{21} &= 0 & ^-a_{21} &= 0 \\
a_{22} &= 4 & ^-a_{22} &= ^-4
\end{aligned}
$$

The matrix $^-A$ is given by

$$^-A = \begin{pmatrix} ^-3 & 2 \\ 0 & ^-4 \end{pmatrix}$$

so that

$$^-A \oplus A \ominus \begin{pmatrix} ^-3 + 3 & 2 + ^-2 \\ 0 + 0 & ^-4 + 4 \end{pmatrix} \ominus \begin{pmatrix} 0 & 0 \\ 0 & 0 \end{pmatrix} = (0)$$

the zero matrix. By the commutativity of the additive operation in the ring $Z$, it follows that $A \oplus {}^-A \ominus (0)$, so that the matrix ${}^-A$ is the additive inverse of the matrix $A$.

The associativity of the operation $\oplus$ may be shown in a similar manner. Thus, if $(a_{ij})$, $(b_{ij})$, and $(c_{ij})$ are three $m \times n$ matrices, then

$$
\begin{aligned}
(a_{ij}) \oplus [(b_{ij}) \oplus (c_{ij})] &\ominus (a_{ij}) \oplus (b_{ij} + c_{ij}) \\
&\ominus (a_{ij} + [b_{ij} + c_{ij}]) \\
&\ominus ([a_{ij} + b_{ij}] + c_{ij}) \\
&\ominus (a_{ij} + b_{ij}) \oplus (c_{ij}) \\
&\ominus [(a_{ij}) \oplus (b_{ij})] \oplus (c_{ij})
\end{aligned}
$$

Thus the set of all $m \times n$ matrices is a group with respect to $\oplus$. It is also an abelian group, since the entries are elements of a ring, which is, of course, an abelian group with respect to the additive operation. Thus

$$
\begin{aligned}
(a_{ij}) \oplus (b_{ij}) &\ominus (a_{ij} + b_{ij}) \\
&\ominus (b_{ij} + a_{ij}) \\
&\ominus (b_{ij}) \oplus (a_{ij})
\end{aligned}
$$

**Product of 2 × 2 matrices**

The product of two $2 \times 2$ matrices

$$
(a_{ij}) = \begin{pmatrix} a_{11} & a_{12} \\ a_{21} & a_{22} \end{pmatrix}
$$

and

$$
(b_{ij}) = \begin{pmatrix} b_{11} & b_{12} \\ b_{21} & b_{22} \end{pmatrix}
$$

is defined by

$$
(a_{ij}) \odot (b_{ij}) \ominus \begin{pmatrix} a_{11}b_{11} + a_{12}b_{21} & a_{11}b_{12} + a_{12}b_{22} \\ a_{21}b_{11} + a_{22}b_{21} & a_{21}b_{12} + a_{22}b_{22} \end{pmatrix}
$$

**Example 4-7.** Let $A$ and $B$ be $2 \times 2$ matrices over the ring $Z$ given by

$$
A = (a_{ij}) = \begin{pmatrix} 3 & {}^-2 \\ 0 & 4 \end{pmatrix} \qquad B = (b_{ij}) = \begin{pmatrix} 1 & 2 \\ 7 & {}^-6 \end{pmatrix}
$$

Identifying the entries with those of the definition of the product of two matrices, we have

$$
\begin{aligned}
&a_{11} = 3 \qquad a_{12} = {}^-2 \qquad a_{21} = 0 \qquad a_{22} = 4 \\
&b_{11} = 1 \qquad b_{12} = 2 \qquad b_{21} = 7 \qquad b_{22} = {}^-6 \\
&a_{11}b_{11} + a_{12}b_{21} = 3(1) + {}^-2(7) = {}^-11 \\
&a_{11}b_{12} + a_{12}b_{22} = 3(2) + {}^-2({}^-6) = 18
\end{aligned}
$$

$a_{21}b_{11} + a_{22}b_{21} = 0(1) + 4(7) = 28$
$a_{21}b_{12} + a_{22}b_{22} = 0(2) + 4(^-6) = ^-24$

The product of $A$ and $B$ is therefore

$$A \odot B \ominus \begin{pmatrix} ^-11 & 18 \\ 28 & ^-24 \end{pmatrix}$$

In the same manner, we may find the product of $B$ and $A$:

$$B \odot A \ominus \begin{pmatrix} 3 & 6 \\ 21 & ^-38 \end{pmatrix}$$

Observe that the product of two $2 \times 2$ matrices defined over $Z$ is again a $2 \times 2$ matrix defined over $Z$. Also note that $A \odot B \not\oplus B \odot A$.

From the definition and the preceding example it is clear that the product of two $2 \times 2$ matrices defined over a ring $S$ is a $2 \times 2$ matrix over $S$, so that the set of all $2 \times 2$ matrices satisfies the closure postulate G-1. That the operation is not commutative is demonstrated in Example 4-7. The operation of multiplication is, however, an associative one, and the proof of this fact is left as an exercise (Exercise 6). It is also a fact that multiplication distributes over addition (Exercise 7). Consequently, we have the following theorem:

**Theorem 4-2. The set of all $2 \times 2$ matrices defined over a ring is a ring.**

If $S$ is a ring with multiplicative identity $e$, then the $2 \times 2$ matrix

$$E = \begin{pmatrix} e & 0 \\ 0 & e \end{pmatrix}$$

is a multiplicative identity for the ring of $2 \times 2$ matrices defined over $S$, for if $A = (a_{ij})$, then

$$A \odot E \ominus \begin{pmatrix} a_{11} & a_{12} \\ a_{21} & a_{22} \end{pmatrix} \odot \begin{pmatrix} e & 0 \\ 0 & e \end{pmatrix}$$
$$\ominus \begin{pmatrix} a_{11}e + a_{12}(0) & a_{11}(0) + a_{12}e \\ a_{21}e + a_{22}(0) & a_{21}(0) + a_{22}e \end{pmatrix}$$
$$\ominus \begin{pmatrix} a_{11} & a_{12} \\ a_{21} & a_{22} \end{pmatrix}$$
$$= A$$

Thus $A \odot E \ominus A$. In a similar manner, it can be shown that $E \odot A \ominus A$, so that $E$ is identity element, called the *identity matrix*. Consequently, **Identity matrix** we have our next result:

**Theorem 4-3. The set of all $2 \times 2$ matrices defined over a ring with identity is a ring with identity.**

Since the matrix (0) is the additive identity of the ring of $2 \times 2$ matrices, (0) is an annihilator element, or a zero, of the ring. The following example demonstrates that such a ring may also have zero divisors.

**Example 4-8.** Let $A$ and $B$ be $2 \times 2$ matrices defined over $Z$:

$$A = \begin{pmatrix} 1 & {}^-1 \\ {}^-1 & 1 \end{pmatrix} \qquad B = \begin{pmatrix} 1 & 1 \\ 1 & 1 \end{pmatrix}$$

Neither $A$ nor $B$ is a zero matrix. Their product is found as follows:

$$A \odot B \ominus \begin{pmatrix} 1(1) + {}^-1(1) & 1(1) + {}^-1(1) \\ {}^-1(1) + 1(1) & {}^-1(1) + 1(1) \end{pmatrix}$$

$$\ominus \begin{pmatrix} 0 & 0 \\ 0 & 0 \end{pmatrix}$$

$$= (0)$$

It follows, therefore, that $A$ and $B$ are zero divisors.

For simplicity, we have restricted the definition of the product of the matrices to those with two rows and two columns. The definition of the product for $n \times n$ matrices in general will be given at the end of Chap. 5. With this more general definition, the proofs of Theorems 4-2 and 4-3, with $2 \times 2$ replaced by $n \times n$, still hold, since the definition of the sums of such matrices remains as given.

EXERCISES

**1.** Let $S = \{a,b\}$ and $*$ and $\circ$ be operations on $S$ defined by the tables

| $*$ | $a$ | $b$ |
|---|---|---|
| $a$ | $a$ | $b$ |
| $b$ | $b$ | $a$ |

| $\circ$ | $a$ | $b$ |
|---|---|---|
| $a$ | $a$ | $a$ |
| $b$ | $a$ | $b$ |

Prove that $S$ is a ring.

**2.** Let $S = \{a,b,c\}$ and the operations $\not\!c$ and $\$$ be defined† by the tables

† $x \not\!c y$ and $x \$ y$ may be read "x cent y" and "x dollar y," respectively, but regardless of how they are read, their meanings are given by the tables.

| ¢ | a | b | c |
|---|---|---|---|
| a | a | b | c |
| b | b | c | a |
| c | c | a | b |

| $ | a | b | c |
|---|---|---|---|
| a | a | a | a |
| b | a | b | c |
| c | a | c | b |

Prove that S is a ring.

3. Let $S = \{a,b\}$ and $P_S$ be the power set of $S$ (see Example 1-6). If $\cap$ and $\cup$ are the two operations on $P_S$, for each operation write out the table corresponding to that operation on the elements of $P_S$. Using these two operations, determine whether the system is a ring. Does there exist an annihilator for either operation? If so, what is it?

4. Let $S = \{a,b,c\}$ and $P_S$ be the power set of $S$. With respect to the operation of intersection $\cap$ on $P_S$, which of the postulates for an abelian group hold? With respect to the operation of union $\cup$ on $P_S$, which of the postulates for an abelian group hold? Is $P_S$ a ring? If not, which postulates fail? Is there an annihilator with respect to either operation?

5. Show that, with respect to the usual operations of addition and multiplication, the set of all even integers is a commutative ring without an identity.

6. Show that the operation of multiplication of $2 \times 2$ matrices defined over a ring is associative; that is, show that

$$(a_{ij}) \odot [(b_{ij}) \odot (c_{ij})] \ominus [(a_{ij}) \odot (b_{ij})] \odot (c_{ij})$$

7. Show that for the set of $2 \times 2$ matrices multiplication distributes over addition; that is, show that

$$(a_{ij}) \odot [(b_{ij}) \oplus (c_{ij})] \ominus [(a_{ij}) \odot (b_{ij})] \oplus [(a_{ij}) \odot (c_{ij})]$$

and

$$[(b_{ij}) \oplus (c_{ij})] \odot (a_{ij}) \ominus [(b_{ij}) \odot (a_{ij})] \oplus [(c_{ij}) \odot (a_{ij})]$$

8. Show directly, using the operation of multiplication of $2 \times 2$ matrices, that the matrix (0) is an annihilator element.

9. If $S$ is a ring with a multiplicative identity $e$ and

$$E = \begin{pmatrix} e & 0 \\ 0 & e \end{pmatrix}$$

then show that for any $2 \times 2$ matrix $A$, defined over $S$, $E \odot A \ominus A$.

## 4-3. DEFINITION OF AN INTEGRAL DOMAIN

The ring $Z$ of integers is a commutative ring with identity, but it has the important additional property of having no divisors of zero. An algebraic system which has the same algebraic structure as $Z$ is called an *integral domain*.

Integral domain

**Definition 4-5. An integral domain is a commutative ring with identity which has no zero divisors.**

One of the fundamental properties of an integral domain is that it satisfies the well-known Cancellation Law:

**Cancellation Law. Let a, b, and c be any three elements of a ring; if $c \neq 0$ and $a \circ c = b \circ c$, then $a = b$.**

Some writers define an integral domain as a commutative ring with identity which satisfies the Cancellation Law. In the presence of the other ring postulates, the Cancellation Law is equivalent to the property of having no zero divisors, as we shall now see.

Cancellation Law

**Theorem 4-4. If R is a ring which has no divisors of zero, then it satisfies the Cancellation Law.**

*Hypothesis:* $R$ is a ring which has no divisors of zero
*Conclusion:* $R$ satisfies the Cancellation Law

**Proof:** Let $a, b,$ and $c$ be any three elements of $R$ such that $a \circ c = b \circ c$ and $c \neq 0$. It must be shown that $a = b$.

| Statement | Reason |
|---|---|
| 1. $a \circ c = b \circ c$ | 1. Why? |
| 2. $(a \circ c) * (b \circ c)' = (b \circ c) * (b \circ c)'$ | 2. Why? |
| 3. $(a \circ c) * (b \circ c)' = 0$ | 3. Why? |
| 4. $(a \circ c) * (b \circ c)' = (a * b') \circ c$ | 4. Theorem 4-1 |
| 5. $(a * b') \circ c = 0$ | 5. Why? |
| 6. $a * b' = 0$ or $c = 0$ | 6. 5; no divisors of zero |
| 7. $c \neq 0$ | 7. Why? |
| 8. $a * b' = 0$ | 8. 6, 7; Rule of Disjunction |
| 9. $(a * b') * b = 0 * b$ | 9. Why? |
| 10. $(a * b') * b = b$ | 10. Why? |
| 11. $(a * b') * b = a * (b' * b)$ | 11. Why? |
| 12. $\qquad = a * 0$ | 12. Why? |
| 13. $\qquad = a$ | 13. Why? |
| 14. $a = b$ | 14. Why? |

**Theorem 4-5. If R is a ring which satisfies the Cancellation Law, then R has no divisors of zero.**

*Hypothesis:* R is a ring which satisfies the Cancellation Law
*Conclusion:* R has no divisors of zero

**Proof:**   Let $a$ and $b$ be arbitrary elements of $R$ such that $a \circ b = 0$. It must be shown that $a = 0$ or $b = 0$. If $b = 0$, then we are through (why?). Assume $b \neq 0$.

| Statement | Reason |
|---|---|
| 1. $a \circ b = 0$ | 1. Why? |
| 2. $b \neq 0$ | 2. Why? |
| 3. $0 \circ b = 0$ | 3. Why? |
| 4. $a \circ b = 0 \circ b$ | 4. Why? |
| 5. $a = 0$ | 5. 4,2; Cancellation Law |

By the last two theorems we have shown that an integral domain may be defined with either the Cancellation Law or the property of having no divisors of zero. In each case the system will have exactly the same properties. Many examples of finite rings and integral domains can be constructed with the concept of the congruence relation $\equiv$ on the set of integers.

## 4-4. THE CONGRUENCE RELATION

In Sec. 1-2 a congruence relation $\equiv$ was defined as follows:

Let $m$ be a positive integer; for $a, b \in Z$, $a \equiv b \pmod{m}$ if and only if $a - b$ is divisible by $m$

If no ambiguity may result, we may write simply $a \equiv b$, and say that "$a$ and $b$ are congruent modulo $m$" or "$a$ is congruent to $b$ modulo *Congruence modulo m* $m$." If $a - b$ is not divisible by $m$, we write $a \not\equiv b \pmod{m}$ and say that "$a$ and $b$ are not congruent modulo $m$."

**Example 4-9.**   Let $m = 2$. The difference of any two odd integers is an even integer; therefore, if $a$ and $b$ are odd integers, then $a \equiv b \pmod 2$. Similarly, the difference of any two even integers is an even integer, so that if $a$ and $b$ are even integers, we may write $a \equiv b \pmod 2$.

Consider the integers 3 and 5; since $3 - 5 = {}^-2$, which is divisible by 2, we may write $3 \equiv 5 \pmod 2$.

Consider the integers 7 and 12; since $7 - 12 = {}^-5$, which is not divisible by 2, we may write $7 \not\equiv 12 \pmod 2$.

The relation $\equiv$ of congruence modulo $m$, for $m$ a positive integer, is an equivalence relation. If $x \in Z$, then $x - x = 0$, which is divisible by $m$; consequently, $x \equiv x$ (mod $m$), and the relation is reflexive. If $x$, $y \in Z$ and $x \equiv y$ (mod $m$), then $x - y$ is divisible by $m$; consequently, $-(x - y) = y - x$ is divisible by $m$, and therefore $y \equiv x$ (mod $m$), and it follows that the relation is symmetric. If $x, y, z \in Z, x \equiv y$, and $y \equiv z$ (mod $m$), then $x - y$ and $y - z$ are divisible by $m$; consequently, $m$ divides the sum $(x - y) + (y - z) = x - z$; it follows that $x \equiv z$ (mod $m$), and the relation is transitive.

The integers congruent to 0, 1, 2, 3, 4, and 5 are indicated in Table 4-2 for the modulus 6.

TABLE 4-2

| a | Integers congruent to a, modulo 6 |
|---|---|
| 0 | . . . , $^-12$, $^-6$, 0,  6, 12, . . . |
| 1 | . . . , $^-11$, $^-5$, 1,  7, 13, . . . |
| 2 | . . . , $^-10$, $^-4$, 2,  8, 14, . . . |
| 3 | . . . ,  $^-9$, $^-3$, 3,  9, 15, . . . |
| 4 | . . . ,  $^-8$, $^-2$, 4, 10, 16, . . . |
| 5 | . . . ,  $^-7$, $^-1$, 5, 11, 17, . . . |

It should be apparent from the table that every integer is congruent, or equivalent, to some element of the set $S = \{0,1,2,3,4,5\}$ and that no two elements of $S$ are equivalent modulo 6. For this reason we say that $S$ is the *set of integers reduced, modulo 6*. Consider the usual operations of addition and multiplication on the set $S$ with the stipulation that the sum, or product, be replaced by that element of $S$ with which it is equivalent. Thus $3 + 5 = 8$, and since $8 \equiv 2$ (mod 6), we write $3 + 5 \equiv 2$. Similarly, $3(5) \equiv 3$. With these instructions, we see that the set $S$ is closed with respect to addition and multiplication. It is a simple exercise to verify that the addition and multiplications modulo 6 are those of Example 4-4 (see Exercise 1 following Sec. 4-5). From that example we have that the set of integers reduced, modulo 6, is a commutative ring with identity which has zero divisors. In Example 4-10 we use the same procedure to construct a commutative ring with identity which has no zero divisors and is therefore an integral domain.

**Example 4-10.** Let $m = 3$ and let $\equiv$ represent congruence modulo 3. Let $S = \{0,1,2\}$; then $S$ is the set of integers reduced, modulo 3. If we consider all possible sums and products of elements in $S$, we obtain the tables representing addition and multiplication modulo 3:

| + | 0 | 1 | 2 |
|---|---|---|---|
| 0 | 0 | 1 | 2 |
| 1 | 1 | 2 | 0 |
| 2 | 2 | 0 | 1 |

| · | 0 | 1 | 2 |
|---|---|---|---|
| 0 | 0 | 0 | 0 |
| 1 | 0 | 1 | 2 |
| 2 | 0 | 2 | 1 |

A check with the group postulates will show that with respect to the operation $+$ the set $S$ is an abelian group of order 3. With respect to the operation $\cdot$ the set $S$ satisfies all the postulates for an abelian group except G-4. With respect to the operation $\cdot$, it can be seen from the table that there are no zero divisors; it can also be shown that the distributive property of $\cdot$ with respect to $+$ holds, so that the system is an integral domain. Note that if we eliminate the element 0 from the set, the elements 1 and 2 form, with respect to $\cdot$, an abelian group of order 2.

For any modulus $m$ the set of integers reduced, modulo $m$, forms a commutative ring with identity. However, if $m$ is a prime number, the system is an integral domain. Whether a finite ring has zero divisors can be readily determined by a consideration of the multiplication table for that ring. It is possible, but often tedious, to determine directly whether a ring satisfies the Cancellation Law, but if it has no zero divisors, then, by Theorem 4-4, we know that it satisfies the Cancellation Law.

## 4-5. EQUIVALENCE CLASSES

It is useful to consider, briefly, the partition which is induced upon any given set by an equivalence relation defined on that set. A *partition* of a set $S$ is a collection of subsets of $S$ such that (1) every element of $S$ is in some subset of the collection and (2) any two different subsets of the collection are disjoint (have no elements in common). It can be shown that any equivalence relation on a set determines a partition of the set. Each of the subsets of the partition, or collection, is called an *equivalence class*.

Table 4-2 exhibits a partition of the set $Z$ of integers which is determined by the equivalence relation *congruence modulo 6*. One of these equivalence classes, for example, is the set $\{. . . , ^{-}12, ^{-}6, 0, 6, 12, . . .\} = \{6k | k \in Z\} = \{x | x \in Z, z \equiv 0 \pmod 6\}$. From the table it should be clear that every integer is included in some class and that no

**Partition**

**Equivalence class**

integer is included in two different classes. Furthermore, any two integers from the same class are equivalent—that is, they are congruent modulo 6—and two integers from different classes are not equivalent—that is, they are not congruent modulo 6. Such a property is characteristic of equivalence classes which are determined by a given equivalence relation. When an equivalence relation is a congruence, the equivalence classes are sometimes called *congruence classes*.

**Congruence classes**

Given an algebraic system with set $S$ and an equivalence relation on $S$, there is correspondingly determined a partition of $S$. One or more binary operations may be defined on the collection of equivalence classes thus determined. With appropriate definitions of the operations, an additional algebraic system can be determined which is closely related to the given system. A detailed study of this situation is beyond the scope of this book, but it is appropriate to indicate the procedure, as it can be used in studying the set of integers reduced, modulo 6.

Consider the six equivalence classes indicated in Table 4-2. These classes may be written as follows:

$$A_0 = \{6k + 0 \mid k \in Z\}$$
$$A_1 = \{6k + 1 \mid k \in Z\}$$
$$A_2 = \{6k + 2 \mid k \in Z\}$$
$$A_3 = \{6k + 3 \mid k \in Z\}$$
$$A_4 = \{6k + 4 \mid k \in Z\}$$
$$A_5 = \{6k + 5 \mid k \in Z\}$$

The partition $P$ determined by the equivalence relation congruence modulo 6 is

$$P = \{A_0, A_1, A_2, A_3, A_4, A_5\}$$

An operation $\oplus$ can be defined on $P$ as

$A_r \oplus A_s = A_t$, where $r, s \in \{0,1,2,3,4,5\}$ and $t$ is the smallest nonnegative integer such that $r + s \equiv t \pmod{6}$

For example, $A_2 \oplus A_3 = A_5$ and $A_3 \oplus A_5 = A_2$. It can be shown that the operation $\oplus$ is well defined, and furthermore that the system $<P, \oplus>$ is an abelian group. Similarly, another operation $\odot$ can be defined on $P$ such that $A_r \odot A_s = A_t$, where $t$ is the smallest nonnegative integer such that $rs \equiv t \pmod{6}$. This operation is also well defined, and it can be shown that the system $<P, \oplus, \odot>$ is a commutative ring with identity (see Exercise 5). With some justification, each equivalence class can be denoted by any element of the class. Thus $A_2$ is the class containing the integer 2, and we may use that integer to denote the class. In this way the set of integers reduced, modulo 6, can be discussed in terms of equivalence classes and be shown to be a commutative ring with identity.

A similar procedure will be used in Chap. 5 in considering the set of rational numbers as a set of ordered pairs of integers.

## EXERCISES

1. Construct the addition and multiplication tables for the ring of integers reduced, modulo 6.
2. Construct the addition and multiplication tables for the ring of integers reduced, modulo 4. Determine whether the Cancellation Law holds for this ring. Is it an integral domain?
3. Construct the addition and multiplication tables for the ring of integers reduced, modulo 5. Does it have any zero divisors? Is it an integral domain?
4. For each of the following, determine whether the ring of integers reduced, modulo $m$, is an integral domain. If it is not an integral domain, find at least one pair of zero divisors.

   (a) $m = 2$       (e) $m = 10$
   (b) $m = 7$       (f) $m = 19$
   (c) $m = 8$       (g) $m = 51$
   (d) $m = 9$       (h) $m = 101$

5. Consider the discussion of Sec. 4-5. If $A_r \in P$, then any element $x \in A_r$ may be written as $x = 6k_1 + r$ for some $k_1 \in Z$. Similarly, if $A_s \in P$ and $y \in A_s$, then $y = 6k_2 + s$ for some $k_2 \in Z$. $x$ and $y$ are sometimes called *representative elements* of $A_r$ and $A_s$, respectively. It can be shown that the definition of $\oplus$ is equivalent to the following:

   $$A_r \oplus A_s = A_t \text{ if and only if, for } x \in A_r \text{ and } y \in A_s, x + y \in A_t$$

   Assume that $\oplus$ and $\odot$ are well-defined operations on $P$.

   (a) Write an equivalent definition of $\odot$.
   (b) Show by using representative elements that $\oplus$ is a commutative operation, $\oplus$ is an associative operation, $\odot$ is an associative operation, and $\odot$ distributes over $\oplus$.
   (c) Construct the addition and multiplication tables for the operations $\oplus$ and $\odot$ defined on $P$.

   From parts (b) and (c), show that $<P,\oplus>$ is an abelian group, $<P,\oplus,\odot>$ is a commutative ring with identity, and $<P,\oplus,\odot>$ is not an integral domain.

**6.** Let $P_1$ be the partition determined by the equivalence relation congruence modulo 3. Then $B_0 = \{3k + 0 | k \in Z\}$, $B_1 = \{3k + 1 | k \in Z\}$, and $B_2 = \{3k + 2 | k \in Z\}$ are the three equivalence classes of $P_1$. Following the pattern of discussion in Sec. 4-5 and Exercise 5:

(a) Define operations $\oplus$ and $\odot$ on $P_1$.
(b) Show by using representative elements that $\oplus$ and $\odot$ are associative operations.
(c) Show that $<P_1, \oplus, \odot>$ is an integral domain.

**7.** Let $P_2$ be the partition determined by the equivalence relation congruence modulo 4. Define operations $\oplus$ and $\odot$ on $P_2$ similar to those of Exercises 5 and 6. Show that $<P_2, \oplus, \odot>$ is a commutative ring with identity but is not an integral domain.

**8.** Determine whether the ring of even integers is an integral domain.

## Invitations to Extended Study

**1.** Let $G$ be an abelian group with operation $*$ and identity $e$. If a second operation $\circ$ is defined between pairs of elements of $G$ so that $a \circ b = e$ for every $a, b \in G$, show that the resulting algebraic system is a ring. Is it an integral domain?

**2.** Let $S$ be the ring of integers reduced, modulo 3 and $M$ be the set of all $2 \times 2$ matrices defined over $S$. Show that with respect to the operations of addition and multiplication as defined in Sec. 4-2, the system is a ring. Is it an integral domain?

**3.** In the ring of $2 \times 2$ matrices over the ring of integers $Z$, every matrix has an additive inverse, whereas not all such matrices have multiplicative inverses. Find at least three matrices of the system which have multiplicative inverses.

**4.** Let $S$ be the ring of integers reduced, modulo 7. Construct the multiplication table and show that each nonzero element has a multiplicative inverse in $S$.

**5.** If $p$ is a prime, let $Z_p$ be the set of integers reduced, modulo $p$. Show that each nonzero element of $Z_p$ has a multiplicative inverse in $Z_p$.

# CHAPTER 5

# THE CONCEPTS OF FIELD AND VECTOR SPACE

## Guidelines for Careful Study

In Chaps. 3 and 4 certain algebraic systems were studied; the concept of group was found to be a basic building block in the formation of systems such as rings and integral domains. In this chapter we shall see how the group concept is useful in defining a field and a vector space, and certain important fields will be studied in some detail. The following questions will provide a guide to the careful study of Chap. 5.

1. What is a field? How does it differ from an integral domain?
2. Give a definition of the field of rational numbers.
3. If the ring of integers is extended to a field, can the ordering relation also be extended?
4. What is an ordered field?
5. What is the difference between a square root and a principle square root?
6. What is an irrational number?
7. What is an upper bound for a set of numbers? Does every set of numbers have an upper bound? A smallest upper bound?
8. What is a real number?
9. What properties distinguish the set of real numbers from the set of rational numbers?
10. What is a vector space? How does it differ from a field?
11. What is meant by a basis and the dimension of a vector space?
12. How may vectors be represented geometrically?

**13.** What is a complex number?

**14.** What is the axis of reals? The axis of imaginaries?

**15.** What are the real and imaginary components of a complex number?

**16.** How may the set of complex numbers be regarded as a vector space?

**17.** How may the set of complex numbers be regarded as a number field?


## Introduction

As we have seen, a ring and an integral domain are algebraic systems which consist of a set and two operations defined on that set along with certain basic properties which characterize each system. In this chapter we shall define a *field,* a system which also consists of one set and two operations, but with properties that are a bit more restrictive than those of either a ring or integral domain. The only operations postulated are addition and multiplication; however, we may use these operations, together with the concept of inverse elements, to define two additional operations in a field, subtraction and division. We shall then define a *vector space,* which, in contrast to a field, consists of two sets, each with its own algebraic structure. One of these structures is a field, and the other is an abelian group; it will also be necessary to define an additional operation which establishes a relationship between the two structures.


## 5-1. THE DEFINITION OF A FIELD

As in the case of an integral domain, a field may be defined in terms of a ring.

Field    **Definition 5-1. A field is a ring in which the set of nonzero elements form an abelian group with respect to the multiplicative operation of the ring.**

A field, then, is a commutative ring with identity such that each element other than zero (the additive identity) has a multiplicative inverse, that is, an inverse with respect to the second operation of the ring. The following frequently used definition of a field is equivalent to Definition 5-1:

**Definition 5-1'. A field is a set F with two operations, $*$ and $\circ$, such that F is an abelian group with respect to $*$, the set F less the zero element is an abelian group with respect to $\circ$, and $\circ$ distributes over $*$. A field may be denoted by $<F,*,\circ>$.**

The proof of the equivalence of these two definitions is left as an exercise (Exercise 6).

Not every integral domain is a field; for example, the set of integers with the usual operations of addition and multiplication is an integral domain, but the only elements which have multiplicative inverses are 1 and ⁻1. It can be proved, however, that every finite integral domain is a field; consequently, several systems of Sec. 4-4 are *finite* fields. In particular, the ring of integers reduced, modulo $p$, for a prime number $p$, is an integral domain which consists of a finite number of elements **Finite field** and is, consequently, a field. The set of rational numbers constitutes a field, as does the set of real numbers and also the set of complex numbers. These are three examples of *infinite* fields. **Infinite field**

If should be observed that a field must have a minimum of two elements. With respect to the first operation, addition, a field must be an abelian group, which implies that the set must contain an additive identity 0. Furthermore, the nonzero elements must satisfy the group properties, so that there is guaranteed the existence of an element 1, the multiplicative identity, which is distinct from the additive identity.

Although every integral domain is not a field, every field is an integral domain. To prove this statement we note that a field is a commutative ring with identity, so that we need only show that in a field there are no zero divisors, or equivalently, that the Cancellation Law holds. Since the multiplicative operation is commutative, we need only show that if $ab = ac$ and $a \neq 0$, then $b = c$. If $a \neq 0$, there exists an element $a'$ in the field such that $a'a = 1$. Assuming, then, that $ab = ac$, we have

$$a'(ab) = a'(ac)$$
$$(a'a)b = (a'a)c$$
$$1b = 1c$$
$$b = c$$

This proves that the Cancellation Law with respect to multiplication holds in a field, and it follows that a field is an integral domain.

Two operations other than addition and multiplication are usually associated with a field, but they may be defined as inverses of the given operations, and no additional postulates need be added to the system. Let $G$ be an abelian group with operation $*$. If $b$ is an arbitrary element of $G$, then the inverse of $b$ will be denoted as $b'$, and the identity element of $G$ will be denoted as $e$. Thus

$$b * b' = b' * b = e$$

We define an operation $\Delta$ (del) on $G$ as follows: If $a, b \in G$, then $a \Delta b = a * b'$. The "product" $a \Delta b$ is read "$a$ del $b$." The operation

$\Delta$, which is a well-defined binary operation, is called the *inverse operation of* $*$. In general, it satisfies only one of the postulates of an abelian group, that of closure.

For the ring of integers, subtraction is the inverse operation of addition, and in accordance with the preceding paragraph, we may define the *difference* of two integers $x$ and $y$ by

$$x - y = x + {}^{-}y \tag{5-1}$$

**Subtraction**   In this way the operation of *subtraction* associates with any two integers $x$ and $y$ an integer, namely, the sum of $x$ and the additive inverse of $y$. This definition is equivalent to other definitions of subtraction of integers. For example, the difference $x - y$ may be defined† as the integer $d$ such that $d + y = x$. From this definition we may solve for $d$:

$$(d + y) + {}^{-}y = x + {}^{-}y$$
$$d + (y + {}^{-}y) = x + {}^{-}y$$
$$d + 0 = x + {}^{-}y$$
$$d = x + {}^{-}y$$

Conversely, if $d = x + {}^{-}y$, as in Eq. (5-1), it then follows that

$$d + y = (x + {}^{-}y) + y$$
$$= x + ({}^{-}y + y)$$
$$= x + 0$$
$$= x$$

The two definitions are thus seen to be equivalent, since each implies the other.

**Division**   In a similar manner, over any field an operation of *division* may be defined as the inverse of multiplication. For example, if $x$ and $y$ are elements of a field, with $y \neq 0$, then

$$x \div y = x \frac{1}{y}$$

where $1/y$ is the multiplicative inverse of $y$. The exclusion of the element 0 from the definition is necessary, since 0 has no multiplicative inverse. Thus division by 0 is never allowed; that is, $x \div 0$ is not defined for any element $x$ of the field. However,

$$0 \div y = 0 \frac{1}{y} = 0$$

for every $y \neq 0$. The symbol $x/y$ is used to represent the unique num-

---

† F. Lynwood Wren, "Basic Mathematical Concepts," pp. 80, 83, McGraw-Hill Book Company, New York, 1965.

ber $z$ such that $z = x \div y$. We could have defined the quotient of $x$ and $y$ as the number $z$ such that $zy = x$,† but, as before, the definitions are equivalent.

## EXERCISES

1. Construct addition and multiplication tables for a field of order 2 (a field with exactly two elements).
2. Construct addition and multiplication tables for a field of order 3.
3. Construct addition and multiplication tables for a field of order 5.
4. Give an example of an infinite integral domain which is not a field.
5. Write a formal proof showing that the Cancellation Law holds in a field.
6. Prove the equivalence of Definitions 5-1 and 5-1′.
7. Show that in a field each of the following properties holds:

(a) $^-(x - y) = y - x$

(d) $\dfrac{1}{xy} = \dfrac{1}{x}\dfrac{1}{y}$   $x \neq 0,\ y \neq 0$

(b) $\dfrac{1}{x/y} = \dfrac{y}{x}$   $x \neq 0,\ y \neq 0$

(e) $xz - yz = (x - y)z$

(c) $^-(x + y) = {}^-x - y$

8. Prove the equivalence of the two definitions of division given in this section.

## 5-2. THE FIELD OF RATIONAL NUMBERS

If $a$ and $b$ are arbitrary elements of a field $F$, then the expression $a^2 - b^2$ is an element of $F$ which may be expressed as the product of the factors $a + b$ and $a - b$, each of which is an element of $F$. However, the expression $a^2 + b^2$ may or may not be expressible as the product of factors in $F$. In this case there is a question of whether $F$ can be extended to a "larger" field in which such expressions can be factored. In fact, a more general question may be asked: Can an algebraic system be extended to a "larger" system which satisfies at least the same postulates? Is it possible, for example, to extend an integral domain to such a "larger" system? It is the purpose of this section to extend the domain of integers $Z$ to the field $Q$ of rational numbers without losing any of the properties of the integral domain. The technique used is fundamentally the same as that for extending any arbitrary integral domain to a field.

† *Ibid.*, pp. 107, 112.

Our procedure is first to define a set $S$, whose elements are ordered pairs of integers, and then to define an equivalence relation on $S$. This equivalence relation, in turn, will determine a partition $Q$ of equivalence classes of $S$. Appropriate operations will be defined on $Q$ in such a manner that the resulting system will be a field. A proper subset of $Q$ will be identified with the set $Z$ of integers, and this subset will have the same algebraic structure as the domain of integers. When this has been accomplished, we may say that we have *extended* the integral domain $Z$ to the field $Q$ or that we have *embedded* $Z$ in $Q$. The set $Q$ will be defined as the set of rational numbers.

The postulates of an integral domain will be assumed to hold on the set $Z = \{\ldots, -3, -2, -1, 0, 1, 2, 3, \ldots\}$, where the additive and multiplicative operations will be represented, as usual, by $+$ and $\cdot$. Juxtaposition of symbols will also be used to represent multiplication, and the minus sign will be used to represent additive inverses as well as the inverse operation of subtraction. In the following development additional symbols will be used to represent equivalence, addition, subtraction, and multiplication of rational numbers, and these symbols are to have only the properties with which we endow them; no additional properties should be inferred from any previous knowledge of rational numbers.

**Definition 5-2. Let $S = \{(a,b)|a,b \in Z; \; b \neq 0\}$. For $(a,b)$ and $(c,d)$ in $S$, $(a,b) \ominus (c,d)$ if and only if $ad = bc$.**

The symbol $\ominus$ may be called "circle equal," but the expression $(a,b) \ominus (c,d)$ is to be read "the ordered pair $(a,b)$ is equivalent to the ordered pair $(c,d)$." Theorem 5-1, which justifies the expression "is equivalent to," is easy to prove, and its proof is left as an exercise (Exercise 1).

**Partition of S**

**Theorem 5-1. The relation $\ominus$ is an equivalence relation on $S$.**

The equivalence relation $\ominus$ determines a partition of $S$ into equivalence classes (Sec. 4-5), where any two ordered pairs of $S$ are in the same equivalence class if and only if they are equivalent in the sense of Definition 5-2. For example, $(2,3)$, $(4,6)$, and $(-2,-3)$ are in the same equivalence class. If $(a,b) \in S$, we shall denote by $a/b$ the equivalence class containing $(a,b)$ and all ordered pairs of $S$ which are equivalent to $(a,b)$. That is, if $(a,b) \ominus (c,d)$, then the equivalence class $a/b$ is the same as the equivalence class $c/d$, or $a/b = c/d$. For example, since $\cdots -6/-9 = -4/-6 = -2/-3 = 2/3 = 4/6 = 6/9 = \cdots$, these symbols all represent the same equivalence class, and any one of them, say $2/3$, may be used as the symbol to indicate the designated set of ordered pairs of $S$, namely, the equivalence class $\frac{2}{3} = \{\cdots, (-6,-9), (-4,-6), (-2,-3), (2,3), (4,6), (6,9), \cdots\}$.

**Definition 5-3. A rational number is any equivalence class of the partition of the set S which is determined by the equivalence relation ⊜.**

As a consequence of this definition and Definition 5-2,

$$\frac{a}{b} = \frac{c}{d} \text{ if and only if } ad = bc$$

This statement may be read "the rational number $a/b$ is the same as the rational number $c/d$ if and only if the integer $ad$ is the same as the integer $bc$." We shall use $Q$ to denote the set of all rational numbers, that is, the set of all equivalence classes $a/b$ for $(a,b) \in S$. Thus

$$Q = \left\{ \frac{a}{b} \middle| a, b \in Z; b \neq 0 \right\}$$

Elements $a/b$ of $Q$ are sometimes called *fractions*, of which $a$ is the numerator and $b$ the denominator. It should be emphasized that $a/b$ denotes a set of ordered pairs of integers any two of which are equivalent in the sense of Definition 5-2. Furthermore, at this point, there should be no association of this symbol with an operation of division.

We shall now define a binary operation ⊕, called "circle plus," which will serve as an additive operation on $Q$ and may be read as "plus." The definition will be given in terms of the additive operation on the set $Z$ of integers:

**Definition 5-4. Let a/b, c/d ∈ Q: then**

$$\frac{a}{b} \oplus \frac{c}{d} = \frac{ad + bc}{bd}$$

By the definition of $Q$, neither of the integers $b$ and $d$ in Definition 5-4 is zero; hence their product is not zero; consequently, the sum of two rational numbers is a rational number. For example, $\frac{1}{2}$ and $\frac{2}{3}$ are elements of $Q$, so

$$\frac{1}{2} \oplus \frac{2}{3} = \frac{1(3) + 2(2)}{2(3)} = \frac{7}{6}$$

From the definition it is clear that ⊕ is a binary operation, but before we proceed, we must make certain that the operation is well-defined. To show that the operation is well-defined we must prove the proposition:

$$\text{If } \frac{a}{b} = \frac{w}{x} \text{ and } \frac{c}{d} = \frac{y}{z}, \text{ then } \frac{a}{b} \oplus \frac{c}{d} = \frac{w}{x} \oplus \frac{y}{z}$$

By Definition 5-3, the assumption $a/b = w/x$ is equivalent to the statement $ax = bw$, and the assumption $c/d = y/z$ is equivalent to the statement $cz = dy$. As a consequence of Definitions 5-2 and 5-4, proving the statements $a/b \oplus c/d = w/x \oplus y/z$ is equivalent to proving that $(ad + bc)/bd = (wz + xy)/xz$, which in turn is equivalent to proving that $(ad + bc)xz = bd(wz + xy)$. The substitution rule now makes it possible to prove that the operation $\oplus$ is well-defined by proving the equivalent proposition:

If $ax = bw$ and $cz = dy$, then $(ad + bc)xz = bd(wz + xy)$

But the proof of this is just an exercise in using the postulates of an integral domain:

$$
\begin{aligned}
(ad + bc)xz &= adxz + bcxz & &\text{why?} \\
&= zd(ax) + bx(cz) & &\text{why?} \\
&= zd(bw) + bx(dy) & &\text{hypothesis, substitution} \\
&= bd(zw) + bd(xy) & &\text{why?} \\
&= bd(wz + xy) & &\text{why?}
\end{aligned}
$$

It follows, then, that the operation $\oplus$ is well-defined.

We now proceed to examine the postulates for an abelian group with respect to the operation $\oplus$ on the set $Q$. That the property of closure holds is obvious from the definition of $\oplus$ and the subsequent discussion. The element $0/1$ is an element of $Q$, and since

$$
\frac{0}{1} \oplus \frac{a}{b} = \frac{0b + 1a}{1b} = \frac{a}{b}
$$

and, similarly,

$$
\frac{a}{b} \oplus \frac{0}{1} = \frac{a}{b}
$$

**Additive identity for Q**

the element $0/1$ is an identity with respect to $\oplus$. It should be observed that for any integer $c \neq 0$, $0/c = 0/1$, so that $0/c$ may serve equally well as an identity element.

If $a/b$ is an element of $Q$, then so is $^-a/b$, where $^-a$ is the additive inverse of the integer $a$. Since

$$
\frac{^-a}{b} \oplus \frac{a}{b} = \frac{^-ab + ab}{bb} = \frac{0}{b^2} = \frac{0}{1}
$$

and similarly,

$$
\frac{a}{b} \oplus \frac{^-a}{b} = \frac{0}{1}
$$

we see that $^-a/b$ is the additive inverse of $a/b$; that is,

$$
{}^-\!\left(\frac{a}{b}\right) = \frac{^-a}{b}
$$

In this connection, it should also be noted that $^-a/b = a/^-b$ (why?), so that the additive inverse may be represented in several ways. In general, we use $^-a/b$ for the additive inverse of $a/b$. The operation $\oplus$ is associative and commutative, and the proof of these properties is left as an exercise (Exercise 2). From the foregoing we have our next result:

**Theorem 5-2. The set Q of rational numbers is an abelian group with respect to the operation $\oplus$.**

If $c$ is any nonzero integer, and if $a/b \in Q$, then from the fact that $a(bc) = b(ac)$ it follows that

$$\frac{a}{b} = \frac{ac}{bc}$$

From this fact and the definition of $\oplus$, we see, by a straightforward argument, that

$$\frac{a}{c} \oplus \frac{b}{c} = \frac{a+b}{c}$$

For example,

$$\frac{1}{4} \oplus \frac{2}{4} = \frac{3}{4}$$

Thus we may add two or more fractions by converting each of them to an equivalent fraction with a common denominator and then finding the sum of the resulting fractions.

**Example 5-1.**   Find the sum $\dfrac{1}{3} \oplus \dfrac{2}{5} \oplus \dfrac{3}{10}$.

The integers 3, 5, and 10 have as a common multiple the integer 30. Thus we may write

$$\frac{1}{3} = \frac{1(10)}{3(10)} = \frac{10}{30} \qquad \frac{2}{5} = \frac{2(6)}{5(6)} = \frac{12}{30} \qquad \frac{3}{10} = \frac{3(3)}{10(3)} = \frac{9}{30}$$

so that

$$\begin{aligned}
\frac{1}{3} \oplus \frac{2}{5} \oplus \frac{3}{10} &= \frac{10}{30} \oplus \frac{12}{30} \oplus \frac{9}{30} \\
&= \frac{10 + 12 + 9}{30} \\
&= \frac{31}{30}
\end{aligned}$$

The sum of the three rational numbers is $\frac{31}{30}$. The result would have been the same had we made direct use of Definition 5-4.

We now define a multiplicative operation on the set $Q$ of rational numbers. The operation will be denoted by $\odot$, called "circle times," and the set of nonzero elements of $Q$ will be seen to satisfy the postulates of an abelian group with respect to $\odot$. The definition will be given in terms of the usual multiplicative operation of the integers:

**Product of two rational numbers**

**Definition 5-5. Let a/b, c/d $\in$ Q; then**

$$\frac{a}{b} \odot \frac{c}{d} = \frac{ac}{bd}$$

Since neither $b$ nor $d$ is zero (why?), it follows that $bd \neq 0$, so that the definition assigns to two rational numbers a third rational number, called the product, or "circle product." We must determine that the operation is well-defined; that is,

$$\text{If } \frac{a}{b} = \frac{w}{x} \text{ and } \frac{c}{d} = \frac{y}{z}, \text{ then } \frac{a}{b} \odot \frac{c}{d} = \frac{w}{x} \odot \frac{y}{z}$$

The proof of this is left as an exercise (Exercise 3).

From Definition 5-5, it is clear that the operation $\odot$ is a binary operation, and the set $Q$ is closed with respect to that operation. The element $1/1$ is an identity with respect to multiplication (explain). If

**Multiplicative identity for Q**

$c \neq 0$, then $c/c = 1/1$, so that the multiplicative identity may be written in many forms. The proof that the multiplicative operation is associative and commutative is left as an exercise (Exercise 4).

Let us now consider which of the elements of $Q$ have a multiplicative inverse. If the element $a/b$ were to have a multiplicative inverse, say $x/y$, then their product must be the identity element; that is,

$$\frac{a}{b} \odot \frac{x}{y} = \frac{1}{1}$$

or

$$\frac{ax}{by} = \frac{1}{1}$$

which is equivalent to the statement

$$ax = by$$

provided, of course, that we do not allow the integer 0 to occur in any of the denominators. From what we know about integers, we can see

**Multiplicative inverse for Q**

that if $x = b$ and $y = a$, then the last equality will hold. Therefore we can produce an inverse of the element $a/b$, namely, $b/a$, provided $a \neq 0$. Thus each of the elements of $Q$ except the additive identity $0/1$ will have an inverse. From the preceding discussion we have the following theorem:

**Theorem 5-3.** The set of nonzero elements of Q form an abelian group with respect to the operation $\odot$.

The property of distributivity of $\odot$ over $\oplus$ is stated in the usual way:

If $r, s, t \in Q$, then $r \odot (s \oplus t) = (r \odot s) \oplus (r \odot t)$ and
$$(s \oplus t) \odot r = (s \odot r) \oplus (t \odot r)$$

The proof is left as an exercise (Exercise 5). We are now able to state our next result:

**Theorem 5-4.** The set of rational numbers is a field.

To prove the additive and multiplicative properties for equality of rational numbers we must show that if $a/b = c/d$, then

$$\frac{a}{b} \oplus \frac{x}{y} = \frac{c}{d} \oplus \frac{x}{y}$$

and

$$\frac{a}{b} \odot \frac{x}{y} = \frac{c}{d} \odot \frac{x}{y}$$

for rational numbers $a/b$, $c/d$, and $x/y$. The proof of the additive property is left as an exercise (Exercise 8). To prove the multiplicative property we first assume that $a/b = c/d$. Consequently, $ad = bc$, and if $x$ and $y$ are integers, then

$$(ad)(xy) = (bc)(xy) \qquad \text{why?}$$

and

$$(ax)(dy) = (cx)(by) \qquad \text{why?}$$

From our assumption, $b \neq 0$ and $d \neq 0$; if $y \neq 0$, then we also have $by \neq 0$, and $dy \neq 0$ (why?). Consequently,

$$\frac{ax}{by} = \frac{cx}{dy} \qquad \text{why?}$$

or

$$\frac{a}{b} \odot \frac{x}{y} = \frac{c}{d} \odot \frac{x}{y} \qquad \text{why?}$$

Similarly, it can be shown that

$$\frac{x}{y} \odot \frac{a}{b} = \frac{x}{y} \odot \frac{c}{d}$$

This proves that equality of rational numbers has the multiplicative property. Note that there is no indication of how the proof may have

been discovered. An examination of the steps, in reverse order, should suggest the technique of discovery.

**Division**

Since the nonzero rational numbers form an abelian group with respect to multiplication, we may consider the corresponding inverse operation, called *division*. Let $a/b$, $c/d \in Q$; then $a$, $b$, $c$, $d \in Z$ and $b$, $d \neq 0$. Furthermore, if $c \neq 0$, then the multiplicative inverse of $c/d$ is $d/c$, since

$$\frac{c}{d} \odot \frac{d}{c} = \frac{cd}{dc} = \frac{1}{1}$$

If we let $\ominus$ represent the operation of division, then we define†

$$\frac{a}{b} \ominus \frac{c}{d} = \frac{a}{b} \odot \frac{d}{c} = \frac{ad}{bc}$$

**Example 5-2.** $\quad \dfrac{3}{4} \ominus \dfrac{5}{7} = \dfrac{3}{4} \odot \dfrac{7}{5} = \dfrac{3(7)}{4(5)} = \dfrac{21}{20}$

**Example 5-3.** $\quad \dfrac{1}{4} \ominus \dfrac{3}{2} = \dfrac{1}{4} \odot \dfrac{2}{3} = \dfrac{1(2)}{4(3)}$

Since $\dfrac{1(2)}{4(3)}$ may be written as $\dfrac{1(2)}{6(2)}$ and, from the discussion following Theorem 5-2, $\dfrac{1(2)}{6(2)} = \dfrac{1}{6}$, we have

$$\frac{1}{4} \ominus \frac{3}{2} = \frac{1(2)}{4(3)} = \frac{1}{6}$$

**Example 5-4.** $\quad \dfrac{3}{4} \ominus \dfrac{3}{2} = \dfrac{3}{4} \odot \dfrac{2}{3} = \dfrac{3(2)}{4(3)} = \dfrac{1(3)(2)}{2(3)(2)} = \dfrac{1}{2}$

We shall now consider an ordering of the rational numbers. Following our pattern of development, our definition will depend on the usual ordering of the integers. Recall that if $a \in Z$ and $a > 0$, then $a$ is called a positive integer. If $a < 0$, then $a$ is a negative integer. By the trichotomy property of integers, exactly one of the following holds: $a > 0$, $a < 0$, or $a = 0$. If $a/b \in Q$, then $a$, $b \in Z$ and $b \neq 0$. If $a$ and $b$ are both positive, or if $a$ and $b$ are both negative, then we say that $a/b$ is *positive*. If $a = 0$, then $a/b$ is *zero*. If $a/b$ is neither positive nor zero, then it is said to be *negative*. Thus we have a corresponding trichotomy

† For a different but equivalent definition of division see *ibid.*, pp. 107, 112.

property for the rational numbers. Since we now have the concept of positive rational numbers, it is possible to define an order relation ⧀, read "less than," on the set of rational numbers.

**Definition 5-6.** If r, s ∈ Q, then r ⧀ s if and only if there exists a positive number t ∈ Q such that r ⊕ t = s.

Order relation
on set Q

To determine the order property of two rational numbers it is sometimes convenient to use a test different from but equivalent to Definition 5-6. This test, which involves subtraction (see discussion, p. 114), may be stated in either of two forms:

1. r ⧀ s if and only if s ⊖ r is positive.
2. r ⧀ s if and only if r ⊖ s is negative.

Notice that if r ∈ Q, then there exist integers a and b, b ≠ 0, such that r = a/b. Here the symbol = refers to an identification of the variable r with the equivalence class a/b, and it refers neither to the equality of integers nor to the equality of rational numbers.

**Example 5-5.**  Show that ⁻1/2 ⧀ ⁻2/5.

$$\frac{^-2}{5} \ominus \frac{^-1}{2} = \frac{^-2}{5} \oplus \frac{1}{2} \qquad \text{why?}$$
$$= \frac{^-4}{10} \oplus \frac{5}{10} \qquad \text{why?}$$
$$= \frac{^-4 + 5}{10}$$
$$= \frac{1}{10}$$

which is a positive rational number. Consequently, the difference is positive, and ⁻1/2 ⧀ ⁻2/5.

It is easy to show (see Exercise 6) that if r, s ∈ Q, then s ⊖ r is positive if and only if r ⊖ s is negative. From this, together with the foregoing, we can show (Exercise 7) that the following theorem holds:

**Theorem 5-5. If r and s are two rational numbers, then exactly one of the following holds: r ⧀ s, r = s, or s ⧀ r.**

Trichotomy for set Q

Given two rational numbers, we sometimes say that we have *determined their ordering* when we have determined which of the conditions of Theorem 5-5 holds. Also, if r ⧀ s, then we may also say that *r precedes s*.

**Example 5-6.**  Determine the ordering of $\frac{17}{8}$ and $\frac{18}{9}$.

$$\frac{18}{9} \ominus \frac{17}{8} = \frac{18}{9} \oplus \frac{^{-}17}{8} \qquad \text{why?}$$

$$= \frac{18(8) + {}^{-}17(9)}{9(8)} \qquad \text{why?}$$

$$= \frac{144 - 153}{9(8)} \qquad \text{why?}$$

$$= \frac{^{-}1}{8} \qquad \text{why?}$$

Thus $\frac{18}{9} \ominus \frac{17}{8}$ is negative; consequently, $\frac{18}{9} \oslash \frac{17}{8}$.

A more detailed study of the ordering relation will be discussed in Chap. 9. At this point, however, we can identify the set of integers with a proper subset of the set of rational numbers. For each integer $a$ the equivalence class $a/1$ is to be identified with $a$. That is, we allow the rational number $a/1$ to be replaceable by the integer $a$. In this way the set of integers may be regarded as a proper subset of the rational numbers. For example, the integer 2 may be used to denote any of the elements $2/1$, $4/2$, $6/3$, . . . , $^{-}2/^{-}1$, $^{-}4/^{-}2$, $^{-}6/^{-}3$, . . . . With this identification, some of our calculations may be simplified. For example, $\frac{17}{8}$ may be written as $\frac{16}{8} \oplus \frac{1}{8}$, or $\frac{2}{1} \oplus \frac{1}{8}$, or, using our convention, as $2 \oplus \frac{1}{8}$. Similarly, we may write $\frac{18}{9}$ as 2. The problem in Example 5-6 could then be written as

If $s = \dfrac{18}{9}$ and $r = \dfrac{17}{8}$

then

$$r \ominus s = \left(2 \oplus \frac{1}{8}\right) \ominus 2$$

$$= \left(\frac{1}{8} \oplus 2\right) \ominus 2$$

$$= \frac{1}{8} \oplus (2 \ominus 2)$$

$$= \frac{1}{8}$$

So that $r \ominus s$ is positive.

It is now possible to define division of integers in terms of the division operation defined on the set of rational numbers. Let $r, s \in Z$, with $s \neq 0$; then

$$r \div s = \frac{r}{1} \oplus \frac{s}{1} = \frac{r}{1} \odot \frac{1}{s} = \frac{r}{s}$$

Thus, since the set $Z$ of integers has been identified as a proper subset of $Q$, we have that the quotient of two integers $r$ and $s$, for $s \neq 0$, may be expressed as the rational number $r/s$.

Other examples are

$$3 \div 4 = \frac{3}{1} \div \frac{4}{1} = \frac{3}{1} \odot \frac{1}{4} = \frac{3}{4}$$

$$12 \div 4 = \frac{12}{1} \odot \frac{1}{4} = \frac{3}{1} = 3$$

$$24 \div 15 = \frac{24}{15} = \frac{8}{5}$$

To adopt the convention of replacing some of the rational numbers by integers might seem to introduce confusion concerning what symbols to use for the different operations and the relations of equality and inequality. There will be no ambiguity if we drop the circle from each of the symbols used in the development of $Q$. When we are dealing only with integers, the symbols intended will be the uncircled symbols. Since integers may be identified with a subset of the set of rational numbers, the circled symbols will be intended when we are dealing with both integers and rational numbers. By this procedure we shall encounter no ambiguities, and we henceforth use the symbols $=$, $+$, $-$, $\cdot$, $\div$, $<$, and $>$ for both $Z$ and $Q$.

## EXERCISES

**1.** Prove Theorem 5-1.
**2.** Prove that the operation $\oplus$ is an associative and commutative operation.
**3.** Prove that the operation $\odot$ is well-defined.
**4.** Prove that the operation $\odot$ is an associative and commutative operation.
**5.** State and prove the property that $\odot$ distributes over $\oplus$.
**6.** Show that for rational numbers $r$ and $s$, $s \ominus r$ is positive if and only if $r \ominus s$ is negative.
**7.** Prove Theorem 5-5.
**8.** Prove the additive property for $\oplus$; that is, prove that

$$\text{For } \frac{a}{b}, \frac{c}{d}, \frac{x}{y} \in Q, \text{ if } \frac{a}{b} = \frac{c}{d'} \text{ then } \frac{a}{b} \oplus \frac{x}{y} = \frac{c}{d} \oplus \frac{x}{y}$$

In the remaining exercises letters represent integers which do not result in zero denominators. In Exercises 9 to 16 express each answer as a single fraction in which the numerator and denominator have no common factors except, possibly, 1 or ‾1.

9. $\dfrac{1}{2} + \dfrac{1}{3} - \dfrac{1}{4}$

10. $\dfrac{2}{3} - \dfrac{3}{4} + \dfrac{4}{5}$

11. $\dfrac{a-2}{3} + \dfrac{a+2}{4}$

12. $\dfrac{2-1}{3-b} - \dfrac{a-2}{b-3}$

13. $\dfrac{a}{9} - \dfrac{5a}{3} - 2$

14. $\dfrac{4a+6b-3}{11} - \dfrac{\,^{-}a+2b-3}{11}$

15. $\dfrac{a^2}{a} - \dfrac{a}{a^2} - \dfrac{2(a^2-1)}{a}$

16. $\dfrac{a}{a-3} - \dfrac{a+4}{a-2} + \dfrac{3a-7}{a^2-5a+6}$

In Exercises 17 to 21 perform the indicated operations and express the result as a fraction in which the numerator and denominator have no common factors except, possibly, 1 or ‾1.

17. $3ab \left(\dfrac{7c}{6a}\right)$

18. $\dfrac{5a^7b^2}{15c^3} \left(\dfrac{27c^3}{9a^3b^5}\right)$

19. $\dfrac{a-b}{c+d} \left(\dfrac{d+c}{b-a}\right)$

20. $\dfrac{a-2}{10} \left(\dfrac{4a-9}{a-2} - \dfrac{a-1}{2-a}\right)$

21. $\dfrac{a^2}{2} \left(\dfrac{3a+8}{4a^2} - \dfrac{2a-1}{a^3}\right) - \dfrac{5}{8a}$

22. In each case determine whether the inequality is true or false:

$$\dfrac{7}{8} < \dfrac{10}{11} \qquad \dfrac{16}{25} < \dfrac{17}{26} \qquad \dfrac{11}{19} < \dfrac{8}{17} \qquad \dfrac{34}{32} > \dfrac{28}{27}$$

In Exercises 23 to 26 let $a$ and $b$ be integers, each greater than 1, with $a < b$, for which the corresponding ordered pairs represent rational numbers. For each exercise indicate whether the statement is true or false and prove your result.

23. $\dfrac{a}{b} < \dfrac{a+1}{b+1}$

24. $\dfrac{a}{b} < \dfrac{a-1}{b+1}$

25. $\dfrac{a}{b} < \dfrac{a+1}{b-1}$

26. $\dfrac{a}{b} < \dfrac{a-1}{b-1}$

## 5-3. THE FIELD OF REAL NUMBERS

In the last section we saw how the integral domain Z can be extended to the field Q of rational numbers. The operations of addition and multiplication in Q were defined in terms of the corresponding operations in Z, and the ordering relation $<$ was defined in terms of the corresponding ordering relation on Z. The field of rational numbers may thus be considered as an *ordered field* in that it is a field with an ordering relation defined on it satisfying the trichotomy, additive, and multiplicative properties.† Since the number of elements of Q is infinite, it is also known as an *infinite ordered field*. The field of real numbers is also an infinite ordered field and, in fact, may be regarded as an extension of the field of rational numbers. The process of extension, which is different from that used in the previous section and is beyond the scope of this book, also extends the field operations and the ordering relation of Q to the field R of real numbers. The purpose of this section is to consider which properties of the real numbers distinguish them from the rational numbers and other ordered fields.

Ordered field

Infinite ordered field

If $x$ is an element of a field $F$, then, of course, $x^2$ is also an element of $F$. However, if $y$ is an arbitrary element of $F$, then there may or may not be an element $x$ in $F$ such that $x^2 = y$. For example, if $y$ is the rational number 9/4, then there are two possible rational numbers $x$ satisfying this property, 3/2 and $^-$3/2. However, if $y$ is the rational number 2, or 2/1, then there is no rational number $x$ such that $x^2 = 2$ (Exercise 1).

If for an element $y$ of a field there exists an element $x$ such that $x^2 = y$, then $x$ is called a *square root* of $y$. It is clear that if a square root of a number exists, it may or may not be unique; if $x$ is a square root of $y$, then both $x^2 = y$ and $(^-x)^2 = y$, and unless $x = ^-x$, in which case $x = 0$, the element $y$ will have two square roots. For real numbers one of the two square roots will be negative and the other will be positive. The positive square root, if it exists, is called the *principal square root* and is denoted by the symbol $\sqrt{\phantom{x}}$. For example, $\sqrt{4} = 2$. It is emphasized that the symbol $\sqrt{\phantom{x}}$, called a *radical*, is used to denote the positive square root. Thus $\sqrt{4}$ *never* denotes the number $^-2$. The rational number $\frac{1}{2}$ is often used as an exponent to denote the principal square root of a number when it exists; $4^{1/2} = \sqrt{4}$ and $^-(4^{1/2}) = -\sqrt{4}$.

Square root

Principal square root

The mathematicians of ancient Greece were familiar with the properties of rational numbers and used such numbers to express the ratios of lengths of line segments. However, when they considered the length of the diagonal of a square each of whose sides was of length one unit, they discovered that there were numbers that are not rational. Such numbers were called *irrational numbers.*‡

Irrational numbers

There exist irrational numbers other than the square roots of inte-

---

† *Trichotomy property:* For every $a, b \in Q$, exactly one of $a < b$, $a = b$, or $a > b$ holds.
*Additive property:* For every $a, b, c \in Q$, if $a < b$, then $a + c < b + c$.
*Multiplicative property:* For every $a, b, c \in Q$, if $a < b$ and $c > 0$, then $ac < bc$.

‡ Given a square with sides of length 1, a diagonal forms, with two of the sides, a right triangle. By the Pythagorean Theorem, the diagonal (hypotenuse of the right triangle) is of length $\sqrt{1^2 + 1^2} = \sqrt{2}$, which can be shown to be irrational (Exercise 1).

gers. The ratio of the circumference of any given circle to its diameter cannot be expressed as a rational number. This ratio, which remains constant for all circles, is expressed by the irrational number $\pi$ (pi). The set $R$ of real numbers consists of all rational numbers and all irrational numbers. Just as $Q$, the set of rational numbers, was defined in terms of the extension of the set $Z$ of integers, $R$ is defined in terms of the extension of $Q$. This extension, as has been mentioned, is beyond the scope of this book.

**R, the set of real numbers**

The arithmetic of elementary mathematics is confined largely to a study of rational numbers. When an irrational number is used, it is usually approximated by some rational number, as is illustrated by the use of 3.14, 3.1416, or $\frac{22}{7}$ as replacements for $\pi$. Every rational number can be expressed either as a finite decimal or as an infinite repeating decimal. An irrational number may be expressed as an infinite nonrepeating decimal;[†] for example, $\frac{15}{4} = 3.75$, a finite decimal, and $\frac{5}{6} = 0.83333 \cdot \cdot \cdot$, an infinite repeating decimal, but $\pi = 3.14159265 \cdot \cdot \cdot$, an infinite decimal with no repeating pattern.

When two numbers are expressed in decimal form, we can decide which precedes the other with respect to the ordering relation $<$.

**Example 5-7.**   Use decimal representation to determine which is the larger, $\frac{7}{5}$ or $\frac{11}{8}$.

If $x = \frac{7}{5}$ and $y = \frac{11}{8}$, then $x = 1.400$ and $y = 1.375$; hence $x - y = .025$. Since $x - y$ is positive, we have $y < x$.

Given two real numbers we can decide which of the two is larger by comparing the digits in the corresponding decimal positions.

**Example 5-8.**   Let $s = 3.1416$, one of the previously mentioned rational approximations to the number $\pi$. Determine which of the two numbers, $s$ or $\pi$, is the larger.

Since $s$ is expressed to four decimal places, we must find an expression for $\pi$ which is correct to at least five decimal places. We know that, correct to five decimal places,

$$\pi = 3.14159 \cdot \cdot \cdot$$

The digit in the fourth decimal place is 5, which is less than the digit in the fourth decimal place of the number 3.1416. Therefore $\pi < s$.

Irrational numbers do not lend themselves to forms of symbolic representation which permit much simplification under the operational

† *Ibid.*, pp. 143–147, 159.

rules of combination. We may write $\sqrt{2} + \sqrt{2} = 2\sqrt{2}$, which is irrational, and $\sqrt{2}\sqrt{2} = 2$, which is rational. The sum of $\sqrt{2}$ and $\sqrt{3}$ can be indicated only as $\sqrt{2} + \sqrt{3}$, but the product of these numbers permits some degree of simplification, as in $\sqrt{2}\sqrt{3} = \sqrt{6}$. There are, in fact, classifications which give some insight as to when simplifications can be effected. We shall be content, however, merely to indicate the results of addition, subtraction, multiplication, and division when they do not lend themselves readily to such simplification. With this sketchy discussion, we shall refer to these operations as the *usual operations on R.*

There exist fields which contain Q as a subfield and which are, in fact, subfields of R. In Example 5-9 we see that the field Q can be extended to a field $F = \{a + b\sqrt{2} \mid a, b \in Q\}$ in which those elements for which $b = 0$ are precisely the elements of Q; however, if $a = 0$ and $b = 1$, then we see that $\sqrt{2} \in F$. In a similar manner, Q can be extended to a field which includes $\sqrt{3}$, $\sqrt{5}$, or other irrational numbers.

**Example 5-9.** Let Q be the set of rational numbers and let $F = \{a + b\sqrt{2} \mid a, b \in Q\}$. The operations defined on F will be the usual operations of addition and multiplication of real numbers. As a consequence, we automatically have the associative and commutative properties satisfied for each of the operations and the distributivity of multiplication with respect to addition. We need only show that postulates G-1, G-3, and G-4 hold with respect to addition on F and that the same postulates hold with respect to multiplication on the elements of F *other than the additive identity* to establish that F is a field.

Let $a + b\sqrt{2}$ and $c + d\sqrt{2}$ be arbitrary elements of F, where a, b, c, $d \in Q$. By the properties of addition and multiplication for real numbers, their sum is $(a + c) + (b + d)\sqrt{2}$ and their product is $(ac + 2bd) + (ad + bc)\sqrt{2}$. Since Q is closed with respect to addition and multiplication, the sum and product of elements of F are again elements of F, and postulate G-1 is satisfied with respect to both operations.

The element $0 + 0\sqrt{2}$ is the additive identity of F, and with respect to this identity, the inverse of $a + b\sqrt{2}$ is $^-a + {}^-b\sqrt{2}$ (verify this). The element $1 + 0\sqrt{2}$ is the multiplicative identity of F, and with respect to this identity, the inverse of $a + b\sqrt{2}$ is, for $a \neq 0$ and $b \neq 0$,

$$\frac{a}{a^2 - 2b^2} + \frac{{}^-b}{a^2 - 2b^2}\sqrt{2}$$

which is an element of F (verify this). It follows that F is a field.

The property which distinguishes the real numbers from the rational numbers is called the *completeness property* and is expressed in terms of the ordering relation $<$ of the set $R$ of real numbers and the additional concept of an upper bound for a subset of $R$.

**Upper bound of a set**

**Definition 5-7. A subset T of real numbers is bounded above if there exists a real number r such that for every t $\in$ T, t $\leq$ r. The number r is called an upper bound for T.**

As an illustration of a set for which there exists no upper bound, consider the set of positive integers. The set has no upper bound, since there is no real number larger than or equal to each element of the set. However, if $T$ is the set of all negative real numbers, then any positive number is an upper bound for $T$; hence $T$ is bounded above. As a matter of fact, every negative number is smaller than zero, so that zero is also an upper bound for the set of negative numbers. There is no number smaller than zero which is an upper bound, so that zero is the smallest of all of the upper bounds for $T$.

**Example 5-10.**   Find the set of all upper bounds for the set

$$T = \left\{ 1, \frac{3}{2}, \frac{7}{115}, \frac{-2}{3}, 14, -4 \right\}$$

Since $T$ has both positive and negative numbers, and a negative number is smaller than any positive number, we may reject negative numbers as candidates for upper bounds for $T$. Of the positive numbers, we have

$$\frac{7}{115} < 1 < \frac{3}{2} < 14$$

Since all the numbers of $T$ are either smaller than or equal to 14, we see that 14 is an upper bound and, in fact, is the smallest of the upper bounds for the set $T$. The set $S$ of all upper bounds for $T$ is

$$S = \{x \mid x \geq 14\}$$

Note that, whereas the smallest upper bound for the set of negative numbers was not an element of that set, in this case the smallest of the upper bounds for the set $T$ is an element of $T$.

If $T$ is a subset of real numbers and is bounded above, we let $S$ be the set of all upper bounds for $T$. The smallest element of $S$, if it exists, **Smallest upper bound** is called the *smallest upper bound* for the set $T$.

From the preceding examples we see that the smallest upper bound may or may not be in the set $T$. We now state the conditions under which the existence of a smallest upper bound for a set is guaranteed.

**Completeness property. If any nonempty set T of real numbers is bounded above, then T has a smallest upper bound.**

A consequence of the completeness property is the following: If $a$ is any positive real number and $n$ is any natural number, then there exists a real number $x$ such that $x^n = a$; the real number $x$ is called an $n$th root of $a$. In particular, if $n = 2$, then there are two possible values of $x$, $\sqrt{2}$ and $-\sqrt{2}$. The number $\sqrt{2}$ is, for example, the smallest upper bound in $R$ for the set $\{x|x \in R, x > 0, x^2 < 2\}$. Although $\sqrt{2}$ is the smallest upper bound in $R$ for $\{x|x \in Q, x > 0, x^2 < 2\}$, it is not an element of $Q$; in fact, it can be shown that this set has no smallest upper bound in $Q$. These two examples show how the completeness property distinguishes the field of real numbers from the field of rational numbers.

If $n$ is an odd integer, then it can be shown that for every real number $y$ there exists a real number $x$ such that $x^n = y$. However, if $n$ is an even integer, then real numbers which are $n$th roots exist only for nonnegative values of $y$. For example, if $n = 3$ and $y = -8$, then $x = -2$; but if $n = 2$ and $y = -8$, then there exists no real number $x$ such that $x^2 = -8$. To obtain a field in which there exists an $n$th root of any element of the field it is necessary to extend $R$ to the larger field $C$ of complex numbers. This will be done in Sec. 5-5.

## EXERCISES

**1.** Two integers $a$ and $b$ are said to be *relatively prime* if they have no common integer factors except 1 and $-1$. If $a$ is an integer and $p$ is a prime number such that $p$ is a factor of $a^2$, then $p$ is also a factor of $a$. Supply the missing reasons in the following proof that $\sqrt{2}$ is an irrational number

*Theorem:* If $x$ is a real number such that $x^2 = 2$, then $x$ is an irrational number

*Hypothesis:* $x$ is a real number and $x^2 = 2$

*Conclusion:* $x$ is an irrational number

*Type of proof:* Indirect (see Sec. 2-2)

**Proof:**

| Statement | Reason |
|---|---|
| 1. $x^2 = 2$ | 1. |
| 2. $x$ is a rational number | 2. Assumption |
| 3. For integers $a$ and $b$, $a$ and $b$ relatively prime, $b \neq 0$, $x = a/b$ | 3. Definition of rational number, a rational number may be reduced to lowest terms |

| | |
|---|---|
| 4. $x^2 = a^2/b^2$ | 4. |
| 5. $x^2b^2 = a^2$ | 5. |
| 6. $2b^2 = a^2$ | 6. |
| 7. 2 is a prime number and 2 is a factor of $a^2$ | 7. |
| 8. 2 is a factor of $a$ | 8. |
| 9. For some integer $c$, $a = 2c$ | 9. From 8, $a$ is an even integer |
| 10. $a^2 = 4c^2$ | 10. |
| 11. $2b^2 = 4c^2$ | 11. |
| 12. $b^2 = 2c^2$ | 12. |
| 13. 2 is a prime number and 2 is a factor of $b^2$ | 13. |
| 14. 2 is a factor of $b$ | 14. |
| 15. 2 is a factor of $a$ and of $b$ | 15. |
| 16. $a$ and $b$ are not relatively prime | 16. |
| 17. $a$ and $b$ are relatively prime | 17. |
| 18. $x$ is not a rational number | 18. |
| 19. $x$ is an irrational number | 19. |

**2.** Following the pattern of Exercise 1, show that $\sqrt{3}$ is an irrational number.

**3.** Find the set of all upper bounds for each of the following sets of real numbers.

(a) $\{3, ^-7, 2, ^-\frac{1}{2}, 4, ^-37, ^-3, 7\}$    (e) $\{x \mid x \leq ^-2\}$

(b) $\{x \mid x < 4\}$    (f) $\{x \mid x \text{ is a negative integer}\}$

(c) $\{x \mid x \leq 4\}$    (g) $\{x \mid x \text{ is a negative even integer}\}$

(d) $\{x \mid x < ^-2\}$

**4.** For each of the sets in Exercise 3 find the smallest upper bound.

## 5-4. THE DEFINITION OF A VECTOR SPACE

We shall now define a system which involves two sets. Let $F$ be a field and $V$ an abelian group. That is, $F$ is a set with the operations of addition and multiplication (denoted by $+$ and $\cdot$) which satisfy the field postulates, and $V$ is a set with an operation (called addition and denoted by $\oplus$) which satisfies the postulates for an abelian group. The elements of $F$ are called *scalars* and will be denoted by Latin letters

**Scalars**

**Vectors**

$(a, b, c, \ . \ . \ .)$; the elements of $V$ are called *vectors* and will be denoted by boldface Greek letters ($\alpha$, $\beta$, $\gamma$, . . .). The symbols 0 and 1 will represent the additive and multiplicative identities, respectively, of F. $\alpha \oplus \beta$ denotes the *vector sum* of the vectors $\alpha$ and $\beta$, and **o** (omicron) will represent a vector which is the identity of V with respect to $\oplus$. Furthermore we denote by * an operation between scalars and vectors defined so that if a $\in F$ and $\alpha \in V$, then a * $\alpha$ is an element of V. a * $\alpha$ is called the *scalar product* of the scalar a and the vector $\alpha$ or *scalar multiple* of $\alpha$ by a. Certain properties will be listed which establish relationships between the four given operations. These properties are similar in appearance to some of the postulates we have listed previously, but they are of a somewhat different character.

*Vector sum*

*Scalar product*

**Definition 5-8.** A vector space over a field F is an algebraic system which consists of a field F, with operations + and ·, an abelian group V, with operation $\oplus$, and an operation * defined between elements of F and elements of V satisfying the following properties:

*Vector space*

1. If a $\in$ F and $\alpha \in$ V, then a * $\alpha$ is an element of V.
2. If a $\in$ F and $\alpha$, $\beta \in$ V, then a * ($\alpha \oplus \beta$) = (a * $\alpha$) $\oplus$ (a * $\beta$).
3. If a, b $\in$ F and $\alpha \in$ V, then (a + b) * $\alpha$ = (a * $\alpha$) $\oplus$ (b * $\alpha$).
4. If a, b $\in$ F and $\alpha \in$ V, then ab * $\alpha$ = a * (b * $\alpha$).
5. If $\alpha \in$ V, then 1 * $\alpha = \alpha$.

**V** is called a *vector space over F* and is sometimes denoted by **V**(F). Property 1 is similar to a closure property (how is it different?), whereas properties 2 and 3 resemble a distributive property (how are they different?). Property 4 is similar to an associative property (how does it differ?), and property 5 is much like the property of an identity with respect to multiplication (how does it differ?). We shall now consider an important example of a vector space.

**Example 5-11.**   Let R be the field of real numbers and **V** the set of all ordered pairs of real numbers; that is, for every a, b $\in$ R, $\alpha$ = (a,b) is an element of **V**. a will be called the *first component* of $\alpha$, and b will be called the *second component* of $\alpha$. Two ordered pairs will be considered as equal if and only if their first components are equal and their second components are equal. In other words,

(a,b) = (c,d) if and only if a = c and b = d

The operations of $\oplus$ and * are defined as follows:

(a,b) $\oplus$ (c,d) = (a + c, b + d)
  c * (a,b) = (ca, cb)

With these definitions, we first show that **V** is an abelian group, and then we shall verify that each of properties 1 to 5 of the definition of a vector space is satisfied.

If $\alpha$ and $\beta$ are ordered pairs of real numbers, then, by the definition of $\oplus$, $\alpha \oplus \beta$ is an ordered pair of real numbers, so that postulate G-1 is satisfied with respect to the operation $\oplus$. If $a, b, c, d, e, f \in R$, then

$$
\begin{aligned}
(a,b) \oplus [(c,d) \oplus (e,f)] &= (a,b) \oplus (c + e, d + f) \\
&= (a + [c + e], b + [d + f]) \\
&= ([a + c] + e, [b + d] + f) \\
&= (a + c, b + d) \oplus (e,f) \\
&= [(a,b) \oplus (c,d)] \oplus (e,f)
\end{aligned}
$$

so that $\oplus$ is an associative operation. Since

$$
\begin{aligned}
(a,b) \oplus (c,d) &= (a + c, b + d) \\
&= (c + a, d + b) \qquad \text{why?} \\
&= (c,d) \oplus (a,b)
\end{aligned}
$$

it follows that $\oplus$ is a commutative operation.

Let $o = (0,0)$; since $\oplus$ is commutative and

$$
(0,0) \oplus (a,b) = (0 + a, 0 + b) = (a,b)
$$

it follows that $o$ is the identity element of $V$. The inverse of $(a,b)$ is $(^-a,^-b)$, since $\oplus$ is commutative and

$$
(^-a,^-b) \oplus (a,b) = (^-a + a, ^-b + b) = (0,0) = o
$$

It follows that $V$ is an abelian group with respect to the operation $\oplus$.

We shall now verify properties 1 to 5. From the definition of the operation $*$, if $c \in R$ and $\alpha = (a,b)$, then $c * \alpha$ is the ordered pair of real numbers $(ca,cb)$ and hence is an element of $V$. This verifies property 1. Also, for $(a,b) \in V$,

$$
1 * (a,b) = (1a,1b) = (a,b)
$$

so that property 5 is verified. If $(a,b), (c,d) \in V$ and $r \in R$, then

$$
\begin{aligned}
r * [(a,b) \oplus (c,d)] &= r * (a + c, b + d) \\
&= (r[a + c], r[b + d]) \\
&= (ra + rc, rb + rd) \\
&= (ra,rb) \oplus (rc,rd) \\
&= [r * (a,b)] \oplus [r * (c,d)]
\end{aligned}
$$

so that property 2 is verified. Similarly, if $r, s \in R$ and $(c,d) \in V$, then

$$
\begin{aligned}
(r + s) * (c,d) &= ([r + s]c, [r + s]d) \\
&= (rc + sc, rd + sd) \\
&= (rc,rd) \oplus (sc,sd) \\
&= [r * (c,d)] \oplus [s * (c,d)]
\end{aligned}
$$

which verifies property 3. Finally,

$$rs * (c,d) = (rsc, rsd)$$
$$= r * (sc,sd)$$
$$= r * [s * (c,d)]$$

which verifies property 4. All the properties of a vector space have been verified, and it follows that **V** is a vector space over $R$.

The vector space in the preceding example is sometimes denoted by **R**$_2$, where the subscript indicates that ordered pairs are to be selected from the field $R$ of real numbers. Similarly, **R**$_3$ may denote the set of ordered triples, or *3-tuples* of real numbers; more generally, if $n$ is a positive integer, **R**$_n$ may denote the set of *n-tuples* of elements from $R$. For each positive integer $n$ a vector space of *n*-tuples, **R**$_n$, may be constructed following the pattern of the example. The field $R$ itself may be regarded as a vector space, where each element of $R$ is to be regarded as a 1-tuple (see pages 139–140).    **n-tuple**

People who work in the fields of physics and engineering frequently define a vector as "a quantity which is completely determined by its magnitude and direction." Examples of such vectors are velocity, acceleration, and force. In some cases vectors may be represented geometrically by directed line segments, or arrows, drawn in a plane. For example, in Fig. 5-1 three arrows emanate from the origin: $\boldsymbol{\alpha}$ de-

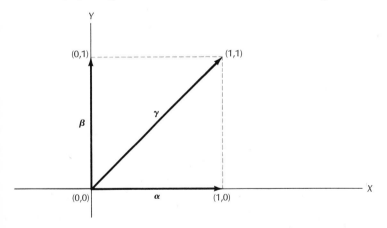

FIG. 5-1

notes that arrow along the x axis with its tip at the point (1,0), $\boldsymbol{\beta}$ denotes that arrow along the y axis with tip at the point (0,1) and $\boldsymbol{\gamma}$ denotes the arrow with its tip at the point (1,1). These arrows are called *geometric representations* of the vectors (1,0), (0,1), and (1,1), respectively, of **R**$_2$. Geometrically, the sum of $\boldsymbol{\alpha}$ and $\boldsymbol{\beta}$ is usually defined to be the arrow emanating from the origin and forming the diagonal of the parallelogram determined by the origin and the tips of $\boldsymbol{\alpha}$ and $\boldsymbol{\beta}$. Thus $\boldsymbol{\gamma} =$    **Geometric representation of vectors**

$\boldsymbol{\alpha} \oplus \boldsymbol{\beta}$. This definition is in agreement with the corresponding definition of the sum of vectors from the space $\mathbf{R}_2$. Thus, by Example 5-11, we may write $(1,1) = (1,0) + (0,1)$, which agrees with the geometric representation.

Geometrically, the origin represents the additive identity, and for practical reasons, the additive identity vector may be regarded as an arrow with length 0 but with no direction. The negative of a geometric vector, or arrow, is that arrow which has the same length but opposite direction. For example, the negative (or additive inverse) of $\boldsymbol{\alpha}$ in Fig. 5-1 would lie along the negative x axis, with its tip resting at the point $(^-1,0)$.

As a practical matter, arrows representing vectors may be drawn anywhere in the plane; they need not emanate from the origin. For example, since the three arrows in Fig. 5-2 are of the same length and

**FIG. 5-2**

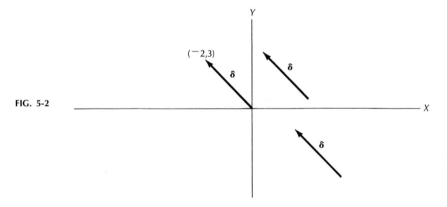

have a common direction, they represent vectors which are equivalent, and each is designated by $\boldsymbol{\delta}$. In effect, the set of all arrows with the same magnitude and direction are said to be members of the same equivalence class, and that member emanating from the origin may be considered as a typical vector. In this way any arrow in the plane can be made to correspond to some element of $\mathbf{R}_2$. Similarly, three-dimensional arrows may be used to represent vectors in three-space, and with a corresponding three-axis coordinate system, points in three dimensions may be considered as vectors in the vector space $\mathbf{R}_3$.

**Length of a vector**    The magnitude of a vector is also called the *length* of the vector. In $\mathbf{R}_2$ the length of a vector $\boldsymbol{\alpha} = (a,b)$ is defined to be $|\boldsymbol{\alpha}| = \sqrt{a^2 + b^2}$ (see Fig. 5-3). For an arbitrary arrow drawn in the plane (not necessarily emanating from the origin), the arrow may have its origin at the point $(c,d)$ and its tip at the point $(e,f)$. In this case the length of the vector is given by the formula $\sqrt{(c - e)^2 + (d - f)^2}$ (see Fig. 5-3).

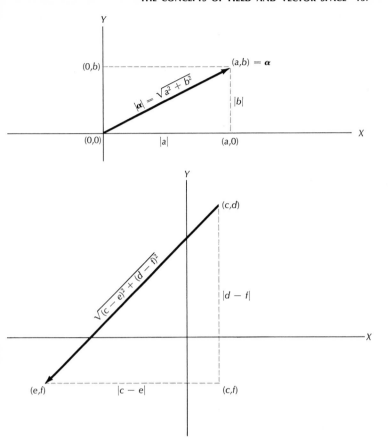

FIG. 5-3

It is beyond the scope of this book to study vector spaces in detail, but two additional concepts are of sufficient importance to mention, namely, the concepts of *basis* and of *dimension*. Let **S** be a set of vectors of a vector space **V** (over a field *F*). From **S** we may generate other vectors by adding scalar multiples of elements from **S** (using the operations ⊕ and *). If every element of **V** can be generated from **S** by this procedure, then we say that the set **S** *spans* **V**. IF **S** is the smallest set which spans **V**—that is, if there is no set that spans **V** which has fewer elements—then **S** is called a *basis* for **V**, and the number of elements in **S** is called the *dimension* of **V**. A vector space may have more than one basis, but its dimension is a unique positive integer.

**Basis**

**Dimension of a vector space**

**Example 5-12.** Consider the vector space $\mathbf{R}_2$ (see Example 5-11). Let $\boldsymbol{\alpha} = (1,0)$ and $\boldsymbol{\beta} = (0,1)$. If $\mathbf{S} = \{\boldsymbol{\alpha}, \boldsymbol{\beta}\}$, then any vector in $\mathbf{R}_2$ can be generated from the set **S**. For example, if $\boldsymbol{\epsilon} = (a,b)$ for $a$, $b \in R$, then

$$\boldsymbol{\epsilon} = (a + 0, 0 + b)$$
$$= (a,0) \oplus (0,b)$$
$$= [a * (1,0)] \oplus [b * (0,1)]$$

so that by multiplying $\boldsymbol{\alpha}$ by the scalar $a$ and $\boldsymbol{\beta}$ by the scalar $b$ and adding we get the vector $\boldsymbol{\epsilon}$. Since any vector in $\mathbf{R}_2$ can thus be generated, the set $\mathbf{S}$ spans $\mathbf{R}_2$. It can be shown that there is no "smaller" set which generates $\mathbf{R}_2$, so that $\mathbf{S}$ is a basis for $\mathbf{R}_2$. Since $\mathbf{S}$ has two elements, the dimension of $\mathbf{R}_2$ is 2.

The set $\mathbf{S}$ is not the only basis for $\mathbf{R}_2$. For example, the arbitrary vector $\boldsymbol{\epsilon} = (a,b)$ can be generated from the set $T = \{(1,1), (1,^-1)\}$:

$$\boldsymbol{\epsilon} = (a,b) = \left(\frac{a + b}{2} * (1,1)\right) \oplus \left(\frac{a - b}{2} * (1,^-1)\right)$$

so that $T$ also spans $\mathbf{R}_2$ and is, in fact, also a basis for $\mathbf{R}_2$.

It is sometimes helpful to consider the geometric representation of a basis. Thus, for the basis $\mathbf{S}$ of the preceding example, the vectors $\boldsymbol{\alpha}$ and $\boldsymbol{\beta}$ are represented in Fig. 5-1 as arrows along the coordinate axes. In Fig. 5-4 the vector $(^-3,4)$ is represented as the geometric sum of arrows

**FIG. 5-4**

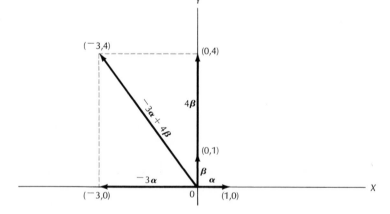

corresponding to $^-3\boldsymbol{\alpha}$ and $4\boldsymbol{\beta}$. The vector $^-3\boldsymbol{\alpha}$ is represented by an arrow emanating from the origin with its tip at the point $(^-3,0)$, and the vector $4\boldsymbol{\beta}$ is represented by an arrow emanating from the origin with its tip at the point $(0,4)$; the vector sum is represented by an arrow with its tip at the point $(^-3,4)$. In a similar way, every point in the plane, and consequently every vector in $\mathbf{R}_2$ can be generated by the elements of the basis $\mathbf{S}$.

In Fig. 5-5 the same vector, $(^-3,4)$, is represented as generated from a different basis. The basis $T$ of Example 5-12 contains the vector $\boldsymbol{\gamma} =$

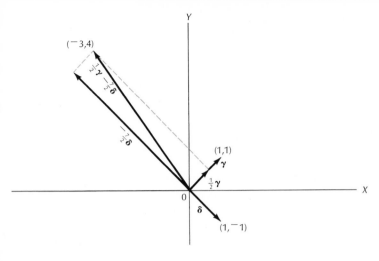

FIG. 5-5

(1,1) and $\delta = (1,{}^-1)$. These vectors are represented as arrows emanating from the origin, with tips, respectively, at the points (1,1) and (1,$^-$1). Since

$$\frac{1}{2}\gamma \ominus \frac{7}{2}\delta = \frac{1}{2}(1,1) \oplus \frac{-7}{2}(1,{}^-1)$$

$$= \left(\frac{1}{2},\frac{1}{2}\right) \oplus \left(\frac{-7}{2},\frac{7}{2}\right)$$

$$= ({}^-3,4)$$

the vector ($^-$3,4) can be said to be generated by the vectors $\gamma$ and $\delta$ of the basis $T$. In a similar way, every vector in $\mathbf{R}_2$ can be generated by the elements of $T$.

Points on a number line can be used to represent real numbers. With every real number $a$ there is associated an arrow emanating from the origin, with its tip at the point corresponding to the number $a$ on the number line (see Fig. 5-6). From a geometric consideration we see that real numbers may be considered as vectors. The real number $a$ con-

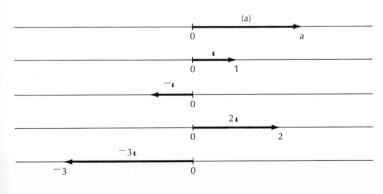

FIG. 5-6

sidered as a vector may be denoted by the 1-tuple (a); in this way we can distinguish, when necessary, between a real number considered as a scalar and that same number considered as a vector.

The vector (1) will be denoted by $\iota$ (iota), and the vector $(^-1)$ will be denoted by $^-\iota$. If a is any real number, then the vector (a) may be written as a scalar multiple of $\iota$; that is, (a) may be written as $a * \iota$, or more simply as $a\iota$. For example, $(2) = 2\iota$; the vector $(^-3)$ may be represented by $^-3 * \iota$, $3 * {}^-\iota$, or simply $^-3\iota$. Every vector of this type, then, can be represented as a scalar multiple of $\iota$, and we say that $\{\iota\}$ is a basis for $\mathbf{R}_1$ and that the dimension of $\mathbf{R}_1$ is 1. The arrow associated with the vector $\iota$ is of length 1, or unit length, so that the length of $\iota$ is 1; that is, **Unit vector** $|\iota| = 1$. The vector $\iota$ is consequently called a *unit vector*.

Although the vector spaces $\mathbf{R}_2$ and $\mathbf{R}_1$ have an infinite number of elements, they are finite dimensional, since they have finite bases. It is only fair to mention that there are examples of infinite-dimensional vector spaces. It is possible to construct examples of vector spaces with a finite number of elements, and such vector spaces will, of course, be finite dimensional. Using a finite field (as, for example, the integers reduced, modulo $p$, a prime), and following the pattern of Example 5-11, we may construct examples of finite vector spaces (see Exercises 1 to 4).

In Sec. 4-2 we found that the set of all $m \times n$ matrices defined over a ring is, with respect to addition, an abelian group. As a consequence, since a field $F$ is also a ring, the set of all $m \times n$ matrices defined over $F$ is also an abelian group. If $a \in F$ and $(a_{ij})$ is an $m \times n$ matrix defined over $F$, then we define $a * (a_{ij})$ as that $m \times n$ matrix $(b_{ij})$ such that for each $i$ and $j$, $b_{ij} = aa_{ij}$. For example, if the field is the field $R$ of real numbers, then the matrix

$$\begin{pmatrix} 2 & 3 & ^-1 \\ ^-5 & 4 & 0 \end{pmatrix}$$

is a $2 \times 3$ matrix defined over $R$. If $a \in R$, then

$$a * \begin{pmatrix} 2 & 3 & ^-1 \\ ^-5 & 4 & 0 \end{pmatrix} = \begin{pmatrix} 2a & 3a & ^-a \\ ^-5a & 4a & 0 \end{pmatrix}$$

which is also a $2 \times 3$ matrix defined over $R$.

Let $M$ be the set of all $m \times n$ matrices defined over a field $F$ and $*$ be the product of elements of $F$ with elements of $M$ defined in the preceding paragraph. If $a \in F$ and $\boldsymbol{\alpha} \in M$, then it follows from the definition that $(a * \boldsymbol{\alpha}) \in M$, so that property 1 of Definition 5-8 holds.

For $\boldsymbol{\alpha}, \boldsymbol{\beta} \in M$, let $\alpha = (a_{ij})$, $\boldsymbol{\beta} = (b_{ij})$, and $\boldsymbol{\gamma} = \boldsymbol{\alpha} \oplus \boldsymbol{\beta}$; thus, if $\boldsymbol{\gamma} = (c_{ij})$, then $c_{ij} = a_{ij} + b_{ij}$ for each $i$ and $j$. If $a \in R$, then, since

$$ac_{ij} = a[a_{ij} + b_{ij}]$$
$$= aa_{ij} + ab_{ij}$$

it follows that

$$a * (\pmb{\alpha} \oplus \pmb{\beta}) \ominus (a * \pmb{\alpha}) \oplus (a * \pmb{\beta})$$

so that property 2 of Definition 5-8 holds.

In a similar way, properties 3, 4, and 5 can be shown to hold (see Exercise 6), and we have the following theorem:

**Theorem 5-6. The set of all m × n matrices defined over a field F is a vector space over F.**

## EXERCISES

In Exercises 1 and 2 let F be the field of integers reduced, modulo 2.

**1.** Let $F_3$ be the set of all ordered triples of elements of F.

   (a) How many elements are there in $F_3$?
   (b) Prove that $F_3$ is a vector space $\mathbf{F}_3$. *Hint:* Use Example 5-11 as a pattern for the proof.
   (c) Find a basis for $\mathbf{F}_3$.
   (d) What is the dimension of $\mathbf{F}_3$?

**2.** Let M be the set of all 2 × 2 matrices defined over F.

   (a) How many elements are there in M?
   (b) Prove that M is a vector space $\mathbf{M}$ over F.
   (c) Find a basis for $\mathbf{M}$.
   (d) What is the dimension of $\mathbf{M}$?

In Exercises 3 and 4 let F be the field of integers reduced, modulo 3.

**3.** Let $F_2$ be the set of all ordered pairs of elements of F.

   (a) How many elements are there in $F_2$?
   (b) Prove that $F_2$ is a vector space $\mathbf{F}_2$.
   (c) Find a basis for $\mathbf{F}_2$.
   (d) What is the dimension of $\mathbf{F}_2$?

**4.** Let M be the set of all 3 × 2 matrices defined over F.

   (a) How many elements are there in M?
   (b) Prove that M is a vector space $\mathbf{M}$.
   (c) Find a basis for $\mathbf{M}$.
   (d) What is the dimension of $\mathbf{M}$?

**5.** Prove that $R_3$ is a vector space $\mathbf{R}_3$.

**6.** Verify that properties 3, 4, and 5 of Definition 5-8 hold for the set of all m × n matrices defined over a field.

**7.** Find a basis and the dimension of the vector space consisting of the set of all $2 \times 2$ matrices defined over the field of real numbers.

## 5-5. THE FIELD OF COMPLEX NUMBERS

In Example 5-11 it was shown that the set $R_2$ of all ordered pairs of real numbers is, with appropriate definitions, a vector space $\mathbf{R_2}$, and in Example 5-12 it was shown that the vectors (1,0) and (0,1) form a basis for this vector space. With respect to vector addition, $\mathbf{R_2}$ is, consequently, an abelian group. In this section we shall first review some of the properties of a vector space and then define a multiplicative operation between the elements of $\mathbf{R_2}$ such that with respect to addition and multiplication the field properties are satisfied. In this way we shall construct the set $C$ of complex numbers which may be regarded either as a vector space or as a field. In this development it will be desirable to deviate from our convention of representing vectors by Greek letters.

Let $\mathbf{I} = (1,0)$ and $\mathbf{i} = (0,1)$. Then, by Example 5-12, the vectors $\mathbf{I}$ and $\mathbf{i}$ constitute a basis for the vector space $\mathbf{R_2}$. Thus every ordered pair $(a,b)$ of real numbers can be written as $a\mathbf{I} + b\mathbf{i}$. Vectors in this form are called *complex numbers*. If $C$ denotes the set of complex numbers, then $C = \{a\mathbf{I} + b\mathbf{i} | a, b \in R\}$. If $a = 0$, the complex number $0\mathbf{I} + b\mathbf{i}$ may be written simply as $b\mathbf{i}$, and if $b = 0$, the complex number $a\mathbf{I} + 0\mathbf{i}$ may be written as $a\mathbf{I}$. If $a = b = 0$, the complex number $0\mathbf{I} + 0\mathbf{i}$ will be written as $0$. The complex numbers $1\mathbf{I}$, $^-1\mathbf{I}$, $1\mathbf{i}$, and $^-1\mathbf{i}$ are written, respectively, as $\mathbf{I}$, $^-\mathbf{I}$, $\mathbf{i}$, and $^-\mathbf{i}$.

> **C, the set of complex numbers**

Complex numbers may be represented geometrically by arrows in a plane, called the *complex plane*. The coordinate axes are called the *axis of reals* and *the axis of imaginaries*, respectively, and in Fig. 5-7 the complex number $^-3\mathbf{I} + 4\mathbf{i}$ is represented by an arrow emanating from the origin (which represents the complex number 0). The complex numbers $\mathbf{I}$ and $\mathbf{i}$ are represented by arrows emanating from the origin

> **Axes of reals and imaginaries**

**FIG. 5-7**

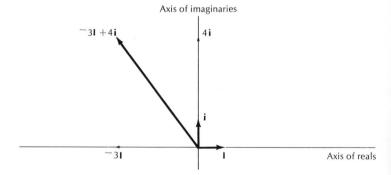

and lying, respectively, along the axis of reals and the axis of imaginaries. Comparing Figs. 5-7 and 5-4, we see that the vectors **l** and **i** are of unit length; that is, $|\mathbf{l}| = 1$ and $|\mathbf{i}| = 1$. For this reason **l** and **i** are called *unit vectors*. Reference to Fig. 5-3 shows that the length of the vector associated with the complex number $a\mathbf{l} + b\mathbf{i}$ is given by $|a\mathbf{l} + b\mathbf{i}| = \sqrt{a^2 + b^2}$. This length is frequently referred to as the *modulus*, or *absolute value*, of the complex number. The scalars $a$ and $b$ are called the *real component* and the *imaginary component*, respectively, of the complex number $a\mathbf{l} + b\mathbf{i}$.

    Two complex numbers are equal if and only if their real components are equal and their imaginary components are equal. Thus, if $a\mathbf{l} + b\mathbf{i}$ and $c\mathbf{l} + d\mathbf{i}$ are complex numbers, then $a\mathbf{l} + b\mathbf{i} = c\mathbf{l} + d\mathbf{i}$ if and only if $a = c$ and $b = d$. In particular, $a\mathbf{l} + b\mathbf{i} = 0$ if and only if $a = 0$ and $b = 0$.

    The sum of two complex numbers is found by adding their real components and by adding their imaginary components. Thus, if $a\mathbf{l} + b\mathbf{i}$ and $c\mathbf{l} + d\mathbf{i}$ are two complex numbers, their sum is given by

$$(a\mathbf{l} + b\mathbf{i}) + (c\mathbf{l} + d\mathbf{i}) = (a + c)\mathbf{l} + (b + d)\mathbf{i}$$

For example,

$$(3\mathbf{l} + 4\mathbf{i}) + (5\mathbf{l} + {}^-12\mathbf{i}) = (3 + 5)\mathbf{l} + (4 + {}^-12)\mathbf{i}$$
$$= 8\mathbf{l} + {}^-8\mathbf{i}$$

For convenience, the last expression will be written simply as $8\mathbf{l} - 8\mathbf{i}$. In general, $a\mathbf{l} - b\mathbf{i}$ will be written for $a\mathbf{l} + {}^-b\mathbf{i}$.

    From Example 5-11 we see that the sum of complex numbers is essentially the same as the sum of ordered pairs of real numbers. Therefore we can state that with respect to addition the set $C$ of complex numbers is an abelian group with identity 0. Also from that example, the scalar product of a real number $r$ with a complex number $a\mathbf{l} + b\mathbf{i}$ is expressed by $r(a\mathbf{l} + b\mathbf{i}) = (ra)\mathbf{l} + (rb)\mathbf{i}$.

    In Fig. 5-8 the scalar multiples of the complex number $5\mathbf{l} + 2\mathbf{i}$ are represented by arrows lying on a common line through the origin.

Unit vectors

Modulus

Real and imaginary
components

Equality of complex numbers

Sum of complex numbers

Scalar multiples of
complex numbers

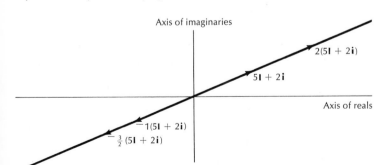

FIG. 5-8

Scalar multiplication by a positive number is represented by an arrow with the same direction as the given complex number. The result of scalar multiplication by a negative number is represented by an arrow with its direction opposite to that of the given complex number (how may scalar multiplication by the real number 0 be represented?). The lengths of the arrows are the same as those of the vectors they represent. If $r$ is a real number and $a\mathbf{l} + b\mathbf{i}$ is a complex number, then the length of the scalar product can be found as follows:

$$
\begin{aligned}
|r(a\mathbf{l} + b\mathbf{i})| &= |(ra)\mathbf{l} + (rb)\mathbf{i}| \\
&= \sqrt{(ra)^2 + (rb)^2} \quad \text{definition of length} \\
&= \sqrt{r^2a^2 + r^2b^2} \\
&= \sqrt{r^2(a^2 + b^2)} \\
&= \sqrt{r^2}\sqrt{a^2 + b^2} \\
&= |r|\,|a\mathbf{l} + b\mathbf{i}|
\end{aligned}
$$

where $|r|$ represents the *absolute value* of $r$.† Thus, since $|2| = |{}^-2| = 2$,

$$
|2(a\mathbf{l} + b\mathbf{i})| = |{}^-2(a\mathbf{l} + b\mathbf{i})| = 2|a\mathbf{l} + b\mathbf{i}|
$$

In a scalar multiple of a complex number the sign of the scalar affects only the direction or the arrow associated with that number, not its length.

**Example 5-13.**   Find a unit vector with the same direction as $3\mathbf{l} - 4\mathbf{i}$.
     A unit vector is a vector with length 1. The length of $3\mathbf{l} - 4\mathbf{i}$ is given by

$$
\begin{aligned}
|3\mathbf{l} - 4\mathbf{i}| &= |3\mathbf{l} + {}^-4\mathbf{i}| \\
&= \sqrt{3^2 + ({}^-4)^2} \\
&= \sqrt{25} \\
&= 5
\end{aligned}
$$

Consequently, the vector $\tfrac{1}{5}(3\mathbf{l} - 4\mathbf{i})$ will be of length $\tfrac{1}{5}(5) = 1$. The required vector, therefore, is $\tfrac{1}{5}(3\mathbf{l} - 4\mathbf{i})$. Note that the vector ${}^-1/5(3\mathbf{l} - 4\mathbf{i})$ is a unit vector with a direction opposite to that of the given vector.

     Multiplying a complex number by the scalar 1 has the effect of mapping the arrow representing that number into itself, and multiplying the number by the scalar ${}^-1$ has the effect of rotating the arrow about the origin through an angle of 180°. An example is shown in Fig. 5-9, where the given complex number is $10\mathbf{l} - 3\mathbf{i}$. Multiplying by ${}^-1$ gives the complex number ${}^-10\mathbf{l} + 3\mathbf{i}$, and its representation can be obtained

**Absolute value**      † The absolute value of any real number $r$ is nonnegative; in symbols, $|r| = r$ if $r \geqslant 0$, or $|r| = {}^-r$ if $r < 0$.

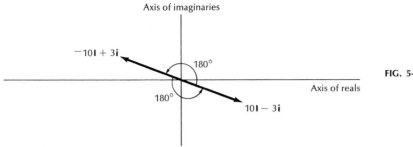

FIG. 5-9

by rotating the original arrow about the origin through 180°. Multiplying this result by $^-1$ has the effect of returning the arrow to its original position. The product $^-1(^-1) = 1$ is thus equivalent to a rotation about the origin through 0°, which is the identity rotation.

This is more than an interesting observation, for multiplication of a complex number by the complex number $\mathbf{i}$ corresponds to a rotation about the origin through 90°. In Fig. 5-10 the successive products of

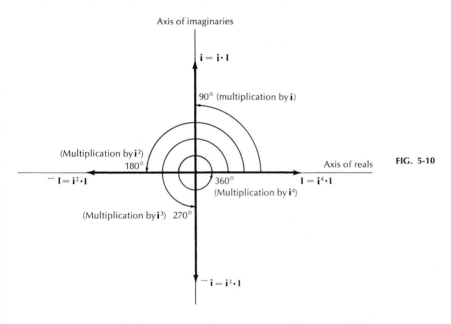

FIG. 5-10

the unit vector $\mathbf{I}$ with the unit vector $\mathbf{i}$ are represented geometrically, rotation is performed in a counterclockwise direction, and the successive products by $\mathbf{i}$ are indicated by $\mathbf{i} \cdot \mathbf{I}$, $\mathbf{i}^2 \cdot \mathbf{I}$, $\mathbf{i}^3 \cdot \mathbf{I}$, and $\mathbf{i}^4 \cdot \mathbf{I}$, and they correspond to rotation about the origin through angles of 90, 180, 270, and 360°, respectively. From the figure we observe that the vector represented by $\mathbf{i}^2 \cdot \mathbf{I}$ is the vector $^-\mathbf{I}$, the vector represented by $\mathbf{i}^3 \cdot \mathbf{I}$ is the vector $^-\mathbf{i}$, and the vector represented by $\mathbf{i}^4 \cdot \mathbf{I}$ is the vector $\mathbf{I}$. The definition of the product of two complex numbers will be given presently. It will then be evident that these products obtained by rotation are entirely compatible with the products obtained by definition.

In a geometric development of complex numbers, constructions for the sum and for the product of any two complex numbers may be given, and through such a development many of the properties of complex numbers can be deduced. Here, however, we only suggest how complex numbers can be represented geometrically and how some of the products may be interpreted in order to motivate the algebraic definition. The definition of the product of two complex numbers will now be given.

**Product of complex numbers**  If $a\mathbf{I} + b\mathbf{i}$ and $c\mathbf{I} + d\mathbf{i}$ are complex numbers, then their product is defined by

$$(a\mathbf{I} + b\mathbf{i})(c\mathbf{I} + d\mathbf{i}) = (ac - bd)\mathbf{I} + (ad + bc)\mathbf{i}$$

**Example 5-14.**  Find the product of $3\mathbf{I} - 4\mathbf{i}$ and $^-8\mathbf{I} + 8\mathbf{i}$.

From the definition, we let $a = 3$, $b = {}^-4$, $c = {}^-8$, and $d = 8$. Then

$$ac - bd = 3({}^-8) - {}^-4(8) = 8$$

and

$$ad + bc = 3(8) + {}^-4({}^-8) = 56$$

so that

$$(3\mathbf{I} - 4\mathbf{i})({}^-8\mathbf{I} + 8\mathbf{i}) = 8\mathbf{I} + 56\mathbf{i}$$

**Example 5-15.**  Use the definition to verify that $\mathbf{i}^2 = {}^-\mathbf{I}$.

By $\mathbf{i}^2$ we mean the product $\mathbf{i} \cdot \mathbf{i}$. Consequently,

$$\mathbf{i}^2 = (0\mathbf{I} + 1\mathbf{i})(0\mathbf{I} + 1\mathbf{i})$$

From the definition, we let $a = 0$, $b = 1$, $c = 0$, and $d = 1$. Then

$$ac - bd = 0(0) - 1(1) = {}^-1$$

and

$$ad + bc = 0(1) + 1(0) = 0$$

It follows that

$$\mathbf{i}^2 = {}^-1\mathbf{I} + 0\mathbf{i} = {}^-\mathbf{I}$$

The operation of multiplication of complex numbers is a well-defined binary operation, and from its definition closure follows. Proof that multiplication is both associative and commutative is left as an exercise (Exercise 8). The complex number $I$ is the identity with respect to multiplication, for if $aI + bi$ is any complex number, then

$$I(aI + bi) = (1I + 0i)(aI + bi)$$
$$= (1a - 0b)I + (1b + 0a)i$$
$$= aI + bi$$

By the commutative property, $(aI + bi)I = (aI + bi)$, and $I$ is the identity element. If $aI + bi \neq 0$, then its multiplicative inverse is given by

$$(aI + bi)^{-1} = \frac{a}{a^2 + b^2} I + \frac{-b}{a^2 + b^2} i$$

Since $aI + bi \neq 0$, the real and imaginary components are not both zero; consequently, $a^2 + b^2 \neq 0$, and the expression on the right side of the equality is defined. We now show that this expression is indeed the inverse of $aI + bi$:

$$(aI + bi)(aI + bi)^{-1} = (aI + bi)\left(\frac{a}{a^2 + b^2} I + \frac{-b}{a^2 + b^2} i\right)$$

$$= \left(a \frac{a}{a^2 + b^2} - b \frac{-b}{a^2 + b^2}\right) I$$

$$+ \left(a \frac{-b}{a^2 + b^2} + b \frac{a}{a^2 + b^2}\right) i$$

$$= \frac{a^2 + b^2}{a^2 + b^2} I + \frac{-ab + ba}{a^2 + b^2} i$$

$$= 1I + 0i$$

$$= I$$

An appeal to the commutative property yields

$$(aI + bi)^{-1}(aI + bi) = I$$

This completes the proof.

**Example 5-16.** Find the multiplicative inverse of $2i$.

Since $2i = 0I + 2i$, we set $a = 0$ and $b = 2$; then $a^2 + b^2 = 4$. Consequently,

$$(2i)^{-1} = \frac{0}{4} I + \frac{-2}{4} i$$

$$= \frac{-1}{2} i$$

We now check our result:

$$2i \frac{^{-1}}{2} i = (0\mathbf{I} + 2i)(0\mathbf{I} + \frac{^{-1}}{2} i)$$

$$= \left[ 0(0) - 2\left(\frac{^{-1}}{2}\right) \right] \mathbf{I} + \left[ 0\left(\frac{^{-1}}{2}\right) + 2(0) \right] i$$

$$= 1\mathbf{I} + 0i$$

$$= \mathbf{I}$$

The process of checking our result in the previous example could have been made easier by noting the following property, which has been suggested from earlier considerations:

If $a$ and $b$ are real numbers, then $(a\mathbf{i})(b\mathbf{i}) = (^-ab)\mathbf{I}$

In the example, the product of $2\mathbf{i}$ and $^-1/2\mathbf{i}$ is just $^-[2(^-1/2)]\mathbf{I} = 1\mathbf{I} = \mathbf{I}$. The stated property follows directly from the definition of multiplication; the proof is left as an exercise.

From the preceding discussion it should be clear that the nonzero complex numbers form an abelian group with respect to multiplication. By Exercise 9, multiplication distributes with respect to addition, and this, with the foregoing, completes the proof of the following theorem:

**Complex number field**

**Theorem 5-7. The set C of complex numbers is a number field.**

The axis of reals is so called because each real number $a$ can be identified with the ordered pair $(a,0)$, or $a\mathbf{I}$, which can be represented as a point on that axis. The identification is similar to that discussed in Sec. 5-4, where a real number was associated with a 1-tuple. The axis of reals, then, may be regarded as a number line. The axis of imaginaries may also be regarded as a number line, and points on that line represent scalar multiples of the complex number $\mathbf{i}$. The scalar multiples of

**Pure imaginary numbers**

$\mathbf{i}$ are called *pure imaginary numbers*. However, there is a difference between the numbers which each axis represents. Real numbers are closed with respect to the operation of multiplication, whereas pure imaginary numbers are not. With respect to addition and scalar multiplication, the set of all multiples of $\mathbf{I}$ is a vector space, as is the set of all multiples of $\mathbf{i}$, and they represent, respectively, subspaces of the vector space $\mathbf{C}$ of complex numbers. With respect to the vector-space postulates, the algebraic structures of these two subspaces are the same.

Because of the identification of the axis of reals with the real numbers, the complex number $a\mathbf{I} + b\mathbf{i}$ may be written simply as $a + b\mathbf{i}$.† This convention often affords some economy in computation, and examples will be given using this convention. Recalling that the distributive property holds on the set of complex numbers, we may find the product of two such numbers without resort to the definition.

† $a + bi$ is often used for $a + b\mathbf{i}$, but the latter is used here for emphasis.

**Example 5-17.** Find the product of $3 + 2i$ and $2 - i$.

$$(3 + 2i)(2 - i) = 3(2 - i) + 2i(2 - i)$$

$$= 3(2) - 3i + 2i(2) - 2i(i)$$

$$= 6 - 3i + 4i - 2i^2$$

$$= 6 + i - 2(^-1)$$

$$= 8 + i$$

Note that in the next-to-last step the number $^-1$ was used instead of $^-I$ for $i^2$.

The complex number $a - bi$ is called the *conjugate* of the complex number $a + bi$ and can be used to simplify certain computations. Consider the following product of the complex number $a + bi$ and its conjugate:

**Conjugate complex numbers**

$$(a + bi)(a - bi) = a(a - bi) + bi(a - bi)$$
$$= a^2 - abi + abi - b^2i^2$$
$$= a^2 + b^2$$

If $a + bi \neq 0$, $a^2 + b^2$ is a real number not zero, so that

$$\frac{1}{a^2 + b^2}(a + bi)(a - bi) = 1$$

Thus

$$(a + bi)^{-1} = \frac{1}{a^2 + b^2}(a - bi)$$

and also

$$(a - bi)^{-1} = \frac{1}{a^2 + b^2}(a + bi)$$

which is in agreement with the given definition of the multiplicative inverse of a nonzero complex number.

Following the convention for real numbers, it is also convenient at times to denote $(a + bi)^{-1}$ by the fraction $1/(a + bi)$. With this convention,

$$(a + bi)(a + bi)^{-1} = (a + bi)\frac{1}{a + bi}$$

$$= \frac{a + bi}{a + bi}$$

$$= 1$$

Since division can be defined in terms of multiplication,

$$(c + di) \div (a + bi) = (c + di)(a + bi)^{-1}$$

$$= (c + di)\frac{1}{a + bi}$$

$$= \frac{c + di}{a + bi}$$

The complex number $a - bi$ can be used to simplify this expression as follows:

$$\frac{c + di}{a + bi} = \frac{c + di}{a + bi} \quad (1)$$

$$= \frac{c + di}{a + bi}\frac{a - bi}{a - bi}$$

$$= \frac{(c + di)(a - bi)}{(a + bi)(a - bi)}$$

$$= \frac{1}{a^2 + b^2}(c + di)(a - bi)$$

The indicated product can be computed so that this quotient can be written in the form $x + yi$ for $x, y \in R$.

**Example 5-18.**  Express $(1 + 2i) \div (3 - 4i)$ in the form $x + yi$ for $x$, $y \in R$.

$$(1 + 2i) \div (3 - 4i) = \frac{1 + 2i}{3 - 4i}$$

$$= \frac{1 + 2i}{3 - 4i}\frac{3 + 4i}{3 + 4i}$$

$$= \frac{(1 + 2i)(3 + 4i)}{(3 - 4i)(3 + 4i)}$$

$$= \frac{-5 + 10i}{25}$$

$$= \frac{-5}{25} + \frac{10}{25}i$$

Compare this technique with the following procedure:

$$(1 + 2i) \div (3 - 4i) = (1 + 2i)(3 - 4i)^{-1}$$

$$= (1 + 2i)\frac{3 + 4i}{3^2 + 4^2}$$

$$= \frac{1}{25}(1 + 2i)(3 + 4i)$$

$$= \frac{1}{25}(-5 + 10\mathbf{i})$$

$$= \frac{-5}{25} + \frac{10}{25}\mathbf{i}$$

By writing $a\mathbf{l} + b\mathbf{i}$ formally as $a + b\mathbf{i}$, where $a$ and $b$ are real numbers, we can form any complex number by "adding" a pure imaginary number to a real number. In this sense we may see how the complex-number field may be regarded as an extension of the field of real numbers. However, the property of completeness, which was so crucial to the field of real numbers, is not a property of the complex-number field. In fact, the ordering properties of the real numbers are lost to the extended field. To illustrate this fact we shall show that the complex number $\mathbf{i}$ does not satisfy the trichotomy property. In order to do this it will be necessary to use two fundamental properties of inequalities, $-1 < 0$ and $a^2 > 0$ for any nonzero number $a$ (for properties of inequality see Chap. 9). First we note that, by definition, $\mathbf{i} \neq 0$. Whether $\mathbf{i} > 0$ or $\mathbf{i} < 0$, we have $\mathbf{i}^2 > 0$. However, by definition, $\mathbf{i}^2 = -1 < 0$. Thus we have a contradiction, and the principle of trichotomy fails to hold. In spite of this fact, a gain is made in that negative numbers have square roots in the extended field. For example, since $\mathbf{i}^2 = -1$, both $\mathbf{i}$ and $-\mathbf{i}$ are square roots of the negative number $-1$.

The field of complex numbers has many interesting properties, some of which will be explored in the exercises which follow. Since, in practice, the complex numbers are expressed in the form $a + b\mathbf{i}$ for $a$ and $b$ real numbers, both this form and the form $a\mathbf{l} + b\mathbf{i}$ will be used.

## EXERCISES

1. Find real numbers $x$ and $y$ which satisfy each of the conditions stated (recall that two complex numbers are equal if and only if their real components are equal and their imaginary components are equal):

   (a) $2x\mathbf{l} + 3y\mathbf{i} = 6\mathbf{l} + 9\mathbf{i}$
   (b) $x\mathbf{l} + y\mathbf{i} = (2\mathbf{l} + 3\mathbf{i}) + (3\mathbf{l} - \mathbf{i})$
   (c) $x\mathbf{l} + y\mathbf{i} = (2\mathbf{l} + 3\mathbf{i})(3\mathbf{l} - \mathbf{i})$
   (d) $x\mathbf{l} + y\mathbf{i} = (2\mathbf{l} - \mathbf{i})^{-1}$
   (e) $x = |2\mathbf{l} + 5\mathbf{i}|$
   (f) $4x - 5y\mathbf{i} = 20 + 35\mathbf{i}$
   (g) $(2x - 8) + (y - 4)\mathbf{i} = 0$
   (h) $(8 - x) + (2 + y)\mathbf{i} = (2 - \mathbf{i})(2 + \mathbf{i})$

(i) $x + yi = (2 - i)^{-1}$

(j) $|x + 3i|^2 = 25$

2. Perform the indicated operations and express the result in the form $x + yi$ for $x$ and $y$ real numbers:

   (a) $(3I + 4i) + (2I - i)$
   (b) $(I + 2i) + (3I + 4i) + (5I - 6i)$
   (c) $(3I - 5i)(3I + 5i)$
   (d) $^-2I(5I - 2i)$
   (e) $(I + i)^2$
   (f) $i^3 + 2i^4$
   (g) $(2I)^3 + i^5 + (2I + i)^3$
   (h) $(2I + 3i)^3 + (^-2)^3I + 27i$
   (i) $(^-7 + 2i) + (^-2 + i)$
   (j) $(2 + 3i) + (2 - 3i)$
   (k) $(1 + i)(1 - i)(2 + 2i)$
   (l) $i(2 + i)$
   (m) $(1 - i)^3$
   (n) $i^6 + i^9$
   (o) $(2 + i)^5 - (2^5 + i^5)$
   (p) $[(2 - 3i) - (3 - 2i)]^2$

3. (a) Show that the additive inverse of $a + bi$ is $^-a - bi$.
   (b) Prove that $(ai)(bi) = ^-(ab)I$, where $a$ and $b$ are real numbers.
   (c) Prove that $(aI)(bi) = (ab)i$, where $a$ and $b$ are real numbers.

4. Subtraction of complex numbers may be defined as the inverse operation of addition. Thus

   $$(a + bi) - (c + di) = (a + bi) + (^-c + ^-di)$$

   Perform the indicated operations and express the result in the form $x + yi$ for $x, y \in R$:

   (a) $(6 - 5i) - (4 + 3i)$
   (b) $(^-6 + 5i) - (4 - 3i)$
   (c) $i - (2 + 3i) - (^-4 - 5i)$
   (d) $(6I + 5i) - (^-4I - 3i)$
   (e) $(^-6I - 5i) - (^-4I + 3i)$
   (f) $(7I - 6i) - (5I - 4i) - (3I + 2i)$

5. Division of complex numbers may be defined as the inverse operation of multiplication. Thus, if $c + di \neq 0$, then

$$(a + bi) \div (c + di) = (a + bi)(c + di)^{-1} = \frac{a + bi}{c + di}$$

Express the result of each indicated operation in the form $x + yi$ for $x, y \in R$:

(a) $(1 + 2i) \div (1 - 2i)$

(b) $(3 + 4i) \div i$

(c) $\dfrac{5 + 10i}{5}$

(d) $\dfrac{1 - 2i}{1 + 2i}$

(e) $\dfrac{14 - 5i}{2 + 4i}$

(f) $\dfrac{(1 + 2i)(3 + 5i)}{(3 - i)(4 + i)}$

(g) $(2I - 4i) \div (I - i)$

(h) $i \div (3I + 4i)$

(i) $\dfrac{5I + 10i}{5i}$

(j) $\dfrac{4I - 8i}{I - 2i}$

(k) $\dfrac{4I}{I + i}$

(l) $\dfrac{(I + 2i)(3I + 5i)}{(3I - i)(I + 2i)}$

**6.** From the definition of addition of complex numbers, prove that the set of complex numbers forms an abelian group.

**7.** Prove that with respect to addition and scalar multiplication of complex numbers the set of complex numbers forms a vector space over the field of real numbers. What is the dimension?

**8.** From the definition of multiplication of complex numbers, show that the operation satisfies the associative and the commutative properties.

**9.** Show that with respect to the set of complex numbers multiplication distributes over addition.

**10.** (a) Show that the sum of a complex number and its conjugate is a real number.

    (b) Show that the product of a complex number and its conjugate is a nonnegative real number.

    (c) Show that a complex number and its conjugate have the same length.

    (d) Show that the complex number $1 + i$ and its conjugate each satisfy the equation $x^2 - 2x + 2 = 0$.

## Invitations to Extended Study

In exercises 1 to 3 assume that $F$ is the field of integers, modulo 5.

**1.** Let $D = \{a/b | a, b \in F; b \neq 0\}$. If $b \neq 0$, then the multiplicative inverse of $b$ may be represented by $1/b$, and the fraction $a/b$ may represent the product $a(1/b)$. For example, in $F$, $3(2) = 1$; the multiplicative inverse of 3 is 2, and we may consequently write $\frac{1}{3} = 2$.

The fraction $\frac{2}{3}$ can be expressed as an element of $F$ as

$$\tfrac{2}{3} = 2(\tfrac{1}{3}) = 2(2) = 4$$

Express each of the elements of $D$ as an element of $F$.

2. Show that the elements 0, 1, and 4 have square roots in $F$, but that the elements 3 and 2 do not.

3. Show that the set of all $n \times n$ matrices defined over $F$ is a vector space.

4. In an $n \times n$ matrix defined over a field $F$, each row and each column may be regarded as $n$-tuples of elements of $F$. If $A = (a_{ij})$ and $B = (b_{ij})$ are two $n \times n$ matrices, then their product is given by $A \odot B = (c_{ij})$, where $c_{ij}$ can be computed from the $i$th row of $A$ and the $j$th column of $B$ as follows: If the $i$th row of $A$ is the $n$-tuple $(a_{i1}, a_{i2}, \ldots, a_{in})$ and the $j$th column of $B$ is the $n$-tuple $(b_{1j}, b_{2j}, \ldots, b_{nj})$, then

$$c_{ij} = a_{i1}b_{1j} + a_{i2}b_{2j} + \cdots + a_{in}b_{nj}$$

Note that the product $AB$ is also an $n \times n$ matrix.

(a) If the base field is the real number field, find the product of

$$\begin{pmatrix} 1 & 2 & 3 \\ 2 & 3 & 1 \\ 3 & 1 & 2 \end{pmatrix} \odot \begin{pmatrix} {}^{-}1 & {}^{-}2 & {}^{-}3 \\ 0 & 2 & 0 \\ 1 & 3 & 5 \end{pmatrix}$$

(b) If the base field is the field $F$ of exercises 1 to 3, find the product of

$$\begin{pmatrix} 1 & 0 & 2 & 0 & 3 \\ 0 & 3 & 0 & 4 & 0 \\ 2 & 0 & 2 & 1 & 2 \\ 0 & 4 & 1 & 0 & 4 \\ 3 & 0 & 2 & 4 & 3 \end{pmatrix} \odot \begin{pmatrix} 1 & 0 & 0 & 0 & 0 \\ 0 & 1 & 0 & 0 & 0 \\ 0 & 0 & 1 & 0 & 0 \\ 0 & 0 & 0 & 1 & 0 \\ 0 & 0 & 0 & 0 & 1 \end{pmatrix}$$

(c) If the base field is the field $C$ of complex numbers, find the product of

$$\begin{pmatrix} 1 & i \\ {}^{-}i & 1 \end{pmatrix} \odot \begin{pmatrix} {}^{-}1 & {}^{-}i \\ i & {}^{-}1 \end{pmatrix}$$

5. Let $M$ be the set of all $n \times n$ matrices defined over a field. Using the definitions of addition and multiplication of matrices:

(a) Show that $M$ has a multiplicative identity.

(b) Show that multiplication is associative.

(c) Show that multiplication distributes over addition.

(d) Show that with respect to addition and multiplication, $M$ is a ring with identity.

6. Show that the set of all matrices of the form

$$\begin{pmatrix} a & {}^-b \\ b & a \end{pmatrix}$$

where $a$ and $b$ are real numbers form a field.

# CHAPTER 6

# THE CONCEPTS OF RELATION AND FUNCTION

## Guidelines for Careful Study

In Chap. 5 a field was defined to be an algebraic system consisting of a set of elements and two well-defined binary operations, addition and multiplication, on the set such that the set forms an abelian group with respect to addition, the nonzero elements form an abelian group with respect to multiplication, and multiplication distributes with respect to addition. In this and subsequent chapters we shall be interested in a more intensive development of certain concepts and properties within the limitations of number fields. For this reason it seems desirable to list here the specific postulates of a number field.

Number field **Definition 6-1. A number field is a set F of numbers with two well-defined binary operations, addition and multiplication, which satisfy the following postulates:**

For a, b, c ∈ F:

F-1  Closure: If $a + b = m$ and $ab = n$, then m and n are unique elements of F.

F-2  Associativity: $(a + b) + c = a + (b + c)$
$(ab)c = a(bc)$

F-3  Commutativity: $a + b = b + a$
$ab = ba$

**F-4** Distributivity: $a(b + c) = ab + ac$

**F-5** Identity: There exists a number 0 in F, called the additive identity, such that for every number $a \in F$, $0 + a = a$. There exists a number $1 \neq 0$ in F, called the multiplicative identity, such that for every number $a \in F$, $1a = a$.

**F-6** Inverse: For every number a in F there exists a number $^-a$ in F, called the additive inverse of a, such that $^-a + a = 0$. For every nonzero number a in F there exists a number $a^{-1}$, or $1/a$, in F, called the multiplicative inverse of a, such that $a^{-1} a = 1$, or $(1/a)a = 1$.

Our primary concern in the remaining chapters will be with the field of rational numbers and the field of real numbers, with some excursion into the field of complex numbers.

The following questions will serve as helpful guidelines for the careful study of Chap. 6.

1. What are the four field operations, and why are they so called?
2. What are the properties of equality?
3. What is an equivalence relation?
4. What is meant by an ordered pair?
5. What is meant by an independent variable? A dependent variable?
6. What is a relation?
7. In what ways may a relation be characterized?
8. What are the domain and range of a relation?
9. What is a function?
10. What are the domain and range of a function?
11. Why are the concepts of function and mapping synonymous?
12. What is meant by a mapping from one set to another?
13. When is the mapping $f: X \rightarrow Y$ said to be into, and when is it said to be onto?
14. When is a mapping said to be one to one?
15. When is a mapping said to be many to one?
16. What is the meaning of absolute value of a real number?
17. What is the formula for the constant function?
18. What is the formula for the linear function?
19. What is meant by the slope of a straight line?
20. What are the x and y intercepts of a straight line?
21. What is the general equation of a straight line?
22. What is the point-slope form of the equation of a straight line?
23. What is meant by direct variation? Joint variation? Inverse variation? Combined variation?
24. What is the formula for the quadratic function?
25. What are the zeros of a function?

**26.** What type curve is the graph of a quadratic function?

**27.** How do the coefficients of the formula for the quadratic function affect its graph?

**28.** How do you find the extremum and the axis of symmetry of the parabola?

**29.** What is the quadratic formula?

**30.** What is the discriminant of a quadratic equation, and how may it be used to determine the nature of the roots of the equation?

**31.** What is the formula for the reciprocal function?

**32.** What is a simple distinction between a continuous curve and a discontinuous curve?

**33.** What is an indeterminate equation?

**34.** What is the euclidean algorithm?

**35.** What does $a \equiv b$ (mod $m$) mean?

**36.** What is the simple form of diophantine analysis discussed in this chapter?

## Introduction

In Chap. 1 the concept of an equivalence relation was defined as a relation on a set of elements which had certain specific characteristics. Further examination exhibited the fact that such relations can be expressed in many different grammatical forms such as "is equal to," "is the same as," "is as tall as," and "has the same area as." For numbers it was found that the order relations "is less than" and "is greater than," while not equivalence relations, do have significant characteristics which distinguish them from other relations. In fact, they were

**Equivalence and order** used in Chap. 5 in one of their most important applications in the discussion of ordered fields.

We have identified as relations two concepts, equivalence and order, which have some very different characteristics, yet have some properties in common. While the order relation does not have either the reflexive or the symmetric property, it does have the transitive property in common with the equivalence relation. Thus we might conjecture that the transitive property characterizes the concept of "relation." This conjecture is disproved, however, by the counterexample of the relation "is the square of," which is neither reflexive, symmetric, nor transitive. What, then, is the meaning to be conveyed by the relation concept?

## 6-1. THE CONCEPTS OF RELATION AND FUNCTION

When applied to integers, rational numbers, or real numbers, the trichotomy principle tells us that for any number $a$ it is true that $a = 0$, or $a > 0$, or $a < 0$. If the heights of two boys, Tom and Jack, are being compared, we expect to find that Tom is the same height as Jack, or Tom is taller than Jack, or Tom is shorter than Jack. In the study of geometric configurations it is true that, under certain conditions, two figures, $f_1$ and $f_2$, will be so related that $f_1$ is congruent to $f_2$ ($f_1 \cong f_2$); under other conditions two figures $f_3$ and $f_4$ may be similar ($f_3 \sim f_4$); and under still other conditions two figures may be equal in area.

Whether the correspondence between two elements as expressed in the previous paragraph was one of equivalence, equality, order, measurement of height, congruence, similarity, or equality of area, it was an expression of a relation. Although there were distinct differences between the types of relations expressed and between the sets of objects considered, there was one thing common to all of them. In every case there were two elements for which there was a symbolic or verbal statement which gave meaning to the relation being expressed. Whether by symbol or by phrase, the correspondence was accomplished by writing in an ordered form one element, then the symbol or phrase, then the other element. In other words, a characteristic common to all of the relations was the existence of an ordered pair of elements.

*Common characteristic of all relations*

**Definition 6-2. The cartesian product P × Q of the sets P and Q is the set of all ordered pairs (p,q) such that p ∈ P and q ∈ Q; that is,**

*Cartesian product*

**P × Q = {(p,q)|p ∈ P, q ∈ Q}**

**Example 6-1.**   If $A = \{2,3,5,7\}$ and $B = \{10,12,14\}$, then $A \times B$ consists of the 12 ordered pairs, each having a first element from $A$ and a second element from $B$:

$$A \times B = \{(2,10), (2,12), (2,14), (3,10), (3,12), (3,14), (5,10),$$
$$(5,12), (5,14), (7,10), (7,12), (7,14)\}$$

A relation between the elements of two sets may be defined as a subset of their cartesian product.

**Definition 6-3. A relation between the elements of two sets P and Q is a subset S of P × Q. The domain of the relation is the set {p|(p,q) ∈ S}, and the range of the relation is the set {q|(p,q) ∈ S}.**

*Relation, domain range*

**Example 6-2.**   The set $F = \{(2,10), (2,12), (2,14), (3,12), (5,10), (7,14)\}$ is a proper subset of the set $A \times B$ of Example 6-1. The domain of $F$ is $A = \{2,3,5,7\}$, and the range of $F$ is $B = \{10,12,14\}$. The relation $F$ may be expressed in verbal form as "is a factor of." Thus, if $(a,b) \in F$, then "$a$ is a factor of $b$" describes the relationship defined by the set $F$ of ordered pairs. It is convenient, at times, to let $a \, F \, b$ denote the fact that $(a,b) \in F$.

The concept of relation is a natural abstraction from the concept of relationship between people. For example, if $B$ stands for the brotherhood relation, then "Albert is a brother of Ralph" may be written as "Albert $B$ Ralph," which, in our terminology, indicates that the ordered pair (Albert,Ralph) is an element of $B$.

Relations used in the study of mathematics are frequently denoted by symbols rather than by a verbal expression. For example, $\in$ is used to denote the relation "is a member of" in an expression such as $a \in Z$. In such cases the symbol $\in$ is used to represent the membership relation between the elements of a set and the set itself. The symbols $\subseteq$ and $\subset$ denote the relations "is a subset of" and "is a proper subset of," respectively, between sets. The symbol $=$ is often used to denote several equivalence relations within the same context. In more elementary textbooks, the subtle differences in their denotation are either disregarded or overlooked, depending on the objectives of the treatment. When symbols such as these are used, one must take care to examine the context of their use and recognize the domain and range of the relation discussed.

Given a relation $S$, there is determined another relation $S'$, called the *inverse relation* of $S$.

**Inverse relation**

**Definition 6-4. If S is a subset of P $\times$ Q, then S' is the inverse relation of S if and only if S' = {(q,p)|(p,q) $\in$ S}.**

From the definition it should be evident that $S'$ is a subset of $Q \times P$, the domain of $S'$ is the range of $S$, and the range of $S'$ is the domain of $S$.

**Example 6-3.**   Let $F$ be the relation defined in Example 6-2. Then

$$F' = \{(10,2), (12,2), (14,2), (12,3), (10,5), (14,7)\}$$

is the inverse relation of $F$. The domain of $F'$ is $\{10,12,14\} = B$, and the range of $F'$ is $\{2,3,5,7\} = A$. Thus $F'$ is a subset of $B \times A$. The relation $F'$ may be described verbally as "is an integral multiple of." Thus $(10,2) \in F'$ may be stated verbally as "10 is an integral multiple of 2," and the relationship may be denoted by 10 $F'$ 2.

Let $S$ be a relation and $S'$ its inverse. If we denote $(a,b) \in S$ by the notation $a\ S\ b$, then $b\ S'\ a$, that is $(b,a) \in S'$. If $S$ is a symmetric relation, then it satisfies the property

If $a\ S\ b$, then $b\ S\ a$

That is, if $(a,b) \in S$, then $(b,a) \in S$. From this and the definition of the inverse relation, it follows that if $S$ is a symmetric relation, then $S = S'$.

Similarly, if $S$ is a reflexive relation, then $a\ S\ a$ for every element $a$ in the domain of $S$; thus $(a,a) \in S$. How may the transitive property be described in terms of ordered pairs?

There is a special kind of relation in which the second element is usually uniquely determined by the first element. If an ordered pair $(a,b)$ is an element of such a relation, then we may say that the element $a$ determines the single element $b$ and no other, or that $a$ determines $b$ uniquely (this is not to say, however, that $b$ is determined only by the element $a$). A relation of this type is called a *function*.

**Definition 6-5. A function is a relation in which there are no two ordered pairs with the same first element and different second elements.**   Function

A function can be written symbolically as a relation $f$ such that if $(a,b)$ and $(a,c)$ are elements of $f$, then $b = c$. If $a$ is an element of the domain of $f$, then the element of the range of $f$ which is uniquely determined by $a$ is often denoted by $f(a)$, read "$f$ of $a$" or "$f$ at $a$." The corresponding ordered pair may then be written as $(a, f(a))$.

Consider, for example, the squaring function with domain $Z$, the set of integers. To each integer $a$ there is in this function one and only one number corresponding to $a$, namely, $a^2$; in other words, the value of $f$ at $a$ is $a^2$. For any element $(x,y) \in f$, $y = f(x) = x^2$. We may write $f$ using the set notation as $f = \{(x,y)|x, y \in Z, y = x^2\}$, or, equivalently, $f = \{(x,x^2)|x \in Z\}$. It is sometimes convenient to denote this function by the equation $y = x^2$. The set $\{(x,y)|x, y \in Z, x = y^2\}$, however, is a relation but not a function; to each $x$ $(x \neq 0)$ there correspond two values of $y$ satisfying the equation $x = y^2$. On the other hand, $\{(y,x)|x, y \in Z, x = y^2\}$ is a function in which the first element is represented by $y$ and the second element is represented by $x$.

An arbitrary element of a function $f$ may be given as an ordered pair $(x,y)$, where $x$ is called the *independent variable* and $y$ is called the *dependent variable*. The independent variable $x$ represents any element **Independent and dependent variable** of the domain of $f$, and $y = f(x)$ denotes that element of the range of $f$ which is determined by $x$; thus the element which $y$ denotes depends on the element which $x$ denotes, hence the term "dependent" variable. We also say that the element $y$ *corresponds* to $x$ with respect to the function $f$, and for this reason $f$ is sometimes called a *correspondence*. The correspondence may be given by some formula, rule, or verbal statement or by an explicit listing of the ordered pairs as a set, or as a table of values. If the correspondence and the domain are given, then the range is automatically determined.

**Example 6-4.**   Consider the variables $x$ and $y$ whose common domain is the set $D = \{0,1,2,3,4,5,6,7,8,9\}$, and let $F$ be the relation between the variable $x$ and $y$ defined by "$y$ is $x$ increased by 1."

**1.** In this statement the relation $F$ has been defined by verbal description.

It may also be defined:

**2.** In symbolic form:

$$F = \{(x,y)|y = x + 1 \text{ for } x, y \in D\}$$

Note that $D$ is neither the domain nor the range of the relation. The domain of $F$ is the set $\{0,1,2,3,4,5,6,7,8\}$ and the range is the set $\{1,2,3,4,5,6,7,8,9\}$, each of which is a proper subset of $D$.

**3.** As a set of ordered pairs:

$$F = \{(0,1), (1,2), (2,3), (3,4), (4,5), (5,6), (6,7), (7,8), (8,9)\}$$

**4.** In formula form:

$$y = x + 1 \qquad \text{where } x, y \in D$$

**5.** As a table of values:

| x | 0 | 1 | 2 | 3 | 4 | 5 | 6 | 7 | 8 |
|---|---|---|---|---|---|---|---|---|---|
| y | 1 | 2 | 3 | 4 | 5 | 6 | 7 | 8 | 9 |

**6.** As a graph (see Fig. 6-1):

FIG. 6-1

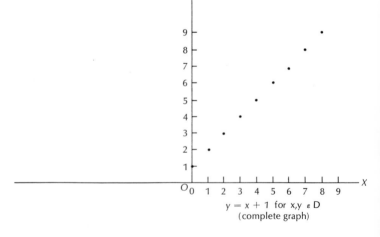

$y = x + 1$ for x,y $\varepsilon$ D
(complete graph)

**Function notation**

The relation $F$ of the example is indeed a function, since to each first element there corresponds one and only one second element. A customary notation to express such functional relationships is $y = f(x)$, which is usually read in either of two ways: "$y$ is a function of $x$" or "y is the value of the function at x," even though the letter y is not the function but is the second member of the ordered pair (x,y) in the function f. In the symbol f(x) the independent variable is x, and it represents the values to be selected from the domain of the function. The function is often denoted by f( ), or merely f, which represents the formula that sets up the correspondence and thus determines the values to be selected from the range of the function. This is the context which justifies the use of y to represent f(x), as is indicated in the frequent use of $y = f(x)$.

**Example 6-5.**   The formula for the function of Example 6-4 might be written as $f(x) = x + 1$. This can be read "the function of x is $x + 1$," "the function at x is $x + 1$," "f of x is $x + 1$," or "f at x is $x + 1$." Keep clearly in mind that the rule for the function is $f( ) = ( ) + 1$. Here the correspondence is defined by a formula which states that 1 is to be added to whatever value is selected from the domain of the function. Thus to find the functional value for any selected value of the independent variable it is only necessary to replace x in the formula by this selected value and complete the indicated operation. At $x = 0$, $f(0) = 0 + 1 = 1$; at $x = 2$, $f(2) = 2 + 1 = 3$.

The concept of *mapping* is synonymous with the concept of function. This is because the unique second element which corresponds to each first element may be considered as the range image of that element selected from the domain. In this context y would be said to be *the image of x under the mapping* $y = f(x)$, and the range of the function might be called the *image set* of the function. If for each element of the domain set X there exists an image element in the set Y, then f is said to be a *function from X into Y*, or f maps X into Y. The notation for this concept is $f: X \rightarrow Y$. In any such mapping the correspondence may be *many to one* or *one to one*. In a function, or mapping, the correspondence is said to be *many to one* when at least one element of the range is the image of two or more distinct elements of the domain. A mapping is said to be *one to one* if and only if to each element of the range there corresponds one and only one element of the domain. Thus a function f is one to one if its inverse relation f' is also a function. Furthermore, if the mapping is such that each element of the set Y is an image under f of at least one element of the domain X, then f is said to map X onto Y.

**Mapping**

**Into**

**Many-to-one correspondence**

**One-to-one correspondence**

**Onto**

The function of Examples 6-4 and 6-5 is a *one-to-one mapping* of a proper subset of the set D into the set D. The domain is the set $X = \{0,1,2,3,4,5,6,7,8\}$ and the range is the set $Y = \{1,2,3,4,5,6,7,8,9\}$, and the function is a one-to-one mapping from X into Y which is onto.

**One-to-one mapping**

As an example of a many-to-one mapping from the set $R$ of real numbers into a proper subset of itself, consider the function $f = \{(x,y) \mid y$ is the greatest integer less than or equal to $x$ for all real numbers $x\}$. In symbolic form it might be written as $f = \{(x,y) \mid y = [x]$ for $x \in R\}$. The graph of this greatest-integer function is shown in Fig. 6-2. The

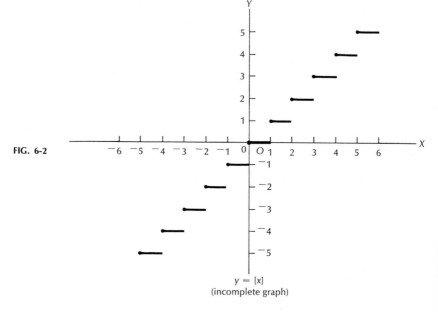

**FIG. 6-2**

$$y = [x]$$
(incomplete graph)

dots on the left end of each short line segment indicate that this value is included in the domain of the function for the interval indicated by the line segment. The fact that there is no dot at the right end of each such line segments means that this value is excluded from the domain of the function for the interval. For example, for $1 \leqslant x < 2$, $y = 1$ and for $^-3 \leqslant x < {}^-2$, $y = {}^-3$. The function $f$ is a many-to-one mapping from the set of real numbers into the set of integers which is onto.

Accepted, and frequently used, notations to indicate intervals on the real-number line are as follows:

$[a,b]$   is synonymous with $a \leqslant x \leqslant b$ and indicates the *closed* interval which includes both $a$ and $b$ and all points between $a$ and $b$.

$(a,b)$   is synonymous with $a < x < b$ and indicates the open interval which includes all points between $a$ and $b$ but does not include either $a$ or $b$.

$[a,b)$   is synonymous with $a \leqslant x < b$ and indicates an interval closed at the lower end but open at the upper end. Such an interval includes $a$ and all points between $a$ and $b$ but does not include $b$ (the intervals of the previous paragraph are of this type and could have been written $[1,2)$ and $[^-3,^-2)$, respectively).

$(a,b]$    is synonymous with $a < x \leqslant b$ and indicates an interval open at the lower end but closed at the upper end. Such an interval includes $b$ and all the points between $a$ and $b$ but does not include $a$.

Since a function is, by definition, a relation, one condition for the existence of the inverse of a function is that expressed in Definition 6-4. Attention is called to the fact that such an inverse, when it exists, may or may not be a function. If a function $f$ is a one-to-one mapping from $X$ onto $Y$, then its inverse relation is a function $f'$ which is a one-to-one mapping from $Y$ onto $X$. If, however, a function $g$ is a many-to-one mapping of the set $P$ onto the set $Q$, then its inverse $g'$ is not a function, but a one-to-many relation such that to each element from $Q$ there corresponds at least one element, and in some cases more than one element, from $P$.

**Inverse function**

**Example 6-6.**    The function $F$ of Example 6-4 is a one-to-one mapping from $X = \{0,1,2,3,4,5,6,7,8\}$ onto $Y = \{1,2,3,4,5,6,7,8,9\}$ which is expressed in formula form as $F(x) = x + 1$ or in verbal form as "increase by one." The inverse relation is the function

$$F' = \{(1,0), (2,1), (3,2), (4,3), (5,4), (6,5), (7,6), (8,7), (9,8)\}$$

which is a one-to-one mapping from $Y$ onto $X$. Expressed in formula form, it is $F'(y) = y - 1$, and in verbal form it is "decrease by one."

**Example 6-7.**    The function defined by the set

$$G = \{(0,1), (1,1), (2,1), (3,1), (4,9), (5,9), (6,7)\}$$

is a many-to-one mapping from $P = \{0,1,2,3,4,5,6\}$ onto $Q = \{1,7,9\}$. The inverse, which is the one-to-many relation whose domain is $Q$ and range is $P$, is not a function.

## EXERCISES

**1.** State in verbal form the relation in each of these situations:

(a) $y$ is the square of $x$.

(b) My car is the same model as your car.

(c) $y$ has the same area as $x$.

(d) $y$ is a square root of $x$.

(e) $y$ is 3 more than 2 times $x$.

(f) $y$ is one-half of $x$.

(g) $y$ is the positive square root of $x$.

2. What is the inverse relation of each relation of Exercise 1?

3. Which of the relations in Exercises 1 and 2 have the property of reflexivity? Symmetry? Transitivity?

4. Consider the relation $W$ for which the domain is the set $Z$ of all integers, the range is the set $\{0,1\}$, and the correspondence is such that if the first element is an even integer, the second element is 0, and if the first element is an odd integer, the second element is 1.

   (a) Is this correspondence one to one, many to one, one to many, or many to many?

   (b) Is $W$ a function?

   (c) Is $W$ a mapping?

5. Consider the relation $S$ for which the domain is the set $\{0,1\}$, the range is the set $Z$ of all integers, and the correspondence is such that if the first element is 0, the second element is an even integer, and if the first element is 1, the second element is an odd integer.

   (a) Is this correspondence one to one, many to one, one to many, or many to many?

   (b) Is $S$ a function?

   (c) Is $S$ a mapping?

6. Consider the relation $C$ for which the domain is the set $P$ of all non-negative integers, the range is the set $D = \{0,1,2\}$, and $C = \{(p,d)\mid p \in P, d \in D, p \equiv d \pmod 3\}$.

   (a) Is this correspondence one to one, many to one, one to many, or many to many?

   (b) Is $C$ a function?

   (c) Is $C$ a mapping?

7. Where appropriate, rewrite the relation $W$, $S$, or $C$ (Exercise 4, 5, or 6) in the phraseology of a mapping. Be careful to state whether the mapping is onto or not.

8. Which of these relations are functions?

   (a) $y$ is the same as $x$.

   (b) $y$ is greater than $x$.

   (c) $y$ is 1 more than twice $x$.

   (d) $y$ is less than or equal to $x$.

   (e) $y$ is the absolute value of $x$.

   (f) $y$ has the value of 5 for all values of $x$.

   (g) $y$ is 6 diminished by one-third of $x$.

(h) y is 1 more than two-thirds of x.

(i) y is the positive square root of x.

(j) y is numerically equal but opposite in sign to x.

**9.** Write a formula for each relation of Exercise 8.

**10.** What is the inverse relation of each relation of Exercise 8? Which of these inverse relations are functions?

**11.** Follow the pattern of Example 6-5 to indicate the function expressed by each of these formulas:

(a) $f(x) = 2x - 3$

(b) $f(x) = 3x$

(c) $f(x) = 6$

(d) $f(x) = 3x^2 - 2x + 7$

(e) $f(x) = \dfrac{4x - 2}{3x + 1}$

(f) $f(x) = \dfrac{2(x + 4)(x - 1)}{5(x - 3)(x + 2)}$

**12.** For each function of Exercise 11 find these function values:

(a) $f(1)$

(b) $f(0)$

(c) $f(^-3)$

(d) $f(\tfrac{1}{2})$

(e) $f(2 + h)$

**13.** For each function of Exercise 11 find the function value:

(a) At $x = 4$

(b) At $x = ^-1$

(c) At $x = \tfrac{2}{3}$

(d) At $x = a - 1$

**14.** Consider the set $D = \{0,1,2,3,4,5,6,7,8,9\}$ and the function $f(x) = |x - 1|$. Is this a mapping from $D$ into $D$? Is the mapping onto?

**15.** Is the mapping of Exercise 14 many to one or one to one?

**16.** Use the following patterns to define the function of Exercise 14:

(a) A descriptive phrase

(b) A set of ordered pairs

(c) A table of values

(d) A graph

**17.** Consider the set $R$ of all real numbers and the function defined by the formula of Exercise 14. Is this a mapping from $R$ into $R$? Is this mapping onto?

**18.** Construct a selected table of values and draw an incomplete graph of the function defined in Exercise 17.

**19.** Write the formula for a function which would be a mapping of a set onto itself.

For Exercises 20 to 23 let $S$ be the set whose elements are

$$0, \pm1, \pm2, \pm3, \pm4, \pm5, \pm6, \pm7, \pm8, \pm9$$

**20.** Consider the function $f(x) = |x|$.

    (a) Is this a mapping of $S$ into $S$?

    (b) Is the mapping onto?

    (c) Draw a graph of the function. Is this a complete graph or an incomplete graph?

**21.** Consider the function $f(x) = 4 - \frac{1}{2}x$.

    (a) Select a proper subset $X$ of $S$ such that this function will be a mapping from $X$ into $S$.

    (b) Select a proper subset $Y$ of $S$ such that this function will be a mapping from $X$ into $Y$ which is onto.

    (c) Write the set of ordered pairs which describes the onto mapping of (b).

    (d) Construct the table of values for the onto mapping of (b).

    (e) Construct the graph for the onto mapping of (b). Is this a complete or an incomplete graph?

**22.** Which of the functions, if any, of Exercise 8 are mappings of $S$ into $S$? Are any of these mappings also onto?

**23.** Construct a table of values and draw the graph for each of the functions of Exercise 8 which are mappings of $S$ into $S$.

**24.** Consider the function $f(x) = |x + 2|$.

    (a) Is this a mapping from the set $R$ of all real numbers into $R$?

    (b) Is the mapping onto?

    (c) Construct a selected table of values and draw the graph of the function. Is this a complete graph or an incomplete graph?

**25.** Consider the function $f(x) = 4 - \frac{1}{2}x$.

    (a) Is this a mapping from $R$ into $R$?

    (b) Is the mapping onto?

    (c) Construct a selected table of values and draw the graph of this function. Is this a complete or an incomplete graph?

**26.** Which of the functions of Exercise 8 are mappings of $R$ into $R$? Are any of these mappings onto?

**27.** (a) If the domain for $y = \frac{1}{3}x + 1$ is $[^-9,6]$, what is the range?

    (b) Is the correspondence in this mapping one to one?

    (c) Is the mapping onto?

    (d) Draw a graph of the function as defined. Is this a complete graph or an incomplete graph?

(e) What differences would there be in the range and graph of this function if the domain were changed to $(^-9,6)$? To $[^-9,6)$? To $(^-9,6]$?

**28.** Rewrite the definition of the concept of "function" in the pattern of Definition 6-2.

## 6-2. TWO CONSTANT RELATIONS

Consider the set of ordered pairs $\{(x,c)|x \in R, c$ is a fixed element of $R\}$. Since to each first element there corresponds one and only one second element, this relation is indeed a function. Furthermore, this function is a many-to-one mapping from the set $R$ onto the set $\{c\}$. Such a function is called a *constant function*. Its formula may be written as $y = c$ or $f(x) = c$, and its graph is a straight line parallel to the $x$ axis at a distance $c$ units from it. What are the domain and range of this function? Figure 6-3 shows the graph of two constant functions, where the values for $c$ are 3 and $^-5$, respectively.

**Constant function**

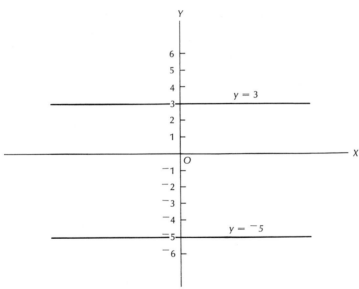

FIG. 6-3

The constant function $y = c$, for $c = 3$ and $c = {}^-5$
(incomplete graph)

In contrast, consider the set of ordered pairs $\{(a,y)|a$ is a fixed element of $R, y \in R\}$. Since in this case the correspondence between the set of first elements and the set of second elements is one to many, this set of ordered pairs defines a relation but not a function. Its formula may be written as $x = a$, and its graph is a straight line parallel to the $y$ axis

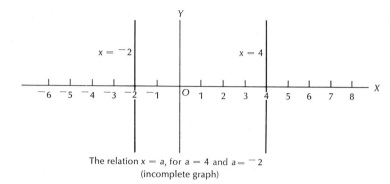

FIG. 6-4

The relation x = a, for a = 4 and a = ⁻2
(incomplete graph)

at a distance of a units from it. What are the domain and range of this relation? Figure 6-4 shows the graphs for two such relations, where the lues of a are 4 and ⁻2 respectively.

## 6-3. THE LINEAR FUNCTION

In Fig. 6-5 a line $\ell$ is drawn which is not parallel to either of the two axes. Let the point Q be the point where this line intersects the y axis. If the length of the line segment $\overline{OQ}$ is k units, then the coordinates of Q are (0,k). Let N(h,0) be the point where this line intersects the x axis

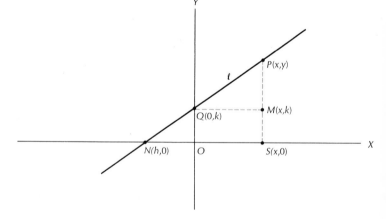

FIG. 6-5

and P(x,y) be any other point on the line. The line segment $\overline{PS}$, drawn parallel to the y axis, and the line segment $\overline{QM}$, drawn parallel to the x axis, will intersect at the point M(x,k). The triangle QMP thus formed will be a right triangle, with right angle at M, which is similar to triangle NOQ. It thus follows that

$$\frac{OQ}{NO} = \frac{MP}{QM}$$

This ratio remains constant independently of the position of the point P on the line or of the length of the line segment associated with it. It provides, therefore, a significant description of the position of a line in the plane. This ratio is called the *slope* of the line. If the point P is considered as moving along the line segment in such a manner that its x coordinate is always increasing, then the slope m of the line is positive if the y coordinate is also increasing, zero if the y coordinate remains constant, and negative if the y coordinate is decreasing.

**Slope of a line**

It should be evident from an examination of Fig. 6-3 that for any line which is parallel to the x axis, the y coordinate remains constant as a point moves along the line. For this reason the slope of the graph of a constant function, that is, any line parallel to the x axis, is said to be zero. However, an examination of Fig. 6-4 also reveals the fact that in the case of a line parallel to the y axis, any effort to interpret the ratio which defines the slope of a line always involves a division by zero. It is for this reason that we say that the slope is undefined for any line which is parallel to the y axis. From this discussion it follows immediately that any line whose slope is defined but is different from zero will be a line which will not be parallel to either axis. Line $\ell$ of Fig. 6-5, which intersects the x axis in the point $N(h,0)$ and the y axis in the point $Q(0,k)$, is a line of this type. The number h is called the x *intercept,* and k is called the y *intercept* of this line.

**x intercept**
**y intercept**

Again from Fig. 6-5, we have $MP = SP - SM = y - k$ and $QM = x$. If we designate the slope of $\ell$ by the symbol m, we may write

$$m = \frac{y - k}{x}$$

or

$$y = mx + k \qquad m \neq 0 \tag{6-1}$$

Equation (6-1) associates with each value of x one and only one value of y and is indeed a formula that defines a function which is called the *linear function,* since its graph is a straight line.

**Definition 6-6. A linear function is any function which can be represented by the set of ordered pairs (x,y) of real numbers, where y = mx + k and m (≠0) and k are both real numbers.**

**Linear function**

The domain and range of the linear function will be the set of all real numbers, unless otherwise specified.

**Example 6-8.**  What is the formula for the linear function in each of these cases?

**1.** Slope 2 and $y$ intercept $^-7$. In this case $m = 2$, $k = {}^-7$, and $y = 2x + (^-7) = 2x - 7$.

**2.** (1,2) and (5,$^-$6) are two of the ordered pairs associated with the function.

The formula for the linear function is $y = mx + k$. For the ordered pair (1,2) we have $2 = m(1) + k$. For the ordered pair (5,$^-$6) we have $^-6 = m(5) + k$. Subtracting the first equation from the second gives $^-8 = 4m$, or $m = {}^-2$. Using this value in the first equation gives $2 = {}^-2 + k$, or $k = 4$. Therefore the formula is

$$y = {}^-2x + 4$$

To check, for (1,2) we have the true statement $2 = {}^-2(1) + 4$, and for (5,$^-$6) we have the true statement $^-6 = {}^-2(5) + 4$.

**Example 6-9.**  Does there exist a linear function $f$ which can satisfy this condition?

$$f(x) = f(x + 2) \text{ for all real numbers } x$$

The formula for a linear function is $f(x) = mx + k$, where $m \neq 0$. Hence

$$f(x + 2) = m(x + 2) + k$$

The condition is that $f(x) = f(x + 2)$ for all real numbers, or

$$mx + k = m(x + 2) + k$$

or

$$mx + k = mx + 2m + k$$

whence

$$0 = m$$

It thus follows that no linear function exists which meets the stated condition. Why? Is there any kind of function which satisfies this condition?

**Example 6-10.**  Does there exist a linear function $f$ which can satisfy this condition?

$$f(x) = f(x) + 2 \text{ for all real numbers } x$$

This time the condition requires

$$mx + k = (mx + k) + 2$$

or

$$mx + k = mx + k + 2$$

Hence

$$0 = 2$$

Since this is an impossible relation, it follows that no linear function exists such that $f(x) = f(x) + 2$.

**Example 6-11.**   Does there exist a linear function $f$ which can satisfy this condition?

$f(2x) = 2f(x)$ for all real numbers $x$

$f(2x) = 2mx + k$
$2f(x) = 2(mx + k)$

The condition states

$$2mx + k = 2(mx + k)$$

or

$$2mx + k = 2mx + 2k$$

whence

$$k = 0$$

Therefore the linear function $f(x) = mx$ for any real number $m \neq 0$ satisfies the stated condition. To check this conclusion we observe that

$$f(2x) = m(2x) = 2mx = 2f(x)$$

Since zero is the second element of the ordered pair which labels the point where the straight line graph of a linear function intersects the x axis, the x intercept of the line frequently is called the *zero of the function*. For example, the zero of the linear function $y = x - 2$ is 2, since this is the value of x which gives the function the value 0.

**Zero of the linear function**

## 6-4. THE GENERAL EQUATION OF A STRAIGHT LINE

The discussion of the two preceding sections may be summarized by saying that the equation of a straight line in the plane is of the form

$$ax + by + c = 0 \qquad\qquad (6\text{-}2)$$

where $a$, $b$, and $c$ are real numbers and $a$ and $b$ cannot both be zero.

In order to establish the truth of this statement it is necessary to show that the graph of the given equation is a straight line, and also that the equation of any arbitrary line is of this form. In the first place it is desirable to raise the question of why it is necessary to impose the condition that both $a$ and $b$ cannot be zero. This is easily answered by noticing that if, in Eq. (6-2), $a = b = 0$, then $c = 0$, and the equation is trivially satisfied by any ordered pair of real numbers $(x,y)$. In other words, the equation loses its significance as an expression of a relation between $x$ and $y$. There remain three cases to consider to show that the graph of the given equation is a straight line.

**1.** $a \neq 0$ and $b = 0$. In this case the equation becomes $ax + c = 0$, or $x = {}^{-}c/a$. Figure 6-4 shows that the graph of such an equation is a straight line.

**2.** $a = 0$ and $b \neq 0$. In this case the equation becomes $by + c = 0$, or $y = {}^{-}c/b$. Figure 6-3 shows that the graph of such an equation is a straight line.

**3.** $a \neq 0$ and $b \neq 0$. In this case the equation may be written as

$$y = \frac{{}^{-}a}{b} x - \frac{c}{b}$$

which is in the form of the linear function for which the graph is a straight line.

The problem still remains of showing that the equation of an arbitrary line in the plane is of the form of Eq. (6-2). The cases for horizontal and vertical lines was covered in Sec. 6-2. A basic postulate of geometry states that through any two distinct points in a plane one and only one line can be drawn. In Fig. 6-6, let the line $\ell$ be the unique line determined by the two distinct points $P_1(x_1, y_1)$ and $P(x,y)$. If $P_1M$ is drawn parallel to the $x$ axis and $MP$ is drawn parallel to the $y$ axis, the coor-

**FIG. 6-6**

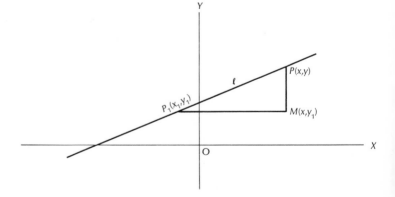

dinates of $M$ will be $(x,y_1)$. The slope $m$ of the line determined by the two points is then

$$m = \frac{y - y_1}{x - x_1}$$

or

$$y - y_1 = m(x - x_1) \qquad\qquad (6\text{-}3)$$

This last equation is called the *point-slope form* of the equation of a straight line. It may be written as

**Point-slope equation**

$$mx - y + (y_1 - mx_1) = 0$$

which is an equation in $x$ and $y$ of the form of Eq. (6-2), where $a = m$, $b = {}^-1$, and $c = y_1 - mx_1$. This completes the informal proof that the equation of any line in a plane is of the form $ax + by + c = 0$, where $a$, $b$, and $c$ are real numbers, with $a$ and $b$ not both zero.

## EXERCISES

1. In each case write the formula for the linear function whose graph satisfies the given conditions:

   (a) Has the slope $^-3$ and $y$ intercept 2.
   (b) Has the slope $\frac{2}{3}$ and $y$ intercept $^-1/2$.
   (c) Passes through the points $(0,3)$ and $(^-1,^-2)$.
   (d) Passes through the points $(2,^-5)$ and $(^-3,4)$.
   (e) Passes through the points $(0,^-4)$ and $(2,0)$.
   (f) Has the slope 6 and passes through the point $(0,5)$.
   (g) Has the slope $^-3/5$ and passes through the point $(^-5,^-2)$.

2. What are the slope, $y$ intercept, and $x$ intercept for each of these lines?

   (a) $2x - y + 8 = 0$             (d) $5x + 2y + 7 = 0$
   (b) $x + 3y - 6 = 0$             (e) $10x - 6y - 12 = 0$
   (c) $8x - 4y + 3 = 0$             (f) $7x + 5y - 3 = 0$

3. In each case what is the equation of the straight line determined by the given conditions?

   (a) Passes through the points $(^-2,0)$, and $(0,^-3)$.
   (b) Has slope $\frac{2}{3}$ and passes through $(0,^-3/2)$.
   (c) Has slope 0 and $y$ intercept 2.
   (d) Has $x$ intercept $\frac{1}{2}$ and $y$ intercept $\frac{2}{3}$.
   (e) Has slope $^-4$ and passes through $(^-1,2)$.

(f) Passes through the points (2,4) and (⁻5,4).

(g) Has undefined slope and x intercept ⁻6.

(h) Has slope 0 and passes through (4,1).

(i) Has slope ⁻3 and x intercept 2.

(j) Has undefined slope and passes through (3,⁻2).

(k) Passes through the points (4,5) and (6,7).

(l) Passes through the points (5,⁻3) and (5,4).

4. Show that the equation of a line with x intercept $h \neq 0$ and y intercept $k \neq 0$ can be written in the form

$$\frac{x}{h} + \frac{y}{k} = 1$$

5. A straight line is determined by two distinct points. For each equation find two suitable points and draw the graph of the line:

(a) $2x + 3y - 6 = 0$            (b) $x + 5y + 10 = 0$

6. On the same set of axes draw the graphs of the three equations $3x + 5y - 27 = 0$, $2x - 3y + 1 = 0$, and $9x - 4y + 33 = 0$. What geometric figure is formed?

7. The area of a triangle can be computed by taking one-half the product of the base and the altitude. What is the area of the triangle formed by the three lines $x = 0$, $y = 0$, and $3x + 5y - 30 = 0$?

8. On the same set of coordinate axes draw the graph of the lines $y = 3x - 4$, $y = 3x$, $y = 3x + 2$, and $y = 3x + 8$.

**Parallel lines**

9. The lines of Exercise 8 illustrate the fact that *parallel lines* are distinct lines which have the same slope. Find the equation of each of these lines:

(a) Is parallel to $2x + y - 3 = 0$ and passes through the point (4,5).

(b) Is parallel to $3x - 2y + 8 = 0$ and has y intercept ⁻3.

(c) Is parallel to $x + 5y + 3 = 0$ and has x intercept 6.

(d) Is parallel to $4x - 6y + 7 = 0$ and passes through the origin.

**Perpendicular lines**

10. Two lines which can be represented by linear functions are said to be *perpendicular* to each other if the slope of each line is the negative reciprocal of the slope of the other. Find the equation of each of these lines:

(a) Is perpendicular to $3x - y + 3 = 0$ and passes through the point (2,3).

(b) Is perpendicular to $2x + 3y - 5 = 0$ at the point (1,1).

(c) Is perpendicular to $x + 4y + 2 = 0$ and passes through the origin.

**11.** Find the formula for the linear function if:

(a) $f(3x) = 3f(x)$
(b) $f(5x) + 4 = 5f(x)$
(c) $f(^-x) = ^-f(x)$

**12.** One variable is said to *vary directly* as a second variable if the ratio between the two is constant. The constant is called the *constant of variation* or the *constant of proportionality*.

**Direct variation**

(a) Write the formula for the linear function which expresses this condition.
(b) Describe fully the nature of the graph of the linear function resulting from direct variation.

**13.** Given that $y$ varies directly as $x$, what is the value of $y$ when $x = 8$ if $y = 105$ when $x = 5$?

**14.** The circumference of a circle varies directly as its diameter.

(a) What is the circumference of a circle whose diameter is 7 in. if 12.56 in. is the circumference of a circle with a 4-in. diameter?
(b) What is the radius of a circle whose circumference is 25.12 ft?

**15.** Radar locates a distant object by measuring the delay in time between the sending of a signal and the reception of an echo from the object. Experiment has shown that the distance varies directly as the delay time. The delay time for a distance of 25 miles is .00027 sec. To the nearest 1/100,000 sec, what would be the delay time for a distance of 35 miles?

**16.** The volume of a sphere varies directly as the cube of its radius. The volume of a sphere with 3-in. radius is 113.04 cu in. What is the volume of a sphere with 6-in. radius, correct to two decimal places?

Another important type of variation is that in which the ratio of one variable to the product of two or more other variables remains constant. This form of variation is called *joint variation*. The formula which states that $y$ varies jointly as $x$ and $z$ may be written in either of the two forms: $y/xz = k$ or $y = kxz$ for $k \neq 0$. In the latter form $y$ would be said to be a function of the two independent variables $x$ and $z$.

**Joint variation**

**17.** Given that $y$ varies jointly as $x$ and $z$ and that $y = 96$ when $x = 9$ and $z = 16$, what is the value of $y$ when $x = 81$ and $z = 36$?

**18.** The area of a triangle varies jointly as the base and altitude of the triangle. What is the area of a triangle with a base of 18 in. and an altitude of 10 in. if a triangle with a base of 6 ft and an altitude of 4 ft has an area of 12 sq ft?

**19.** A triangle whose area is 84 sq in. has a base of 21 in. What is its altitude?

**20.** The volume of a rectangular solid varies jointly as its length, width, and height. The volume of such a solid is 105 cu in. when its dimensions are length 7 in., width 5 in., and height 3 in. What is the volume of a rectangular solid with length 12 in., width 8 in., and height 3 in.?

**21.** What is the height of a rectangular solid which has a volume of 1,680 cu ft and a base which is 15 ft long and 14 ft wide (see Exercise 20)?

## 6-5. THE QUADRATIC FUNCTION

It is important to note that in the formula for the linear function both the dependent variable and the independent variable appear only to the first power. The quadratic function derives its name from the fact that in its functional formula the independent variable appears to the second power.† The quadratic function may be written in either of the forms

**Quadratic function**

$$y = ax^2 + bx + c$$
$$f(x) = ax^2 + bx + c \qquad a \neq 0 \tag{6-4}$$

The condition $a \neq 0$ guarantees that the second power of the independent variable is a part of the formula. The only other condition on the coefficients is that $a$, $b$, and $c$ are real numbers. Unless otherwise restricted, the domain of the quadratic function is the set $R$ of real numbers, and the range is a subset of $R$. The graph will be a parabola.

**Parabola**

**Definition 6-7. Given a line and a point not on the line, a parabola is the set of all points in the plane, determined by the point and the line, which are so situated that they are equidistant from the point and line.**

As an illustration of this definition, consider the point $P(x,y)$ (Fig. 6-7) to be so located in the plane that its distance from the fixed point $F(h,k)$ is equal to its distance from the fixed line $d$, whose equation is $y = {}^-k$. Draw $\overline{PR}$ perpendicular to the line $d$. It will be parallel to the $y$ axis and will intersect the $x$ axis at the point $S$, whose coordinates are $(x,0)$. Draw $\overline{FM}$ parallel to the $x$ axis. These two lines will intersect in the point $M$ whose coordinates are $(x,k)$. The length of $\overline{MP}$ is $|y - k|$, and that of $\overline{FM}$ is $|x - h|$; also, triangle $FMP$ is a right triangle. It follows from the distance formula that

**Distance between two points**

$$FP = \sqrt{(x - h)^2 + (y - k)^2}$$

† The word "quadratic" is derived from the Latin word *quadratus*, which means "squared."

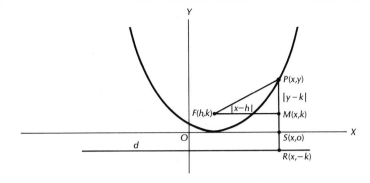

FIG. 6-7

Also,

$$RP = RS + SP$$
$$= k + y$$

Hence, since $FP = RP$,

$$\sqrt{(x-h)^2 + (y-k)^2} = k + y$$
$$(x-h)^2 + (y-k)^2 = (k+y)^2$$
$$x^2 - 2hx + h^2 + y^2 - 2ky + k^2 = k^2 + 2ky + y^2$$

or, for $k \neq 0$,

$$y = \frac{1}{4k} x^2 - \frac{h}{2k} x + \frac{h^2}{4k}$$

This last equation is of the form (6-4), where $a = 1/4k$, $b = {}^-h/2k$, and $c = h^2/4k$.

The assumption $k \neq 0$ simply implies that the point $F$ is not on the $x$ axis. It is not too difficult to show that a similar formula is derived if this restriction is removed. Note also that the line $d$ was taken parallel to the $x$ axis. This was done to guarantee that the derived formula would be of the form of the quadratic formula. If $d$ were taken in any other position, other formulas would result, and the graph in each case would be a parabola.

In order to obtain some information about the nature of a parabola which is the graph of a quadratic function, it is desirable to examine four different cases.

**Case 1:   $a \neq 0$ and $b = c = 0$.** In this case the formula becomes $y = ax^2$. Figure 6-8 shows the graph of this formula for each of three different values of $a$. A comparative study of these curves will reveal these facts:

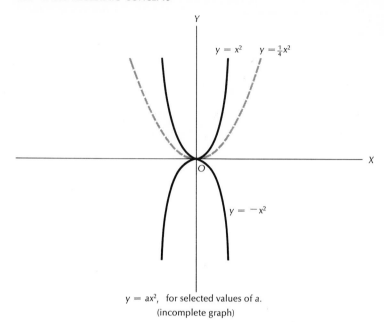

$y = ax^2$,  for selected values of a.
(incomplete graph)

**FIG. 6-8**

1. As $a$ gets larger the curve gets steeper, or closer to the $y$ axis, and as $a$ gets smaller the curve flattens out, or gets closer to the $x$ axis.
2. Since $x^2$ is always positive, the sign of $y$ will be the same as the sign of $a$. This means that when $a$ is positive, the curve will open upward, and there will be a lowest point on the curve; when $a$ is negative, the curve will open downward, and there will be a highest point on the curve.
3. Since $x$ is squared, its values, which differ only in sign, will yield the same value for $y$. This means that in each case the $y$ axis is an *axis of symmetry* for the curve. For example, if the formula is $y = x^2$, then $x = 2$ and $x = {}^-2$ each yield the value of $y = 4$. Note that the lowest point or the highest point, whichever the curve might have, lies on the axis of symmetry of the parabola; this point is at times called an *extremum* of the curve.

**Axis of symmetry**

**Extremum**

**Case 2:  $a \neq 0$ and $b = 0$.** The formula is now of the form $y = ax^2 + c$. Figure 6-9 shows the graphs of this formula for $a = 1$ and $c = 0$ ($y = x^2$), $a = 1$ and $c = 2$ ($y = x^2 + 2$), and $a = 1$ and $c = {}^-3$ ($y = x^2 - 3$). An examination of these curves reveals that there is no difference in their shapes. The only difference is in the position of the curve. Thus, for no change in $a$ but a positive change in $c$, the curve is shifted upward, and for a negative change in $c$, it is shifted downward. Again note that, in each case, the $y$ axis is the axis of symmetry. For the curves used in the illustration $a$ is positive. The only difference in the

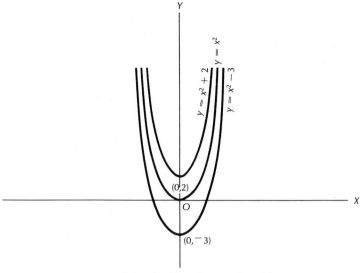

**FIG. 6-9**

$y = ax^2 + c$,  for selected values of a and c.
(incomplete graphs)

discussion and the illustration for a negative would be that the curves
would open downward rather than upward, and the extremum would
be a highest rather than a lowest point.

**Case 3:   a ≠ 0   and   c = 0.** The formula for this case is $y = ax^2 +$
$bx$. Figure 6-10 shows the graphs of this formula for $a = 1$ and $b = 0$
$(y = x^2)$, $a = 1$ and $b = 2$ $(y = x^2 + 2x)$, $a = 1$ and $b = {}^-2$ $(y = x^2 - 2x)$.

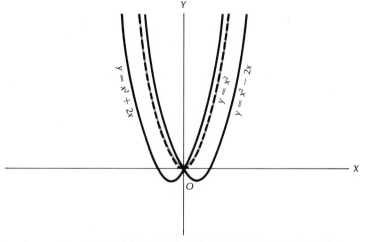

**FIG. 6-10**

$y = ax^2 + bx$ for selected values of a and b.
(incomplete graphs)

Again the shape of the curve remains the same, but this time the axis of symmetry is shifted to the left if $b$ is positive and to the right if $b$ is negative. In each case, for $b \neq 0$ the low point of the curve is shifted either to the right or left and downward but remains on the axis of symmetry, which is a line parallel to the $y$ axis. Thus, for no change in $a$ but a positive change in the coefficient $b$, the parabola will be shifted to the left and downward, and a negative change in $b$ will shift it to the right and downward. Again $a$ is positive for the discussion and illustration. As in the previous case, a negative $a$ would cause the curves to open downward, and the extremum would be a highest point, and the parabola would be shifted to the right or left and upward.

**Case 4:   $a \neq 0$, $b \neq 0$, and $c \neq 0$.** From the discussion of the three previous cases it should be evident that any change in the coefficient $a$ of $x^2$ in the formula of the quadratic function will have a significant effect on the shape, and possibly the position, of the parabola which is its graph; a change in $b$ alone or $c$ alone or a simultaneous change in both $b$ and $c$ will have a significant effect on the position of the graph but not on its shape.

It is desirable now to determine simple techniques for constructing a representative graph of a quadratic function. While not absolutely necessary, it is quite helpful first to find the position of the extremum of the curve. We know that once the coordinates of this point are determined, the line of symmetry will be a line through it and parallel to the $y$ axis. This makes it possible to find rather simply a sufficient number of points to get a better picture of the shape of the curve.

The procedure for finding the coordinates of the extremum and the equation of the line of symmetry consists of rearranging the formula so that the portion containing the independent variable $x$ may be written in the form of a perfect square.

It may be verified that an expression of the form $x^2 + 2px + p^2$ may be written as $(x + p)^2$ (see page 219), and for this reason it is called a perfect square. Note that $p^2$ is the square of one-half the coefficient of $x$. The formula $y = ax^2 + bx + c$ may be written as

$$y - c = ax^2 + bx$$

or, since $a \neq 0$,

$$\frac{y - c}{a} = x^2 + \frac{b}{a} x$$

One-half the coefficient of $x$ is $b/2a$, and if we add $(b/2a)^2$ to both sides of the equation, the right side becomes a perfect square. Thus

$$\frac{y-c}{a} + \left(\frac{b}{2a}\right)^2 = x^2 + \frac{b}{a}x + \left(\frac{b}{2a}\right)^2$$

or

$$\frac{y-c}{a} + \frac{b^2}{4a^2} = \left(x + \frac{b}{2a}\right)^2$$

Multiplying both sides by a and simplifying the left side, we have

$$y - \frac{4ac - b^2}{4a} = a\left(x + \frac{b}{2a}\right)^2 \qquad (6\text{-}5)$$

An analysis of Eq. (6-5) reveals that any value of x other than $^-b/2a$ will give a positive value for $a(x + b/2a)^2$ when a is positive and a negative value when a is negative, while $x = {}^-b/2a$ gives the value 0. Thus the coordinates of the extremum are $({}^-b/2a, [4ac - b^2]/4a)$, and the axis of symmetry is the line $x = {}^-b/2a$.

**Example 6-12.**   Plot the graph of the quadratic function $y = {}^-2x^2 - 4x + 6$ (see Fig. 6-11).

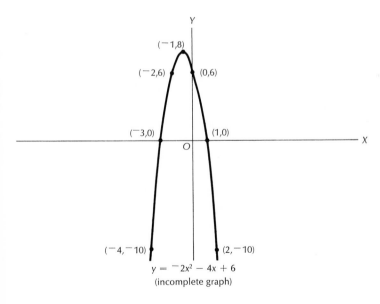

FIG. 6-11

$y = {}^-2x^2 - 4x + 6$
(incomplete graph)

We rewrite the formula as

$$y - 6 = {}^-2(x^2 + 2x)$$

Then, following the procedure of the preceding discussion, we have

$$\frac{y-6}{-2} = x^2 + 2x$$

$$\frac{y-6}{-2} + 1 = x^2 + 2x + 1$$

$$\frac{y-8}{-2} = (x+1)^2$$

$$y - 8 = {}^-2(x+1)^2$$

When $x = {}^-1$, the right side of the equation is zero, and for any other value of $x$ the right side is a negative number. Therefore for $x = {}^-1$ we have $y - 8 = 0$, which is the largest value for $y - 8$, so that the highest point on the graph is the point $({}^-1,8)$. The axis of symmetry is the line $x = {}^-1$. The table shows coordinates of points which are symmetrically distributed along the curve. Note that the values of $x$ which produce these coordinates are equally spaced from $x = {}^-1$.

**INCOMPLETE TABLE OF VALUES**

| $x$ | $^-1$ | $^-2,0$ | $^-3,1$ | $^-4,2$ |
|---|---|---|---|---|
| $y$ | 8 | 6 | 0 | $^-10$ |

## 6-6. THE QUADRATIC EQUATION

A closer study of the curve of Fig. 6-11, or of its supporting table of values, reveals the fact that there are two values of the independent variable $x$ at which the function value is zero. Each of these values is the first element in an ordered pair of real numbers which are the coordinates of the points at which the graph of the function crosses the $x$ axis. These values, $^-3$, and 1, are the real zeros of the function $y = {}^-2x^2 - 4x + 6$.

**Zeros of a function**

**Definition 6-8. The zeros of a function are those values of the independent variable for which the function is zero. If $f(r) = 0$, then $r$ is a zero of the function $f(x)$.**

**Quadratic equation**

Finding the zeros of a quadratic function leads to the necessity of solving the *quadratic equation* which results from assigning the value 0 to the function. Thus to find the zeros of the function of Fig. 6-11 it is necessary to solve the equation

$$^-2x^2 - 4x + 6 = 0$$

This equation may be written as

$$x^2 + 2x - 3 = 0$$

which can be factored easily into

$$(x + 3)(x - 1) = 0$$

Since the domain of $x$ is the set of all real numbers, we have, from the properties of the field of real numbers, that either $x + 3 = 0$ and $x = {}^-3$ or $x - 1 = 0$ and $x = 1$. Substitution of each of these values in the equation will establish that it is a solution. Attention is called to the fact that since $^-3$ and $1$ are zeros of the function, it follows that $x - {}^-3 = x + 3$ and $x - 1$ are factors. This is a property which will be proved later (see page 230).

When the quadratic polynomial can be factored easily, this is the simplest way to find the solution set of the equation. Another technique is that of *completing the square*, the process used in Example 6-12 to find the extremum of the function $y = {}^-2x^2 - 4x + 6$.

**Example 6-13.** Use the technique of completing the square to find the solution set of $x^2 - 2x - 143 = 0$. This technique produces the following chain of equivalent equations:

$$x^2 - 2x - 143 = 0$$
$$x^2 - 2x = 143$$
$$x^2 - 2x + 1 = 143 + 1 = 144$$
$$(x - 1)^2 = 144$$
$$x - 1 = 12 \quad \text{or} \quad x - 1 = {}^-12$$
$$x = 13 \quad \text{or} \quad x = {}^-11$$

Substitution of each of these values in the original equation will establish that the solution set is $\{13, {}^-11\}$.

Still a third technique of great importance is that of the *quadratic formula*. If, in Eq. (6-5), $y$ is replaced by the function value 0, the resulting equation may be written as

$$\left(x + \frac{b}{2a}\right)^2 = \frac{b^2 - 4ac}{4a^2}$$

from which it follows that

$$x + \frac{b}{2a} = \frac{\pm\sqrt{b^2 - 4ac}}{2a}$$

Thus

$$x = \frac{^-b \pm \sqrt{b^2 - 4ac}}{2a} \tag{6-6}$$

These are the two values of $x$ obtained by completing the square in the general quadratic equation

$$ax^2 + bx + c = 0 \qquad a \neq 0$$

It therefore follows that, in factored form,

$$ax^2 + bx + c = a \left( x - \frac{-b + \sqrt{b^2 - 4ac}}{2a} \right) \left( x - \frac{-b - \sqrt{b^2 - 4ac}}{2a} \right)$$

Equation (6-6) is known as the *quadratic formula* and may be used to find the solution set of any quadratic equation. The quadratic formula holds if the coefficients $a$, $b$, and $c$ are real or complex numbers. If the coefficients $a$, $b$, and $c$ are real numbers, then $b^2 - 4ac$, which occurs under the radical sign in the formula, may be used to determine the nature of the roots of the equation. For this reason it is called the *discriminant* of the quadratic equation. There are two significant tests to apply.

**Discriminant**

**Test 1. Given that the coefficients a, b, and c of the quadratic equation $ax^2 + bx + c = 0$ are real numbers:**

  1. **If $b^2 - 4ac = 0$, then the roots are real and equal.**
  2. **If $b^2 - 4ac > 0$, then the roots are real and unequal.**
  3. **If $b^2 - 4ac < 0$, then the roots are conjugate complex numbers.**

**Test 2. If a, b, and c are rational numbers and $b^2 - 4ac$ is a perfect square, then the roots are rational numbers.**

**Example 6-14.**   Without solving the equation, determine the nature of the roots:

$$x^2 - 12x + 36 = 0$$
$$a = 1 \qquad b = {}^-12 \qquad c = 36$$
$$b^2 - 4ac = ({}^-12)^2 - 4(1)(36) = 144 - 144 = 0$$

The roots of this equation are real and equal. In fact, the roots are rational. The graph of the corresponding function would be tangent to the x axis at the point $x = 6$.

**Example 6-15.**   Determine the nature of the roots:

$$3x^2 + 5x - 1 = 0$$
$$a = 3 \qquad b = 5 \qquad c = {}^-1$$
$$b^2 - 4ac = (5)^2 - 4(3)({}^-1) = 25 + 12 = 37$$

The roots of this equation are real and unequal. The graph of the corresponding function would intersect the x axis in two distinct points.

**Example 6-16.** Determine the nature of the roots:

$2x^2 - 7x + 9 = 0$

$a = 2 \qquad b = ^-7 \qquad c = 9$

$b^2 - 4ac = (^-7)^2 - 4(2)(9) = 49 - 72 = ^-23$

The roots of this equation are conjugate imaginary numbers. The graph of the corresponding function would neither intersect nor be tangent to the $x$ axis.

**Example 6-17.** Determine the nature of the roots:

$x^2 - 13x - 68 = 0$

$a = 1 \qquad b = ^-13 \qquad c = ^-68$

$b^2 - 4ac = (^-13)^2 - 4(1)(^-68)$

$\qquad = 169 + 272 = 441$

In this case the coefficients are rational numbers and $b^2 - 4ac = 21^2$, which is a perfect square. The roots of the equation are, therefore, rational numbers.

As a check for each of the above examples, the following solution sets can be verified:

$\{6\}$

$\left\{\dfrac{^-5 + \sqrt{37}}{6}, \dfrac{^-5 - \sqrt{37}}{6}\right\}$

$\left\{\dfrac{7 + \sqrt{23}\,i}{4}, \dfrac{7 - \sqrt{23}\,i}{4}\right\}$

$\{17, ^-4\}$

The next two examples illustrate the importance of the conditions on the coefficients in the use of the discriminant of the quadratic equation.

**Example 6-18.** Consider the equation

$x^2 - 2ix - 10 = 0$

Using the formula with $a = 1$, $b = ^-2i$, and $c = ^-10$, we get

$x = \dfrac{2i \pm \sqrt{(^-2i)^2 - 4(1)(^-10)}}{2}$

$\quad = \dfrac{2i \pm \sqrt{^-4 + 40}}{2}$

$\quad = \dfrac{2i \pm 6}{2}$

$\quad = i \pm 3$

In factored form,

$$x^2 - 2ix - 10 = [x - (i + 3)][x - (i - 3)]$$

In this equation $b^2 - 4ac = 36$ and is positive, but the roots are imaginary. However, they are not conjugate imaginary numbers. Also, note that $b^2 - 4ac$ is a perfect square, but the roots are not rational. Since the coefficient of $x$ is imaginary, neither of the tests applies.

**Example 6-19.**  Consider the equation

$$x^2 - 2\sqrt{2}x - 7 = 0$$

Using the formula with $a = 1$, $b = {}^-2\sqrt{2}$, and $c = {}^-7$, we get

$$x = \frac{2\sqrt{2} \pm \sqrt{({}^-2\sqrt{2})^2 - 4(1)({}^-7)}}{2}$$

$$= \frac{2\sqrt{2} \pm \sqrt{8 + 28}}{2}$$

$$= \frac{2\sqrt{2} \pm 6}{2}$$

$$= \sqrt{2} \pm 3$$

In factored form,

$$x^2 - 2\sqrt{2}\,x - 7 = [x - (\sqrt{2} + 3)][x - (\sqrt{2} - 3)]$$

In this equation $b^2 - 4ac$ is a perfect square, but the roots are not rational. The reason for this is that the coefficients are not all rational. Note, however, that the coefficients are real, and the discriminant could have been used to determine whether or not the roots were real and equal or real and unequal.

EXERCISES

1. Do not draw any graphs, but describe how the graphs in each case would compare if they were drawn:

(a) $y = 2x^2$, $y = {}^-2x^2$, $y = \frac{1}{2}x^2$, $y = 5x^2$

(b) $y = 3x^2$, $y = 3x^2 + 1$, $y = 3x^2 - 4$

(c) $y = 5x^2$, $y = {}^-5x^2$, $y = 5x^2 - 2$

(d) $y = x^2 + 3x$, $y = x^2 + 6x$, $y = x^2 + x$

(e) $y = \frac{3}{2}x^2$, $y = \frac{3}{2}x^2 + 2x$, $y = \frac{3}{2}x^2 - \frac{1}{2}x$

(f) $y = x^2$, $y = x^2 + 2x - 1$, $y = x^2 - 2x + 1$

(g) $y = x^2 + 3x + 2$, $y = x^2 + 4x + 2$, $y = x^2 + x + 2$

(h) $y = x^2 - 3x - 4$, $y = x^2 - 3x - 2$, $y = x^2 - 3x - 10$

(i) $y = x^2 + 5x + 6$, $y = {}^-x^2 + 5x + 6$, $y = {}^-x^2 + 5x + 3$

(j) $y = 2x^2 - 3x + 1$, $y = 2x^2 - 4x + 2$, $y = 2x^2 - x + 2$

2. In each case draw the graph of the given quadratic function:

    (a) $y = 3x^2 + 1$             (d) $y = 6x^2 + x - 1$

    (b) $y = {}^-2x^2 + 1$          (e) $y = 3x^2 + 5x + 4$

    (c) $y = {}^-x^2 + 3x - 2$

3. How may the graph of a quadratic function be used to determine the real zeros of the function?

4. How may the position of the extremum of a graph of a quadratic function be used to gain information about the nature of the zeros of the function?

5. For a quadratic function with real coefficients, what will be the nature of the discriminant in each of these cases:

    (a) The graph of the function intersects the x axis in two points.

    (b) The graph of the function has no point in common with the x axis.

    (c) The graph of the function is tangent to the x axis.

6. If the coefficients of the quadratic function $f(x) = ax^2 + bx + c$ are all real, what relation between $a$ and $c$ will guarantee that the zeros of the function will be real?

7. Solve each of these equations by factoring:

    (a) $x^2 + 5x + 6 = 0$          (f) $6x^2 - x - 1 = 0$

    (b) $x^2 - x - 2 = 0$          (g) $15x^2 + 2x - 8 = 0$

    (c) $x^2 + 9x + 14 = 0$       (h) $12x^2 + 29x + 15 = 0$

    (d) $^-x^2 + 3x + 10 = 0$      (i) $21x^2 + x - 10 = 0$

    (e) $^-x^2 - 7x + 18 = 0$

8. Solve each of these equations by completing the square:

    (a) $x^2 + 4x - 12 = 0$       (d) $4x^2 - 8x - 5 = 0$

    (b) $x^2 - 16x - 132 = 0$     (e) $9x^2 - 4x + 1 = 0$

    (c) $x^2 + 5x + 3 = 0$

9. Write each quadratic function of Exercise 8 in its factored form.

10. Use the quadratic formula to find the solution set of each of these equations:

    (a) $x^2 - 16x - 36 = 0$      (g) $4x^2 - 7x + 1 = 0$

    (b) $x^2 + 15x - 184 = 0$     (h) $x^2 + 2\sqrt{3}\,x - 6 = 0$

    (c) $2x^2 - 3x - 5 = 0$       (i) $x^2 + 4ix - 13 = 0$

    (d) $3x^2 + 7x - 3 = 0$       (j) $x^2 + 12ix - 11 = 0$

    (e) $2x^2 + 2x - 3 = 0$       (k) $2x^2 + 5\sqrt{2}\,x - 6 = 0$

    (f) $x^2 + 5x + 8 = 0$

11. Write each quadratic function of Exercise 10 in its factored form.

**12.** The area of a circle varies as the square of its radius. A circle of radius 3 in. has an area of 28.26 sq in. Correct to two decimal places, what is the area of each of these circles?

(a) A circle with a radius of 9 in.

(b) A circle with a diameter of 24 ft

**13.** When a body falls from rest, the distance it falls varies directly as the square of the time it has been falling. If a body falls from rest a distance of 257.6 in. in 4 sec, how far would it fall in 8 sec?

**14.** The surface area of a sphere varies directly as the square of the radius of the sphere. A sphere whose radius is 2 in. has a surface area of 50.24 sq in. Correct to two decimal places, find the surface area of each of these spheres:

(a) A sphere with radius of 8 in.

(b) A sphere with diameter of 5 ft

**15.** The volume of a right circular cylinder varies jointly as its height and the square of the radius of its base. The volume of such a cylinder is 339.12 cu in. when its height is 12 in. and the radius of its base is 3 in. Correct to two decimal places, find the volume of each right circular cylinder:

(a) Radius of base 14 in., height 9 in.

(b) Diameter of base 12 in., height 10 in.

(c) Radius of base 2 ft, height 15 in.

(d) Diameter of base 7 ft, height 15 in.

**16.** The volume of a right circular cone varies jointly as its height and the square of the radius of its base. The volume of such a cone is 1,356.48 cu in. when its height is 3 in. and the radius of its base is 12 in. Correct to two decimal places, find the volume of each right circular cone:

(a) Radius of base 6 in., height 7 in.

(b) Radius of base 8 in., height 2 ft

(c) Diameter of base 6 ft, height 10 ft

**17.** In each case what would be the form of the quadratic function $f(x) = ax^2 + bx + c$ which satisfies the specified conditions?

(a) $f(2x) = 4f(x) - 3c$          (c) $f(2) = f(3)$

(b) $f(0) = f(^-1)$          (d) $b^2 - 4ac = 0$

**18.** In each case find the quadratic equation whose roots are given:

(a) 2, 3          (b) $^-1$, 4

(c) $^-6, ^-4$

(d) $0, 3$

(e) $1 + \sqrt{5}, 1 - \sqrt{5}$

(f) $\sqrt{2} + 1, \sqrt{2} - 1$

(g) $\dfrac{3 + \sqrt{7}}{2}, \dfrac{3 - \sqrt{7}}{2}$

(h) $2 + \sqrt{3}, 1 - \sqrt{3}$

(i) $\dfrac{^-1}{2} + \dfrac{\sqrt{3}}{2}\,i, \dfrac{^-1}{2} - \dfrac{\sqrt{3}}{2}\,i$

(j) $3 + 3i, 3 - 3i$

(k) $i, ^-i$

(l) $i + 2, i - 2$

(m) $2 + i, 2 - i$

(n) $4i, 1 + i$

**19.** For what values of $k$ will the roots of each equation be equal?

(a) $x^2 + kx + 81 = 0$

(b) $3x^2 + kx + 12 = 0$

(c) $x^4 + kx + (k - 1) = 0$

(d) $x^2 + (k + 2)x + 1 = 0$

(e) $2x^2 + (k - 1)x + (k + 5) = 0$

(f) $x^2 + (k + 3)x + 3 = 0$

**20.** For the obtained values of $k$, find the roots of each equation of Exercise 19.

In Exercises 21 to 24, $r_1$ and $r_2$ represent the two roots of the quadratic equation $ax^2 + bx + c = 0$.

**21.** Show that $r_1 + r_2 = {}^-b/a$ and $r_1r_2 = c/a$.

**22.** Prove this theorem:

$r_1 = r_2 = 0$ if and only if $b = c = 0$

**23.** Prove this theorem:

$r_1$ and $r_2$ are reciprocals of each other if and only if $a = c$

**24.** Prove this theorem:

$r_1 = {}^-r_2$ if and only if $b = 0$

**25.** Prove this theorem:

One root of the quadratic equation is positive and the other is negative if and only if $ac < 0$

## 6-7. THE RECIPROCAL FUNCTION

Two types of variation have been mentioned previously, direct variation and joint variation. There are two further types of significance, *inverse variation* and *combined variation*. Direct variation is characterized by a constant ratio between the two variables involved. *Inverse variation* is characterized by the fact that the *product* of the two involved variables remains constant. The dependent variable is said to *vary inversely* as the independent variable. If $y$ varies inversely as $x$,

**Inverse variation**

then, for $x \neq 0$,

$$xy = k \quad \text{or} \quad y = \frac{k}{x}$$

**Reciprocal function**

Although in inverse variation the dependent variable $y$ cannot be expressed as a polynomial function (see Sec. 7-5) of the independent variable $x$, as in direct variation, the relation between the two variables is indeed that of a function. This function has been called the *reciprocal function*, since, if the formula is written in the form $y = k(1/x)$, the dependent variable is expressed explicitly as a function of the reciprocal of the independent variable. Furthermore, if the constant of variation $k$ has the value 1, the formula becomes

$$xy = 1 \quad \text{or} \quad y = \frac{1}{x}$$

in which $y$ is expressed as the reciprocal of $x$.

**Example 6-20.** The weight of an object above the surface of the earth varies inversely as the square of its distance from the center of the earth. An astronaut who weighs 185 lb on the earth's surface will have what weight when he is 180 miles above the earth? Take the earth's radius to be 3,960 miles, and find the answer correct to the nearest pound.

Let

$w =$ man's weight
$d =$ distance from the earth's center
$k =$ constant of variation

$$w = \frac{k}{d^2}$$

$$185 = \frac{k}{(3,960)^2} \quad \text{or} \quad k = 185[(3,960)^2]$$

The formula may now be written as

$$w = \frac{185[(3,960)^2]}{d^2}$$

To find the astronaut's weight at 180 miles above the earth, we have

$$d = 3,960 + 180 = 4,140$$
$$w = \frac{185[(3,960)^2]}{(4,140)^2}$$
$$= 169 \text{ lb}$$

In both direct and joint variation the resulting polynomial function is a mapping from the set of all real numbers into itself. Since the number 0 must be excluded from both its domain and its range, the reciprocal function is a mapping from a proper subset of the set of real numbers into itself. Figure 6-12 shows the graph of the function $y = 1/x$. When it is contrasted with the straight line and the parabola—the graphs of the linear and quadratic functions, respectively—one very significant difference becomes evident. There are no breaks in either the straight line or the parabola, while the graph of the function $y = 1/x$ shows a distinct break at $x = 0$. Since division by zero is undefined, there exists no functional value for the reciprocal function at $x = 0$. For this reason the curve has a break in it and is said to be *discontinuous* at $x = 0$. The straight line and parabola are said to be *continuous* curves **Continuity** over the set of real numbers, since they have no breaks for any real values of the independent variable.

An examination of Fig. 6-12 may give the impression that the graph

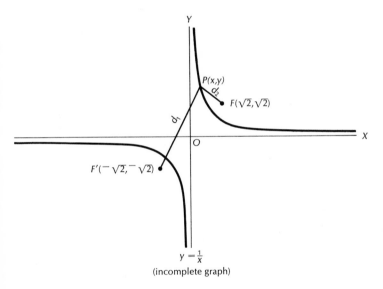

$y = \frac{1}{x}$
(incomplete graph)

FIG. 6-12

is made up of two distinct curves. Since the curve is the graph of the function $y = 1/x$, which is discontinuous at $x = 0$, the picture is that of one curve with two branches which are separated from each other. This particular curve is called a *rectangular* or *equilateral hyperbola*.

**Definition 6-9. Given two fixed points in a plane, a hyperbola is the set of all** **Hyperbola** **points in the plane which are so situated that the difference of the distances of any point of the set from the two fixed points is, in absolute value, equal to a constant.**

As an illustration of this definition, the equation of the curve of Fig. 6-12 may be derived in the following manner. Let $F = (\sqrt{2}, \sqrt{2})$ and

$F' = (^-\sqrt{2}, ^-\sqrt{2})$ be the two fixed points and $2\sqrt{2}$ be the fixed constant. If $P(x,y)$ represents any point of the set, $d_1$ its distance from $F'$, and $d_2$ its distance from $F$, then the condition that $P$ be a point of the hyperbola is

$$|d_1 - d_2| = 2\sqrt{2}$$

Since

$$d_1 = \sqrt{(x + \sqrt{2})^2 + (y + \sqrt{2})^2}$$
$$d_2 = \sqrt{(x - \sqrt{2})^2 + (y - \sqrt{2})^2}$$

it follows that

$$|\sqrt{(x + \sqrt{2})^2 + (y + \sqrt{2})^2}$$
$$- \sqrt{(x - \sqrt{2})^2 + (y - \sqrt{2})^2}| = 2\sqrt{2} \qquad (6\text{-}7)$$

If $d_1 > d_2$ (as drawn in the figure), the difference $d_1 - d_2 > 0$ and Eq. (6-7) may be replaced by

$$\sqrt{(x + \sqrt{2})^2 + (y + \sqrt{2})^2} - \sqrt{(x - \sqrt{2})^2 + (y - \sqrt{2})^2} = 2\sqrt{2}$$

This may be written as

$$\sqrt{(x + \sqrt{2})^2 + (y + \sqrt{2})^2} = 2\sqrt{2} + \sqrt{(x - \sqrt{2})^2 + (y - \sqrt{2})^2}$$

We square and simplify to get

$$(x + y) - \sqrt{2} = \sqrt{(x - \sqrt{2})^2 + (y - \sqrt{2})^2}$$

and again square and simplify to get

$$xy = 1$$

If $d_1 < d_2$, Eq. (6-7) may be replaced by

$$\sqrt{(x + \sqrt{2})^2 + (y + \sqrt{2})^2} - \sqrt{(x - \sqrt{2})^2 + (y - \sqrt{2})^2} = ^-2\sqrt{2}$$

The same pattern of simplification again produces $xy = 1$ as the equation of the curve.

The significance of the adjectives "rectangular" and "equilateral" are not pertinent to this discussion (see Exercise 8 on page 205).

**Combined variation**   *Combined variation* does not imply a new type of variation. It merely provides for the combining of the various individual types already described. As an illustration, consider this example:

**Example 6-21.**   The maximum safe load for a horizontal beam, supported at each end, varies directly as the width and the square of the depth, and inversely as the distance between the supports. If 512 lb is the maximum safe load for a beam 2 in. wide and 8 in. deep and held by

supports 12 ft apart, find the maximum safe load for a beam 5 in. wide
and 10 in. deep with supports 12 ft apart.

Let

$L$ = the maximum safe load
$w$ = width
$d$ = depth
$l$ = distance between supports

The formula is then

$$L = \frac{kwd^2}{l}$$

$$512 = \frac{k(2)(8)^2}{12}$$

or

$k = 48$, for the given unit

The formula now may be written as

$$L = \frac{48wd^2}{l}$$

whence

$$L = \frac{48(5)(10)^2}{12}$$

or

$L = 2{,}000$ lb

## EXERCISES

**1.** Boyle's law in physics states that the volume of a certain gas, at constant temperature, varies inversely as its pressure. The volume at a
pressure of 20 psi (pounds per square inch) is 30 cu ft.

(a) What is the volume at a pressure of 15 psi?
(b) How much pressure would be needed to compress the gas to a
volume of 15 cu ft?

**2.** The intensity of illumination from a given source of light varies inversely as the square of the distance from the source. If the intensity
is 45 ft-candles at a distance of 4 ft, what will the intensity be at a
distance of 6 ft?

**3.** For a constant electromotive force the current in an electric circuit varies inversely as the resistance. The current is 100 amp when the resistance is 0.3 ohm.

(a) What is the current when the resistance is 2.5 ohms?

(b) What resistance will produce a current of 150 amp?

**4.** The number of times a pendulum oscillates in 1 sec varies inversely as the square root of the length of the pendulum. A pendulum 39.1 in. long will oscillate once every second.

(a) What will be the length of a pendulum which oscillates three times a second?

(b) How long will a pendulum have to be to make it oscillate once every 2 sec?

**5.** A 2- by 6-in. beam is to be supported so that the distance between the supports will be 8 ft. It can be placed with either the 2-in. side or the 6-in. side down. In which position will it support the greater weight? How much more weight will it support in this position (see Example 6-21)?

**6.** The correction $C$ for error in measurement with a steel tape due to sagging of the tape varies directly as the square of the weight $w$ in pounds per foot of the tape and the cube of the length $l$ in feet between the supports of the tape, and inversely as the square of the tension $t$ in pounds. A correction of 0.035 ft should be made in a measurement made over a distance of 50 ft between the supports with a tape which weighs 0.065 lb/ft and with a tension of 25 lb.

(a) Correct to the nearest pound, what tension would have reduced this correction to 0.025 ft?

(b) Correct to the nearest 0.01 ft, what would be the correction for a measurement made over a distance of 65 ft between the supports with a tape which weighs 0.075 lb/ft and with a tension of 15 lb?

**7.** To help prevent cars from sliding off the road under slippery conditions, highway grading must meet certain conditions. On curves, the height in feet to which the outer edge of the road must be raised above the inner edge varies as the width of the road in feet and the square of the speed of the car in feet per second, and inversely as the radius $r$ of the curve in feet. For a car traveling at a speed of 40 mph (approximately 60 ft/sec) on a curve with a radius of 750 ft, a height of 3.6 ft is necessary for a roadbed which is 24 ft wide.

(a) Correct to the nearest 0.1 ft, what height would be required on the same curve for a speed of 60 mph?

(b) Correct to the nearest 0.1 ft, what height would be required for a speed of 30 mph on a road 35 ft wide if the radius of the curve were 820 ft?

8. The number of vibrations per second of a stretched cord varies directly as the square root of the stretching force, and inversely as the product of its length and diameter.

  (a) If the stretching force remains constant, what effect will halving the diameter and tripling the length have on the number of vibrations?
  (b) If the length and diameter remain constant, by what factor will the stretching force have to be modified to double the number of vibrations?

9. How may a problem in inverse variation be restated as a problem in direct variation?

## 6-8. DIOPHANTINE EQUATIONS IN TWO AND THREE VARIABLES

In Sec. 6-4 the equation $ax + by + c = 0$ was discussed as the general equation of the straight line. The only condition placed on the coefficients was that they be real numbers, with $a$ and $b$ not both zero. In such a situation, where there is only one equation in two or more variables, it is possible to select at random values for all but one of the variables. Once such a selection has been made, there exists a unique value for the remaining variable. An equation of this type is called an *indeterminate equation*. Similarly, any system of equations involving fewer equations than variables would possess this same characteristic of indeterminateness.

**Indeterminate equation**

If the coefficients $a$ and $b$ of the given linear equation are restricted to being integers, and only integral values are sought for the variables $x$ and $y$, one of the fundamental problems of *diophantine analysis* is introduced. Problems of this type and similar problems of a more general nature have long been of great significance in the study of number theory. Diophantus seems to be associated with the study of such indeterminate equations more because of his contribution to solution technique than because of his origination of problem ideas.†

**Diophantine analysis**

The existence of integral solutions of indeterminate equations in two variables, with integral coefficients, is provided by this theorem:

† E. T. Bell, "Development of Mathematics," pp. 64–65, McGraw-Hill Book Company, New York, 1940. Howard Eves, "An Introduction to the History of Mathematics," pp. 158–161, Holt, Rinehart and Winston, Inc., New York, 1964.

**Theorem 6-1. All equations of the form ax + by + c = 0, where a, b, and c are integers, have integral solutions if and only if c is a multiple of the greatest common divisor of a and b.**

The general proof of this theorem will not be attempted here; rather, the technique will be applied to a specific case to illustrate how the general proof might be developed.

**Example 6-22.**   Prove this theorem:

The equation $22x + 52y = k$ has integral solutions if and only if $k$ is an integral multiple of the greatest common divisor of 22 and 52.

Note that the given equation may be written as $22x + 52y - k = 0$, which is of the form of the general linear equation with $a = 22$, $b = 52$ and $c = {}^-k$.

To prove the sufficiency condition we must show that if $k$ is a multiple of the greatest common divisor of 22 and 52, then the equation has integral solutions. To this end we first find the greatest common divisor of 22 and 52. The steps are exhibited below, with the results summarized on the left in the form of the accompanying division algorithm.

**1.** $52 = 2(22) + 8$    divide 52 by 22:

$$22\underline{|52|}2$$
$$\underline{44}$$
$$8$$

**2.** $22 = 2(8) + 6$    divide 22 by the remainder 8:

$$8\underline{|22|}2$$
$$\underline{16}$$
$$6$$

**3.** $8 = 1(6) + 2$    divide 8 by the remainder 6:

$$6\underline{|8|}1$$
$$\underline{6}$$
$$2$$

**4.** $6 = 3(2)$    divide 6 by the remainder 2:

$$2\underline{|6|}3$$
$$\underline{6}$$
$$0$$

The process ends when the remainder is 0.

In step 4, 2 is exhibited as a divisor of 6, and since $6 = 3(2)$, we substitute in step 3 and use the properties of integers to write $8 = 2(4)$. We now have found 2 as the common divisor of 6 and 8. The process thus guarantees that 2 is the greatest common divisor of 6 and 8. Substituting the results of steps 3 and 4 in step 2 and using a similar argument will reveal that 2 is the greatest common divisor of 22 and 8. Similarly, substitution of the results of steps 2 and 3 in step 1 will show that 2 is the greatest common divisor of 52 and 22.

The algorisms of the first three steps may be rewritten in the respective equivalent forms

$$8 = 52 - 2(22) \tag{6-8}$$

$$6 = 22 - 2(8) \tag{6-9}$$

$$2 = 8 - 1(6) \tag{6-10}$$

Substituting from Eq. (6-9) into Eq. (6-10), we get

$$2 = 8 - 1[22 - 2(8)] = 3(8) - 1(22) \tag{6-11}$$

Substituting from Eq. (6-8) into Eq. (6-11), we get

$$2 = 3[52 - 2(22)] - 1(22)$$

or

$$2 = 3(52) - 7(22) \tag{6-12}$$

Equation (6-12) may be written as $22(^-7) + 52(3) = 2$, from which it is evident that $x = ^-7$ and $y = 3$ would be an integral solution of the given equation if $k = 2$. If $k = 2m$, where $m$ is an integer, then $x = ^-7m$ and $y = 3m$ would be a solution, since multiplication of Eq. (6-12) by $m$ gives $22(^-7m) + 52(3m) = 2m$. For example, if $m = 8$, then $x = ^-56$, and $y = 24$ would be an integral solution of $22x + 52y = 16$.

Conversely, since the given equation may be written in the form $2(11x + 26y) = k$, it follows that $k$ must be an integral multiple of 2 before integral values of $x$ and $y$ can be found to satisfy the equation. This argument has established the necessary condition of the theorem: the equation $22x + 52y = k$ has integral solutions *only if* $k$ is an integral multiple of the greatest common divisor, 2, of 22 and 52.

An important corollary of Theorem 6-1 presents a condition under which there are always integral solutions of the equation $ax + by + c = 0$. If we accept the theorem as proved, it is not too difficult to argue the truth of the corollary in the general case. This proof is left as an exercise for the reader (see Exercise 1).

**Corollary. There exist integral solutions for all equations $ax + by + c = 0$, where a, b, c are integers and a and b are relatively prime.**

In Example 6-22 only one set of values was found for $x$ and $y$. It is now desirable to investigate a general technique for finding all solutions for such an equation. The techniques of modular arithmetic provide a simple and direct pattern for the solution of an indeterminate equation in two variables.

**Example 6-23.**   Find all integral solutions of

$$22x + 52y = 16 \tag{6-13}$$

The techniques of modular arithmetic are suggested by the fact that the given equations may be written in the form

$$22x = 16 - 52y$$

which exhibits $16 - 52y$ as an integral multiple of 22, the coefficient of $x$. Hence, using 22 as a modulus, we have

$$16 - 52y \equiv 0 \ (\text{mod } 22)$$

or

$$52y \equiv 16 \ (\text{mod } 22)$$

In this congruence additional reductions are possible with 22 as a modulus:

$$52 = 22(2) + 8 \qquad \text{or} \qquad 52 \equiv 8 \ (\text{mod } 22)$$
$$16 = 22(1) - 6 \qquad \text{or} \qquad 16 \equiv {}^-6 \ (\text{mod } 22)$$

From these facts it follows that Eq. (6-13) reduces to

$$8y \equiv {}^-6 \ (\text{mod } 22)$$

Thus, for some integer $t$, $8y + 6 = 22t$, or

$$4y + 3 = 11t \tag{6-14}$$

Repeating the process with 4, the coefficient of $y$, as the modulus, we get

$${}^-1 \equiv {}^-t \ (\text{mod } 4)$$

from which it follows that for some integer $s$

$$t - 1 = 4s \tag{6-15}$$

Substituting from Eq. (6-15) into Eq. (6-14), we get

$$y = 2 + 11s \tag{6-16}$$

and substituting from Eq. (6-16) into Eq. (6-13), we get

$$x = {}^-4 - 26s \tag{6-17}$$

Formulas (6-16) and (6-17) give values for $y$ and $x$ which, upon substitution in (6-13), will satisfy the equality for each integer $s$. The condition of formula (6-15) requires that $s$ be an integer. Thus formulas (6-16) and (6-17) will yield an infinite number of pairs of integers $(x,y)$ which are solutions of Eq. (6-13). Note that $s = 2$ will give the values $x = {}^-56$ and $y = 24$ obtained as the particular solution in the previous example.

The technique exhibited in the example for solving an indeterminate equation in two variables may be outlined as follows:

**1.** Select the smaller coefficient of the two variables as a modulus.
**2.** Reduce the equation using this modulus.
**3.** Use the fundamental principle of modular arithmetic to express the resulting congruence in equation form.
**4.** Repeat the process on each such resulting equation until one of the coefficients of the two variables involved in the reduced equation is 1.
**5.** Solve this final equation to express the variable with 1 as its coefficient in terms of the final modulus used.
**6.** Substitute in the chain of reduced equations to express finally the two original variables as functions of the final modulus used. These obtained expressions will be the formulas which yield all integral solutions of the given equation.

An examination of Eqs. (6-16) and (6-17) of Example 6-23 will reveal the fact that, while there are an infinite number of integral solutions of Eq. (6-13), there are no pairs of positive integers which will satisfy the equation. This is evident from the fact that only negative integral values for $s$ can make $x$ positive, while $y$ can be positive for no negative integral value of $s$. This is an illustration of the fact that when the coefficients of the two variables in an indeterminate equation with integral coefficients are of the same sign, there exists either no positive integral solution or, at most, a finite number of positive integral solutions.

The same techniques can be used to advantage to find the integral solutions of any indeterminate system of equations which can be reduced to a single equation in two variables with integral coefficients. The next example illustrates such a solution procedure. It also illustrates the existence of only a finite number of positive integral solutions of the system.

**Example 6-24.** A farmer has $1,280 with which to purchase 100 animals. Calves can be purchased at $45 a head, hogs at $35 a head, and pigs at $10 a head. How many head of each type of animal can he purchase?

Let

$c$ = number of calves purchased
$h$ = number of hogs purchased
$p$ = number of pigs purchased

The conditions of the problem may then be stated in two equations:

$$c + h + p = 100 \tag{6-18}$$

$$45c + 35h + 10p = 1{,}280 \tag{6-19}$$

This presents one indeterminate system of two equations in three variables. It may be reduced to one equation in two variables by solving Eq. (6-18) for one variable, say $p$, in terms of the other two and substituting in Eq. (6-19). This gives

$$7c + 5h = 56 \tag{6-20}$$

This equation reduces to

$$2c \equiv 1 \ (\mathrm{mod}\ 5)$$

or

$$2c - 1 = 5k \qquad \text{for } k \text{ an integer} \tag{6-21}$$

We repeat the process to get

$$^{-}1 \equiv k \ (\mathrm{mod}\ 2)$$

$$k + 1 = 2m \qquad \text{for } m \text{ an integer} \tag{6-22}$$

Substituting from this into Eq. (6-21), we get

$$c = 5m - 2 \tag{6-23}$$

and substituting from this into Eq. (6-20), we get

$$h = 14 - 7m \tag{6-24}$$

Formulas (6-23) and (6-24), with $m$ an integer, yield all integral solutions of Eq. (6-20). The physical conditions of the problem demand that only positive integers be accepted as solutions. The only permissible values of $m$ are, therefore, $m = 1$, and $m = 2$. Equations (6-23), (6-24), and (6-18) then yield these permissible values:

| $m$ | $c$ | $h$ | $p$ |
|-----|-----|-----|-----|
| 1   | 3   | 7   | 90  |
| 2   | 8   | 0   | 92  |

The possible purchases are 3 calves, 7 hogs, and 90 pigs; or 8 calves, no hogs, and 92 pigs.

## EXERCISES

In each of these exercises the word "solve" means to find the formulas which yield the integral solutions of the given equation or equations.

**1.** Prove the corollary to Theorem 6-1.

**2.** Solve the equation $7x - 19y = 31$.

**3.** Is it true that in Exercise 2 there exists an infinite number of positive integral solutions of the equation? How can you substantiate your answer?

**4.** Solve the equation $3x + 4y = 29$.

**5.** Is it true that in Exercise 4 there exists an infinite number of *positive* integral solutions of the equation? How can you substantiate your answer?

**6.** Why does there exist no solution of $9x - 21y = 10$? What in the solution procedure supports your answer?

**7.** Find the positive integral solutions of each of these equations and give reasons for the basic differences that exist:

(a) $15x - 21y = 14$

(b) $15x + 21y = 18$

(c) $15x + 21y = 72$

**8.** Solve $5x + 3y = 38$.

**9.** Solve $78x + 65y = 91$.

**10.** Find the positive integral solutions of $7x - 2y = 4$.

**11.** Find the positive integral solutions of $10x + 9y = 108$.

**12.** Separate 100 into two integral parts $a$ and $b$ such that the quotients $a/3$ and $b/5$ are positive integers.

**13.** How many suckers and cones can Tommy buy for 25 cents if suckers cost 3 cents each and cones 5 cents each?

**14.** A man received a check for a certain amount of money. In cashing the check the cashier carelessly interchanged the number of dollars and the number of cents. This was not detected by the man until he discovered that, after spending 68 cents, he had exactly twice as much money as the amount for which the check was drawn originally. For how much was the check written?†

† J. V. Uspensky and M. A. Heaslet, "Elementary Number Theory," p. 65, McGraw-Hill Book Company, New York, 1939.

**15.** (a) Solve this system:
$$14x + 3y + 5z = 135$$
$$x + y + z = 22$$
(b) Find all positive integral solutions of the system.

**16.** Divide 78 into three positive integral parts $a$, $b$, and $c$ so that the quotients $a/3$, $b/4$, and $c/7$ are integers whose sum is 14.

Exercises 17 and 18 are the Chinese *Hundred Fowls* problem and a European version of it as recorded by the historian David Eugene Smith.†

**17.** "If a cock is worth 5 sapeks; a hen, 3 sapeks; and 3 chickens, 1 sapek; how many cocks, hens, and chickens, 100 in all, will together be worth 100 sapeks?"

**18.** "Twenty persons, men, women, and girls, have drunk 20 pence worth of wine; each man pays 3 pence, each woman, 2 pence, and each girl, $\frac{1}{2}$ penny; required the number of each."

**19.** A department-store buyer has $8,600 to invest in television, stereo, and radio sets. He plans to purchase 50 instruments altogether. Television sets are priced at $336 each, stereo sets at $280 each, and radios at $16 each. How many instruments of each type can he purchase?

## Invitations to Extended Study

**1.** For the general polynomial equation of degree $n$ in $x$

$$a_nx^n + a_{n-1}x^{n-1} + \cdots + a_2x^2 + a_1x + a_0 = 0$$

the discriminant is defined to be $a_n^{2n-2}$ multiplied by the product of the squares of the differences of the roots. For example, if $r_1$, $r_2$, and $r_3$ are the three roots of

$$a_3x^3 + a_2x^2 + a_1x + a_0 = 0$$

the discriminant is

$$a_3{}^4(r_1 - r_2)^2(r_1 - r_3)^2(r_2 - r_3)^2$$

Use this definition to derive $b^2 - 4ac$ as the discriminant of the quadratic equation $ax^2 + bx + c = 0$.

**2.** Investigate techniques for solving equations of the form

$$a[f(x)]^2 + b[f(x)] + c = 0 \qquad a \neq 0$$

† David Eugene Smith, "History of Mathematics," vol. II, p. 585, Ginn and Company, Boston, 1925.

3. Investigate techniques for solving irrational equations which can be put in quadratic form. Pay special attention to the possibility of extraneous roots.

4. Investigate techniques for solving equations that contain rational functions of the variable and can be put into quadratic form. Pay special attention to the possibility of extraneous roots.

5. If $r_1$, $r_2$, and $r_3$ are the roots of

$$ax^3 + bx^2 + cx + d = 0$$

show that

$$r_1 + r_2 + r_3 = \frac{-b}{a}$$

$$r_1r_2 + r_1r_3 + r_2r_3 = \frac{c}{a}$$

$$r_1r_2r_3 = \frac{-d}{a}$$

6. If $r_1$, $r_2$, $r_3$, and $r_4$ are the roots of

$$ax^4 + bx^3 + cx^2 + dx + e = 0$$

show that

$$r_1 + r_2 + r_3 + r_4 = \frac{-b}{a}$$

$$r_1r_2 + r_1r_3 + r_1r_4 + r_2r_3 + r_2r_4 + r_3r_4 = \frac{c}{a}$$

$$r_1r_2r_3 + r_1r_2r_4 + r_1r_3r_4 + r_2r_3r_4 = \frac{-d}{a}$$

$$r_1r_2r_3r_4 = \frac{e}{a}$$

7. Use the definition of exercise 1 and the information of exercise 5 to show that the discriminant of the reduced cubic $x^3 + px + q = 0$ is $-4p^3 - 27q^2$.

8. Find the equation of the curve which is defined as the set of points each of which is such that the absolute value of the difference of its distances from the points $(\sqrt{2},0)$ and $(^-\sqrt{2},0)$ is 2. This is another form of the equation of a rectangular hyperbola. Plot a rough graph of this curve. How does it differ from that of Fig. 6-12?

9. Prove Theorem 6-1.

10. Sets of positive integers, $a$, $b$, and $c$ which satisfy the condition $c^2 = a^2 + b^2$ are called *pythagorean number triples*. Derive formulas which will give all pythagorean number triples.

**11.** In the "Greek Anthology" this summary of the personal life of Diophantus is to be found:† "Diophantus passed one sixth of his life in childhood, one twelfth in youth, and one seventh more as a bachelor. Five years after his marriage was born a son who died four years before his father, at half his father's age [at the time of his death]." How old was Diophantus at the time of his death?

† Eves, *op, cit.,* p. 177.

# CHAPTER 7

# THE CONCEPT OF POLYNOMIALS

## Guidelines for Careful Study

In previous chapters the basic properties of a few important algebraic systems were studied in some detail. In this chapter we shall use these properties to investigate the characteristics of certain types of algebraic expressions called *polynomials*. From one point of view, we shall see that polynomials may be considered as algebraic entities which, with appropriate definitions of addition and scalar multiplication, are vectors, or, with addition and the more general definition of multiplication for finding the product of any two polynomials, are elements of a ring or of an integral domain. From another point of view, we shall see that polynomials may represent functions of which the constant, linear, and quadratic functions are special cases. The following questions will provide a guide to the careful study of Chap. 7.

1. What is the definition of a group? An abelian group?
2. What is the definition of a ring? A commutative ring? A commutative ring with identity?
3. What are divisors of zero?
4. What is the definition of an integral domain?
5. What is the definition of a number field?
6. What are the laws of exponents?
7. What is the definition of a polynomial of degree *n* over a ring? An integral domain? A field?

**8.** How do you find the sum and the product of two polynomials?

**9.** Is the sum or the product of two polynomials of the same degree always a polynomial of the same degree?

**10.** With respect to what operation does the set of polynomials over a field form an abelian group?

**11.** How may the set of polynomials over a ring, integral domain, or field be regarded as a ring?

**12.** How may the set of polynomials over an integral domain or field be regarded as an integral domain?

**13.** For an arbitrary polynomial defined over a field, does there exist a polynomial which is its multiplicative inverse?

**14.** Why may the set of polynomials defined over a field not be considered as a field?

**15.** How may the set of polynomials defined over a field be considered as a vector space?

**16.** How may a polynomial be used to represent a function?

**17.** What is the graph of a polynomial function?

**18.** What is a zero of a polynomial function?

**19.** What is a polynomial equation?

**20.** Does every polynomial function have a zero?

**21.** How does the existence of zeros of a polynomial function depend on the base field and the degree of the polynomial?

**22.** What is the Fundamental Theorem of Algebra?

**23.** What is the Division Algorithm?

**24.** What is the Remainder Theorem?

**25.** What is the Factor Theorem?

## Introduction

**Algebraic expressions**     An *algebraic expression* is an arrangement of symbols, together with indicated operations of addition, subtraction, multiplication, division, raising to powers, or extraction of roots. The symbols may be terms, including numerals or any other constants representing fixed values, or variables with subsets of the set of complex numbers as their domains of value; or the symbols may be merely indeterminates with which no domains of value are associated. In the previous chapter attention was given to four specific types of algebraic expressions, those representing the constant, linear, quadratic, and reciprocal functions. In this chapter we shall define and study some of the basic properties of a more general type of algebraic expression called a *polynomial*. The constant, linear, and quadratic functions, under certain conditions of definition, will be recognized as special cases of this more general concept, whereas the reciprocal function is not. The most general use of poly-nomials, however, is as formal algebraic expressions which involve an indeterminate, usually represented by a letter, and which are ele-ments of significant algebraic systems.

## 7-1. THE CONCEPT OF POLYNOMIAL

If $S$ is an arbitrary algebraic system, such as a ring, an integral do-main, or a field, a polynomial over that system may be defined as a formal algebraic expression utilizing elements from the system and an *indeterminate*, which we shall symbolize by x. Any nonzero element of $S$ is called a polynomial of degree 0 over $S$. If $a_0, a_1 \in S$ and $a_1 \neq 0$, then the expression $a_0 + a_1 x$ is called a polynomial in x of degree 1 over $S$. In general, if $n$ is a nonnegative integer and $a_0, a_1, a_2, \ldots, a_n \in S$, with $a_n \neq 0$, then an expression of the form $a_0 + a_1 x + a_2 x^2 + \cdots + a_n x^n$ is called a *polynomial in x of degree n over S*. The element $a_0$ is called the *constant term*, and the elements $a_0, a_1, a_2, \ldots, a_n$ are called *coefficients*. The *leading coefficient* is $a_n$, and if $a_n = 1$, the polynomial is said to be *monic*. The algebraic system $S$ in which the coefficients of a given polynomial are contained as elements is called the *base system* over which the polynomial is defined. It is emphasized that a poly-nomial has only a finite number of terms. Polynomials of one, two, or three terms are called *monomials, binomials,* or *trinomials*, respectively.

**Polynomial of degree n**

**Base system**

If the set $Q$ of rational numbers is the base field, then the trinomial $3 + 4x + \frac{1}{2}x^2$ is an example of a polynomial of degree 2 over $Q$. If the base field is the set $C$ of complex numbers, then the expression

$$\mathbf{i} + 3x + (^-4 + 2\mathbf{i})x^2 + (1 - \mathbf{i})x^3$$

is an example of a polynomial of degree 3 over $C$. In this case the com-plex number $\mathbf{i}$ is the constant term, the number 3 is the coefficient of $x$, $^-4 + 2\mathbf{i}$ is the coefficient of $x^2$, and $1 - \mathbf{i}$ is the coefficient of $x^3$. Ex-pressions such as $3 + {}^-2x + {}^-7x^2$ are more conveniently written as $3 - 2x - 7x^2$, and, in general, this convention will be used. It is also convenient at times to omit those terms in which the coefficient is zero, and when the coefficient of a term is 1 the coefficient itself is omitted. For example, the expression $x - 4x^5$ is a polynomial of degree 5. It is assumed from the context that the base system has elements 0 and 1, and in this case the constant term is 0, the coefficient of x is 1, the coef-ficients of $x^2$, $x^3$, and $x^4$ are each 0, and the coefficients of $x^5$ is $^-4$.

The definition of a polynomial can be generalized to polynomials in two or more indeterminates. For example, the expression $2x^2 + 3xy + 4y^2 - x^4 y^3$ may be considered as a polynomial of degree 3 in the inde-terminate $y$ with constant term $2x^2$ and other coefficients $3x$, 4, and $^-x^4$, respectively. It also may be considered as a polynomial of degree 4 in $x$ with constant term $4y^2$ and other coefficients $3y$, 2, 0, and $^-y^3$, respectively. In such polynomials it is at times desirable to define the degree as that of the term of highest degree; the degree of each term is the sum of the exponents of its respective indeterminate factors. Thus, for the given polynomial the degrees of the terms are, respectively, 2, 2, 2, and 7. Since $^-x^4y^3$ is the term of highest degree, the given polynomial may be considered as a polynomial of degree 7 in $x$ and $y$ with constant term 0 and other coefficients 2, 3, 4, and $^-1$, respectively. In this chapter we shall confine our attention to polynomials in one indeterminate, and they will be designated by symbols such as $p$, $q$, or $r$; in general, $x$ will represent the indeterminate. Two such polynomials are equal if and only if they have identically the same terms. In other words, the two polynomials

$$p = a_0 + a_1x + a_2x^2 + \cdot \cdot \cdot + a_nx^n$$

and

$$q = b_0 + b_1x + b_2x^2 + \cdot \cdot \cdot + b_mx^m$$

**Equal polynomials**  are equal if and only if $m = n$ and $a_i = b_i$ for $i = 0, 1, 2, 3, \ldots, n$. It will be assumed henceforth that the base system is at least a ring with identity.


## 7-2. POLYNOMIALS AS VECTORS

In general, a polynomial of degree $n$ has $n + 1$ terms. This can be varied, however, through the use of zero coefficients. For example, the polynomial $4x - 7x^3$ may be written equivalently as

$$0 + 4x + 0x^2 + {}^-7x^3 + 0x^4 + 0x^5$$

Although in this form the polynomial has six terms, its degree is still 3. By this device we can define addition of two polynomials of different degrees by adding the corresponding coefficients of "like" terms, that is, terms of the same degree. If

$$p = a_0 + a_1x + \cdot \cdot \cdot + a_nx^n$$

and

$$q = b_0 + b_1x + \cdot \cdot \cdot + b_mx^m$$

are polynomials of degree $n$ and $m$, respectively, over a field $F$, with **Sum of two polynomials**  $n \leqslant m$, then their *sum* is defined by

$$p + q = c_0 + c_1x + c_2x^2 + \cdot \cdot \cdot + c_mx^m$$

where

$$c_k = a_k + b_k \qquad k = 0, 1, \ldots, m$$

and if $n < k \leqslant m$,

$$c_k = b_k \qquad k = n + 1, n + 2, \ldots, m$$

since $a_k = 0$.

**Example 7-1.** Find the sum of $x + 4x^5$ and $3 + x - 7x^3$.

The first polynomial is of degree 5, and the second is of degree 3, so in this case we let $n = 3$ and $m = 5$. Using the stated convention and the notation of the definition of addition, we have

$$
\begin{array}{lll}
a_0 = 3 & b_0 = 0 & c_0 = 3 + 0 = 3 \\
a_1 = 1 & b_1 = 1 & c_1 = 1 + 1 = 2 \\
a_2 = 0 & b_2 = 0 & c_2 = 0 + 0 = 0 \\
a_3 = {}^-7 & b_3 = 0 & c_3 = {}^-7 + 0 = {}^-7 \\
a_4 = 0 & b_4 = 0 & c_4 = 0 + 0 = 0 \\
a_5 = 0 & b_5 = 4 & c_5 = 0 + 4 = 4
\end{array}
$$

The sum of the two polynomials is

$$3 + 2x - 7x^3 + 4x^5$$

It is sometimes easier to find the sum by writing the polynomials to be added one under the other, with the corresponding terms aligned vertically as follows:

$$
\begin{array}{l}
3 + \phantom{2}x - 7x^3 \\
\phantom{3 + {}} x \phantom{{} - 7x^3} + 4x^5 \\
\hline
3 + 2x - 7x^3 + 4x^5
\end{array}
$$

In the preceding example the sum of a polynomial of degree 3 and one of degree 5 is a polynomial of degree 5, the larger of the two degrees of the given polynomials. The sum of two polynomials of the same degree will be one of the same degree or less (when will it be less?). For $n$ a nonnegative integer, $P_n$ is defined to be the set of all polynomials of degree $n$ or less over a field $F$. It then follows that $P_n$ is closed with respect to addition. Furthermore, if $P$ is defined to be the set of all polynomials over $F$, then $P$ is also closed with respect to addition. It is again emphasized that each element of $P$ has only a finite number of terms.

The polynomial $0 + 0x + 0x^2 + \cdots + 0x^n$ for any nonnegative integer $n$ is called the *zero polynomial*. Although the degree of this polynomial is undefined, it is considered to be an element of $P_n$, and consequently, of $P$. Indeed, it is the additive identity of each set. For ex-

*Zero polynomial*

ample, the sum of the zero polynomial and any polynomial $p$, where

$$p = a_0 + a_1 x + a_2 x^2 + \cdots + a_n x^n$$

is

$$(0 + a_0) + (0 + a_1 x) + (0 + a_2)x^2 + \cdots + (0 + a_n)x^n = p$$

This result is the same as the sum of the polynomial $p$ and the additive identity of the base field. Thus we identify 0 with the additive identity of $P_n$. In other words, if we denote the zero polynomial by 0, we have $0 \in P_n$ for each nonnegative integer $n$, and consequently, $0 \in P$.

**Example 7-2.** Consider the following polynomials, each of which is of degree 2:

$$p = 5 + 2x + 2x^2$$
$$q = {}^-4 - 3x + 2x^2$$
$$r = 4 + 3x - 2x^2$$

Then

$$p + q = 1 - x + 4x^2$$

which is of degree 2;

$$p + r = 9 + 5x$$

which is of degree 1;

$$q + r = 0$$

which is the zero polynomial.
Furthermore, note that

$$p + 0 = p$$

where 0 is the zero polynomial.

**Additive inverse**      The additive inverse of a polynomial is that polynomial in which each of the coefficients is replaced by its additive inverse with respect to the base field. In Example 7-2, $q$ and $r$ are additive inverses of each other. With respect to addition the associative and commutative properties hold for each of the sets $P_n$ and $P$ (the proofs are left as exercises). Consequently, with respect to addition both $P_n$ and $P$ are abelian groups. In fact, $P_n$ is a subgroup of $P$.

**Scalar product**      In order to consider polynomials as vectors, let us now define a *scalar product*. Let $F$ be a field and $b$ an element of $F$, and let $p = a_0 + a_1 x + a_2 x^2 + \cdots + a_n x^n$, a polynomial over $F$. The product of $b$ and $p$ is the polynomial

$$bp = c_0 + c_1 x + c_2 x^2 + \cdots + c_n x^n$$

where, for $k = 0, 1, 2, \ldots, n$, $c_k = ba_k$, a product of elements of $F$. For example, if the base field is $R$, then the product of $^-4$ and $2 - x + 5x^3$ is $^-8 + 4x - 20x^3$. Observe that the justification for this definition is the distributive property of a field.

If, in the definition of scalar products, $b = 0$ and $p$ is a polynomial, then $bp$ is the zero polynomial and may be represented by 0. If $b \neq 0$ and $p$ is not the zero polynomial, then the degree of $bp$ is the same as the degree of $p$. The scalar product of a field element with an element of $P_n$ (or $P$) is again an element of $P_n$ (or $P$). Similarly, it can be shown that all of the properties of a vector space, as listed in Definition 5-8, hold for the sets $P_n$ and $P$. Consequently, we have the following theorems:

**Theorem 7-1. The set $P_n$ of all polynomials of degree n or less with coefficients in a field F is a vector space over F.†**

**Theorem 7-2. The set P of all polynomials with coefficients in a field F is a vector space over F.**

## 7-3. POLYNOMIALS AS ELEMENTS OF A RING

Just as in the case of the multiplication of a polynomial by a scalar, the distributive law suggests the pattern for the definition of the product of any two polynomials. If $ax^k$ and $p = b_0 + b_1 x + b_2 x^2 + \cdots + b_n x^n$ are two polynomials defined over the same base field, then their product is defined to be the polynomial

$$ax^k p = (ab_0)x^k + (ab_1)x^{k+1} + \cdots + (ab_n)x^{k+n}$$

For example, if the base field is $Q$, then

$$3x^2(4x + 3x^3 + \tfrac{5}{3}x^4) = 3(4)x^{2+1} + 3(3)x^{2+3} + 3(\tfrac{5}{3})x^{2+4}$$
$$= 12x^3 + 9x^5 + 5x^6$$

† As a consequence of the definition, a polynomial of degree $n$ over a field $F$ is an indicated sum of $n + 1$ monomials, each of which is an indicated product of an element of $F$ with some power of the indeterminate. With the adopted notation, the subscript of each coefficient symbol is the same as the exponent of the power of the indeterminate with which the coefficient is associated. Because of these facts, the symbol +, indicating addition, may be considered merely as a "punctuation symbol" separating the distinct monomials, each of which is completely identified by its coefficient. Thus the polynomials $a_0$, $a_0 + a_1 x$, $a_0 + a_1 x + a_2 x^2$, and $a_0 + a_1 x + a_2 x^2 + \cdots + a_n x^n$ may be represented precisely by the respective symbols $(a_0)$, $(a_0, a_1)$, $(a_0, a_1, a_2)$, and $(a_0, a_1, a_2, \ldots, a_n)$. More specifically, the symbol $(2, ^-3, 0, \tfrac{1}{2}, \tfrac{3}{3})$ would be a symbol representing the polynomial $2 - 3x + \tfrac{1}{2}x^3 + \tfrac{3}{3}x^4$ defined over the field $Q$ of rational numbers. Such ordered $n$-tuples are sometimes used to define polynomials, instead of the pattern of indicated sums of monomials used in this book. If the basic structure is the field $R$ of real numbers, then the vector space of Theorem 7-1 may be denoted by $\mathbf{R}_n$, in accordance with the discussion of Sec. 5-4.

From the definition of addition and the above definition of multiplication, with $k = 0$, it follows that if $a$ and $b$ are elements of a field, $ax^0 + bx^0 = (a + b)x^0$ and $ax^0bx^0 = (ab)x^0$. Thus the correspondence $a_0 \leftrightarrow a_0x^0$ between elements $a_0$ of the base field and the polynomials $a_0x^0$ is a one-to-one correspondence which preserves addition and multiplication. The expression $a_0 \leftrightarrow a_0x^0$ is understood to mean that to each element $a_0$ of the base field there corresponds one and only one polynomial $a_0x^0$, and conversely. Such a correspondence is called an *isomorphism*. It is because of this isomorphic correspondence $a_0 \leftrightarrow a_0x^0$ that we justify considering the nonzero elements of a field as zero-degree polynomials defined over that field. Furthermore, from the above definition of multiplication, the product

**Isomorphism**

$$1x^0(a_0 + a_1x + a_2x^2 + \cdots + a_nx^n) = (1a_0)x^0 + (1a_1)x$$
$$+ (1a_2)x^2 + \cdots + (1a_n)x^n$$
$$= a_0 + a_1x + a_2x^2 + \cdots + a_nx^n$$

Thus $1x^0$ is seen to be the multiplicative identity of the set $P$. Since $1 \leftrightarrow 1x^0$, we shall identify 1 as the multiplicative identity of $P_n$ for each positive integer $n$, and consequently, of $P$.

**Multiplicative identity of P**

Since a polynomial is the sum of monomials of the form $a_ix^i$, the distributive property provides the authority for finding the product of any two polynomials by first multiplying one polynomial by each monomial term of the other polynomial, and then finding the sum of the resulting polynomials. The technique is illustrated in the following example:

**Product of two polynomials**

**Example 7-3.**  Find the product of $x + 3x^2 - 2x^5$ and $2 + 5x - 2x^2 + x^4$.

The two polynomials are arranged one under the other, and the term-by-term products are arranged below on separate lines.

$$2 + 5x - 2x^2 + x^4$$
$$\underline{x + 3x^2 - 2x^5}$$

| | |
|---|---|
| $2x + 5x^2 - 2x^3 \qquad + x^5$ | multiplying by $x$ |
| $6x^2 + 15x^3 - 6x^4 \qquad + 3x^6$ | multiplying by $3x^2$ |
| $\underline{\quad - 4x^5 - 10x^6 + 4x^7 - 2x^9}$ | multiplying by $-2x^5$ |
| $2x + 11x^2 + 13x^3 - 6x^4 - 3x^5 - 7x^6 + 4x^7 - 2x^9$ | adding the three products |

The last line is the product of the two given polynomials.

From the preceding example it can be seen that the products of elements of $P_n$ will not, in general, be elements of $P_n$ (why?). However, the product of two polynomials is a polynomial, so that with respect to multiplication the set $P$ of all polynomials over a field $F$ is closed. While it is beyond the scope of this treatment, it is not too difficult to prove that the set $P$ is associative and commutative under multiplication, and that multiplication is distributive over addition. Furthermore, the multiplicative identity 1 of $F$ is a polynomial of degree 0 and serves as a multiplicative identity for the set $P$. Thus we have our next result:

**Theorem 7-3. The set P of all polynomials over a field F, with addition and multiplication as defined, is a commutative ring with identity.**

From the discussion preceding Theorem 7-3 we also have this theorem:

**Theorem 7-4. The set P of all polynomials with coefficients in a ring, with addition and multiplication as defined, is a ring.**

If $P$ is the set of all polynomials over an integral domain, it is a commutative ring with identity. Furthermore, it can be shown that the system has no zero divisors. From these facts Theorem 7-5 follows:

**Theorem 7-5. The set P of all polynomials with coefficients in an integral domain, with addition and multiplication as defined, is an integral domain.**

## EXERCISES

**1.** Find the indicated sums of polynomials:

(a) $(3 + x) + (3 + x)$
(b) $(3 + x) + (3 - x)$
(c) $(x + 2x^2) + (^-2x^2 - 4x^3) + (4x^3 - x^4)$
(d) $(1 + 2x + 3x^2) + (4x + 5x^2 - 6x^3)$
(e) $(^-2 - 3x + x^4) + (2x + 3x^2 - 4x^6)$
(f) $(x + 4x^2 + 5x^3) + (1 + 2x - 2x^2) + (^-3 - 4x - 2x^2 + x^4)$

**2.** Find the indicated products of polynomials:

(a) $5(1 + x)$
(b) $^-8(2 - x)$
(c) $^-3(^-2 + 3x - 4x^2 + x^3)$
(d) $^-4(2 - x + \frac{1}{2}x^2 - \frac{1}{4}x^4)$
(e) $^-3x^2(^-2x^3)(5x)$
(f) $7x(^-2x^3)(x^5)$
(g) $6x(4 - 2x^2)$
(h) $^-4x^3(^-5 + x^2 - 3x^7)$

(i) $(1 - 2x)(3x + 4x^2)$
(j) $(4 + 3x)(5 + 6x)$
(k) $(^-1 - 2x)(3 - 4x + x^2)$
(l) $(1 + x)(^-1 + x - x^2 + x^3)$
(m) $(^-1 + x)(1 + x + x^2 + x^3)$
(n) $(1 + 3x + x^2)(1 - 3x + x^2)$
(o) $(1 + 3x + x^2)(1 + 3x - x^2)$
(p) $(1 + 3x + x^2)(1 - 3x - x^2)$

$(q)(1 - 3x + x^2)(1 + 3x - x^2)$    $(s)\ x(^-4 + x^2)(4 + x^2)$
$(r)\ (x - 3x^4 + x^5)(9x^3 - 12x^7)$    $(t)\ (1 + x)(1 + x)(^-1 + x)$

3. If 0 and 1 are the additive and multiplicative identities, respectively, of an arbitrary field $F$, show that they are also, respectively, the additive and multiplicative identities for polynomials over $F$.

4. Find the additive inverses of the following polynomials:

(a) $^-2$                               (d) $3$
(b) $^-2 + 3x$                          (e) $2 - 3x$
(c) $3x - 4x^2 + 5x^5$                  (f) $^-2x^3 + 4x^5 - 2x^9$

5. If $p$ and $q$ are polynomials over a field $F$, show that $p + q = q + p$.

6. If $P$ is the set of all polynomials over a field $F$, show that addition is an associative operation on $P$.

7. Why do the arguments in Exercises 5 and 6 establish the same properties for the set $P_n$ of all polynomials of degree $n$ or less over the field $F$?

8. Prove Theorem 7-1.

9. Prove Theorem 7-2.

10. If $p$ and $q$ are polynomials and $^-q$ is the additive inverse of $q$, then subtraction of polynomials is defined by

$$p - q = p + {}^-q$$

Perform the indicated operations in each of the following:

(a) $(3 + x) - (3 - x)$
(b) $(3 - x) - (2 + x^2 - 2x^3)$
(c) $(4 - x^2 - 2x^3) - (x + 3x^3 - x^5)$
(d) $(9x + 4x^3 - 2x^4 - x^5) - (3x + 2x^2 + 3x^3 - 2x^4 - 6x^6)$

11. If the degrees of two polynomials are as given in each case, find the degrees of the sums and products of the polynomials:

(a) 3, 4     (b) 2, 2     (c) 0, 0     (d) 0, 1     (e) 5, 2

12. Prove Theorem 7-3.

13. Prove Theorem 7-4.

14. Under what conditions will the ring of Theorem 7-4 be a commutative ring with identity?

## 7-4. THE DISTRIBUTIVE PROPERTY

In the two previous sections the distributive property was used as a basis for structuring the definition of the product of two polynomials. This definition applies whether the polynomials are considered collectively as elements of the basic set of some algebraic system or in-dependently as formulas representing functions defined over some such system. In the remaining sections of this chapter the functional characteristics of polynomials defined over a field are to be studied. The distributive property will be of further significance as an important aid in the details of this study. For example, by the appropriate use of the ring postulates, the expression $a^2b + cab + dab + acb + c^2b + dcb + adb + cdb + d^2b$ can be shown to be equivalent to the expression $(a + c + d)^2b$, and except for closure, the only postulate used which involves multiplication is that of distributivity of multiplication over addition. In any system in which multiplication is both associative and commutative, further simplifications are possible. For example, if $a$, $b$, $c$, and $d$ are elements of a field, the above expression may be written in the form

$$a^2b + bc^2 + bd^2 + 2abc + 2abd + 2bcd$$

The purpose of this section is to review some of the fundamental patterns in which the distributive property plays an important role. Each example may be thought of as one either of *factoring* or of *expanding*. In each case the reader should make sure that he knows which field properties and definitions are used.

## Pattern 1. Several Terms with a Common Factor

Common factor

The simplest case of this pattern is, of course, factoring by direct use of the distributive property. Thus, in the sum $ab + ac$, the element $a$ is a factor of each term, and we factor by removing this monomial factor:

$$ab + ac = a(b + c)$$

A variation of this is that of the property indicated in Theorem 4-1:

$$ab - ac = a(b - c)$$

The next example shows this same pattern in a trinomial.

**Example 7-4.**  Factor $ab + ac + ad$

| $ab + ac + ad = (ab + ac) + ad$ | see discussion immediately following Example 3-3 |
|---|---|
| $= a(b + c) + ad$ | why? |
| $= a[(b + c) + d]$ | why? |
| $= a(b + c + d)$ | why? |

Thus, in factored form,

$$ab + ac + ad = a(b + c + d)$$

**Example 7-5.**  Factor $a + ab$.

In this case the element $a$ is a factor of the second term, and the first term may be modified by using the multiplicative identity. If 1 is the multiplicative identity, then $a(1) = a$, so that

$$a + ab = a(1) + ab$$
$$= a(1 + b)$$

**Example 7-6.**  Factor $abc + cda$.

In this case the commutative property of multiplication is needed:

$$abc + cda = acb + acd$$

and it follows that

$$abc + cda = ac(b + d)$$

The following example does not, at first, appear to fall into Pattern 1. Appropriate use of the associative property will give terms which do fall into this pattern.

**Example 7-7.**  Factor $ac + bc + ad + bd$.

$$ac + bc + ad + bd = (ac + bc) + (ad + bd)$$
$$= (a + b)c + (a + b)d \qquad \text{why?}$$
$$ac + bc + ad + bd = (a + b)(c + d) \qquad \text{why?}$$

**Pattern 2. The Difference of Two Squares**

In the expansion of the product $(a + b)(a - b)$ we see that the commutative property of multiplication can be used to effect a simplification.

$$(a + b)(a - b) = (a + b)a - (a + b)b \qquad \text{why?}$$
$$= a^2 + ba - ab - b^2 \qquad \text{why?}$$
$$= a^2 + ab - ab - b^2 \qquad \text{why?}$$
$$= a^2 - b^2 \qquad \text{why?}$$

Thus we may factor the difference of two squares,

$$a^2 - b^2 = (a + b)(a - b)$$

Recognition that an expression is the difference of two squares enables us to factor the expression immediately.

**Example 7-8.**  Factor $(a + b)^2 - (c + d)^2$.

$$(a + b)^2 - (c + d)^2 = [(a + b) + (c + d)][(a + b) - (c + d)]$$
$$(a + b)^2 - (c + d)^2 = (a + b + c + d)(a + b - c - d)$$

Factoring patterns of this type may be used to enhance computa-

*Difference of two squares*

tional skills. As a simple illustration of the principle of Pattern 2, consider

$$16^2 - 14^2 = (16 + 14)(16 - 14)$$
$$= 30(2)$$
$$= 60$$

These steps can be performed mentally, and the process is somewhat easier than first squaring 16, then squaring 14, remembering each of these three-digit numbers, and then finding their difference.

## Pattern 3. The Sum or Difference of Two Cubes

Expanding the product, we have

$$(a + b)(a^2 - ab + b^2) = (a + b)a^2 - (a + b)ab + (a + b)b^2$$
$$= a^3 + ba^2 - a^2b - bab + ab^2 + b^3$$
$$= a^3 + a^2b - a^2b - ab^2 + ab^2 + b^3$$
$$= a^3 + b^3$$

which is the sum of the cubes of two elements. Similarly,

$$(a - b)(a^2 + ab + b^2) = a^3 - b^3$$

which is the difference of two cubes.

**Example 7-9.**   Factor the polynomial $x^3 + 27$.
Since $3^3 = 27$, we have

$$x^3 + 27 = x^3 + 3^3$$
$$= (x + 3)(x^2 - 3x + 3^2)$$
$$= (x + 3)(x^2 - 3x + 9)$$

**Example 7-10.**   Factor $64a^3 + b^6$.
Since $4^3 = 64$, $64a^3$ may be written as $4^3a^3 = (4a)^3$. Thus

$$64a^3 - b^6 = (4a)^3 - (b^2)^3$$
$$= (4a - b^2)[(4a)^2 + 4a(b^2) + (b^2)^2]$$
$$= (4a - b^2)(16a^2 + 4ab^2 + b^4).$$

## Pattern 4. A Trinomial Which Is the Square of a Binomial

The expansion of $(a + b)^2$ is a trinomial:

$$(a + b)^2 = (a + b)(a + b)$$
$$= a(a + b) + b(a + b)    \quad \text{why?}$$
$$= a^2 + ab + ba + b^2$$
$$= a^2 + 2ab + b^2    \quad \text{why?}$$

*Sum or difference of two cubes*

*Trinomials*

Thus

$$a^2 + 2ab + b^2 = (a + b)^2$$

and similarly,

$$a^2 - 2ab + b^2 = (a - b)^2$$

The following example utilizes both Patterns 2 and 4.

**Example 7-11.**   Factor $a^4 + a^2b^4 + b^4$.

In Example 7-5 we made use of the multiplicative identity. In this example we utilize the additive identity in the form of adding and subtracting a term:

$$
\begin{aligned}
a^4 + a^2b^2 + b^4 &= (a^4 + a^2b^2 + b^4) + (a^2b^2 - a^2b^2) \\
&= (a^4 + 2a^2b^2 + b^4) - a^2b^2 &&\text{why?} \\
&= (a^2 + b^2)^2 - (ab)^2 &&\text{why?} \\
&= (a^2 + b^2 + ab)(a^2 + b^2 - ab) &&\text{why?} \\
&= (a^2 + ab + b^2)(a^2 - ab + b^2) &&\text{why?}
\end{aligned}
$$

The square of a binomial is a special case of the product of two binomials. When the commutativity of multiplication is allowed, the product of two binomials may be simplified to a trinomial, and a reversal of the steps of the expansion will give the process of factoring the trinomial. Using the distributivity of multiplication over addition, we can obtain the expansion in two ways:

$$(x + b)(x + d) = x(x + d) + b(x + d)$$

$$= x^2 + (xd + bx) + bd$$

or

$$(x + b)(x + d) = (x + b)x + (x + b)d$$
$$= x^2 + (bx + xd) + bd$$

From either of these expressions we obtain the equivalent expansion

$$(x + b)(x + d) = x^2 + (b + d)x + bd$$

## Pattern 5. A Trinomial Which Is the Product of Two Binomials

The discovery of two binomials whose product is a given trinomial is indeed the reversal of the above expansion. As a technique, however, it cannot be as direct, and at best it is a trial procedure. There are essentially two types.

**Type 1:**

$$x^2 + (b + c)x + bc = (xx + bx) + (cx + bc)$$
$$= x(x + b) + c(x + b)$$
$$= (x + c)(x + b)$$

Since $x^2$ and $x$ both occur in the trinomial, $x$ will have to appear in each binomial. The problem then becomes merely one of finding two numbers whose product is the term free of $x$ in the trinomial and whose sum is the coefficient of $x$. If the product term is positive, its two factors must have the same sign, that of the coefficient of $x$ in the trinomial. If the product term is negative, its two factors must have different signs. In this case the sign of the numerically larger factor must be the same as that of the coefficient of $x$ in the trinomial. Some examples are

$$x^2 + 5x + 6 = (x + 2)(x + 3)$$
$$x^2 - 5x + 6 = (x - 2)(x - 3)$$
$$x^2 - x - 6 = (x + 2)(x - 3)$$
$$x^2 + x - 6 = (x - 2)(x + 3)$$

**Type 2:**

$$(de)x^2 + (be + cd)x + bc = [(de)(xx) + (be)x] + [(cd)x + bc]$$
$$= (dx + b)ex + (dx + b)c$$
$$= (dx + b)(ex + c)$$

There is a great deal of trial and error in factoring trinomials of this type. Practice can help one become more proficient in making "educated" guesses in arriving at the correct combination of factors.

**Example 7-12.** Factor the trinomial

$$7x^2 - 18bx + 11b^2 = (x - b)(7x - 11b)$$

Since the coefficient of the product term, $11b^2$, is positive, its two factors must have the same sign. This sign must be negative, since the middle term of the trinomial is negative. The factors of $7x^2$ are $x$ and $7x$; those of $^+11b^2$ are $^-b$ and $^-11b$. They must be combined in such a way that the sum of their cross products is $^-18bx$.

**Example 7-13.** Factor the trinomial

$$8x^2 - 6bx - 54b^2 = 2(4x^2 - 3bx - 27b^2)$$
$$= 2(x - 3b)(4x + 9b)$$

Since the coefficient of the product term is negative, its factors must have opposite signs. The monomial factor has been removed, so we are concerned only with the factors of $^-27b^2$, namely, $b$ and $^-27b$, $^-b$ and $27b$, $3b$ and $^-9b$, and $^-3b$, $9b$. The factors of the first term, $4x^2$, are $x$ and $4x$ and $2x$ and $2x$. These factors must be combined with those of $^-27b^2$ in such a manner that the sum of their cross products will be $^-3bx$.

## Pattern 6. Combination of Basic Patterns

In Example 7-13 a monomial factor was removed, and the resulting trinomial was then factored. Similarly, in Example 7-11 two basic patterns were combined to effect the desired factorization. It is frequently the case that different basic patterns must be employed in order to factor a given polynomial.

**Example 7-14.**   $a^6 - b^6$ may be factored in either of two ways:

1. $a^6 - b^6 = (a^2)^3 - (b^2)^3$
$$= (a^2 - b^2)(a^4 + a^2b^2 + b^4)$$
$$= (a^2 - b^2)[(a^2 + b^2)^2 - a^2b^2]$$
$$= (a + b)(a - b)(a^2 + b^2 + ab)(a^2 + b^2 - ab)$$
2. $a^6 - b^6 = (a^3)^2 - (b^3)^2$
$$= (a^3 - b^3)(a^3 + b^3)$$
$$= (a - b)(a^2 + ab + b^2)(a + b)(a^2 - ab + b^2)$$

**Example 7-15.**   Consider the polynomial $a^5 + a^4 + a^3 + a^2 + a + 1$.

$$a^5 + a^4 + a^3 + a^2 + a + 1 = (a^5 + a^4 + a^3) + (a^2 + a + 1)$$
$$= a^3(a^2 + a + 1) + (a^2 + a + 1)$$
$$= (a^3 + 1)(a^2 + a + 1)$$
$$= (a + 1)(a^2 - a + 1)(a^2 + a + 1)$$

**Example 7-16.**   Consider the polynomial $x^4 + 6x^3 + x^2 - 24x - 20$.

$$x^4 + 6x^3 + x^2 - 24x - 20 = x^4 + 6x^3 + 9x^2 - 8x^2 - 24x - 20$$
$$= (x^2 + 3x)^2 - 8(x^2 + 3x) - 20$$
$$= [(x^2 + 3x) - 10][(x^2 + 3x) + 2]$$
$$= (x + 5)(x - 2)(x + 2)(x + 1)$$

In all the illustrations the factoring has been restricted to those cases which allow only integers as coefficients. In other words, the factoring has been "over the domain of integers." Similar considerations control the possibilities of factorization over a field. A polynomial factorable over one field may or may not be factored over another. Whether or not the obtained coefficients are elements of the specified field will be the determining condition.

**Example 7-17.** The expression $x^4 - \frac{1}{4}$ is not a polynomial over the domain of integers (why?). Its complete factorization is

$(x^2 - \frac{1}{2})(x^2 + \frac{1}{2})$

over the field $Q$ of rational numbers and

$(x - \sqrt{2}/2)(x + \sqrt{2}/2)[x - (\sqrt{2}/2)i][x + (\sqrt{2}/2)i]$

over the field $C$ of complex numbers.

**Example 7-18.** Over the domain of integers, the field $Q$ of rational numbers, or the field $R$ of real numbers, the complete factorization of the polynomial $x^3 - 8$ is $(x - 2)(x^2 + 2x + 4)$. Over the field $C$ of complex numbers it is $(x - 2)[x + (1 - \sqrt{3}i)][x + (1 + \sqrt{3}i)]$.

EXERCISES

1. Expand each of the following:

(a) $a(c + b + a)$
(b) $2(3 + 2a - b)$
(c) $3a(2a + 3b + c)$
(d) $abc(a + b + c)$
(e) $-b^2(a - b - c)$
(f) $(a - b)(c + d)$
(g) $(a - b)(c - d)$
(h) $(a - b)(b - a)$
(i) $(a - b)(c - b)$
(j) $2(a - b)(a + b)$
(k) $-a(a + b)(a + b)$
(l) $(2a + b)(2a - b)$
(m) $(3a - 2b)(3a + 2b)$
(n) $(a - b + c)(a - b - c)$
(o) $(a - b + c - d)(a - b - c + d)$
(p) $(a - b + 2c)(a + b - 2c)$
(q) $(2a + b)(4a^2 - 2ab + b^2)$
(r) $(a - 2b)(a^2 + 2ab + 4b^2)$
(s) $(a^2 + b^2)(a^4 - a^2b^2 + b^4)$
(t) $(5a + 2)^2$
(u) $(3a - 5b^2)^2$
(v) $(a^2 + b^2)^2$
(w) $(5a + 2)(a + 3)$
(x) $(6a^2 - 3ab)(3a^2b + 2b^2)$

2. Factor completely over the domain of integers each of the following:

(a) $12a^2 - 4a$
(b) $-3ab - 9ab^2$
(c) $3ab^2 + 6a^2b + 9ab$
(d) $x^2 - 9$
(e) $x^2 - 9b^2$
(f) $9a^2 - 16b^2$
(g) $27x^3 - 8y^3$
(h) $8a^3 + 27b^3$
(i) $x^2 - 6x + 9$
(j) $b^2 - 20ab + 100a^2$
(k) $a^6 + 2a^4 + a^2$
(l) $6a^3b^4 + 8a^2b^5 - 10a^8b^9$
(m) $2c + 3c + 2d + 3d$
(n) $2a^2c + bc + 2a^2d^2 + bd^2$
(o) $a^8 + a^4b^4 + b^8$
(p) $49a^2 - 56ab + 16b^2$

(q) $81c^4 + 8c^2d^2 + 16d^4$

(r) $x^2 - 3x - 70$

(s) $x^2 + 5x - 14$

(t) $15a^2 + 2ab - 8b^2$

(u) $(a^2 + 6a)^2 + 14(a^2 + 6a) + 45$

(v) $9(a - b)^2 - 16(c - d)^2$

(w) $(c + d)^2 + 5(c + d) - 14$

(x) $81(a + b - c)^4$
$\phantom{(x)}\ + {}^-9(b + a - c)^2 + {}^-12$

(y) $a^2 + 2ab + b^2 + 6a + 6b + 8$

(z) $4a^2 - 12ab + 9b^2 + 4a$
$\phantom{(z)}\ - 6b - 35$

**3.** For each of the given polynomials follow the pattern of Examples 7-17 and 7-18 to give its complete factorization over the fields $Q$, $R$, and $C$, respectively:

(a) $x^4 - 4$

(b) $2x^4 - 32$

(c) $x^3 - 1$

(d) $x^2 + 1$

(e) $3x^3 + 24$

(f) $x^6 - 64$

(g) $x^3 + 1$

(h) $5x^3 + 135$

(i) $x^2 - 2\sqrt{3}x + 4$

(j) $x^2 + x + 2$

(k) $16x^4 - 9$

(l) $81x^4 - 24x$

In Exercises 4 to 9 consider $a$ and $b$ as elements of the integral domain $Z$.

**4.** Show that $(a^2 - b^2)^2 = (a - b)^2(a + b)^2$.

**5.** Show that $(a - b)^2 = (b - a)^2$.

**6.** Show that $(a - b)^3 = {}^-(b - a)^3$.

**7.** Factor $a^{12} - b^{12}$ completely by first considering the expression as the difference of two squares.

**8.** Factor $a^{12} - b^{12}$ completely by first considering the expression as the difference of two cubes.

**9.** Prove that if $a$ is a common factor of each term of a polynomial $p$, then $a^n$ is a factor of $p^n$.

## 7-5. POLYNOMIALS AS FUNCTIONS

In Secs. 7-2 and 7-3 we were concerned with polynomials as elements of certain algebraic systems. In this and the next section we shall be interested primarily in polynomials as formulas representing functions which map subsets of the field $R$ of all real numbers into $R$. Under certain conditions it will be desirable to extend our considerations to the field $C$ of complex numbers. With one exception, there is no change in the definition of a polynomial, the equality of two polynomials, or the associated operations. The one exception is that the indeterminate now assumes the characteristics of a variable with which there is associated a domain of values. We shall indicate this change in point of view by using $p(x)$ to represent a polynomial function in $x$. Thus a polynomial function whose formula is of degree $n$ will be indicated by

$$p(x) = a_0 + a_1x + a_2x^2 + \cdots + a_nx^n \qquad a_n \neq 0$$

Because of their frequent occurrence, polynomials of degree 0, 1, 2, 3, and 4 are given the particular names of *constant, linear, quadratic, cubic,* and *quartic,* respectively. In this notation we shall use $P(x)$ to represent the set of all polynomials in $x$ defined over a specified algebraic system and $P_n(x)$ to represent the proper subset of $P(x)$ whose elements are the polynomials in $x$ of degree $n$ or less. If $p(x)$ is a polynomial defined over a field $F$ and $a \in F$, then $p(a)$ denotes a unique element of $F$. The set of all ordered pairs $(a,p(a))$, where $a \in F$, is thus the function represented by the polynomial formula $p(x)$. If the coefficients of a polynomial function are elements of the set $R$ of real numbers, and the domain and range of the function are subsets of $R$, then each ordered pair $(a,p(a))$ will be the coordinates of a point on the curve which is the graph of the function.

Graph

**Example 7-19.**   Let the base field be the set $R$ of real numbers and $P_3(x)$ be

$$\{p(x)|p(x) = a_0 + a_1x + a_2x^2 + a_3x^3 | a_0,a_1,a_2,a_3 \in R\}$$

If $a_1 = a_2 = a_3 = 0$, then $p_0(x) = a_0$ is the constant function of Sec. 6-2 whose graph is a straight line parallel to the $x$ axis. If $a_2 = a_3 = 0$ and $a_1 \neq 0$, then $p_1(x) = a_0 + a_1x$ is the linear function of Sec. 6-3 whose graph is a straight line with slope $a_1$ and $y$ intercept $a_0$. If $a_3 = 0$ and $a_2 \neq 0$, then $p_2(x) = a_0 + a_1x + a_2x^2$ is the quadratic function of Sec. 6-5 whose graph is a parabola with its axis of symmetry parallel to the $y$ axis. If $a_3 \neq 0$, then $p(x)$ is a cubic function. While curves representing the graphs of polynomial functions of degree higher than 2 are not as simple to draw as those for functions of degree 2 or smaller, we can, by careful selection of values, determine sets of ordered pairs which give a satisfactory approximation to the curve. If

$$p(x) = {}^-6x + x^2 + x^3$$

then the table gives a few selected ordered pairs of the function [the values for $p({}^-1.8)$ and $p(1.1)$ are very close approximations to the true values]. Thus the formula determines a subset of the plane. The selected points are plotted, and a smooth curve is drawn, as in Fig. 7-1, which approximates the position and shape of the significant portion of the curve. It is, of course, an incomplete graph of the function.

| $a$ | $^-4$ | $^-3$ | $^-2$ | $^-1.8$ | $^-1$ | 0 | 1 | 1.1 | 2 | 3 |
|---|---|---|---|---|---|---|---|---|---|---|
| $p(a)$ | $^-24$ | 0 | 8 | 8.2 | 6 | 0 | $^-4$ | $^-4.1$ | 0 | 18 |

**FIG. 7-1**

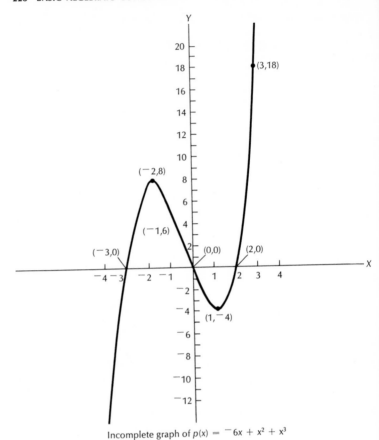

Incomplete graph of $p(x) = {}^-6x + x^2 + x^3$

## 7-6. POLYNOMIAL EQUATIONS

In Example 7-19 it can be seen that there are three real numbers $a$ for which $p(a) = 0$: $a = {}^-3$, $a = 0$, and $a = 2$. In this case we say that the polynomial equation $p(x) = 0$ has three real and distinct roots. The solution set of the equation is $\{^-3,0,2\}$. The graph shows that $a = 3$ is the only number for which $p(a) = 18$.

More generally, assume that $b \in R$ and $p(x)$ is a polynomial over $R$.

**Roots of a polynomial equation**

If there exists a number $a \in R$ such that $p(a) = b$, then we say that $a$ (or $x = a$) is a solution to, or *root* of, the polynomial equation $p(x) = b$.

**Solution set**

The *solution set* for the equation is $\{x \mid p(x) = b\}$. For an arbitrary number $b$ there may or may not exist a real number which is a solution to the equation $p(x) = b$, and if there is a solution it may or may not be unique. Example 7-20 illustrates how the field properties may be used to find solutions to a polynomial equation. The procedure is twofold:

1. Assume that a solution set exists in order to derive the necessary conditions for the existence of elements of the set.
2. Show that the numbers thus obtained are also sufficient; that is, substitute the numbers in the original polynomial to show that the equation is satisfied.

**Example 7-20.** If $p(x) = 5 + x^2$ is a polynomial over $R$, find the solution set in $R$ for the equation $p(x) = 7$.

Assume that a solution exists; then there exists a real number $x$ such that

$$5 + x^2 = 7$$
$$x^2 = {}^-5 + 7$$
$$x^2 = 2$$

From Sec. 5-3 we know that there are two possible real numbers which will satisfy this condition, $x = \sqrt{2}$ and $x = {}^-\sqrt{2}$. We conclude, then, that if there is a solution to the given equation, either $x = \sqrt{2}$ or $x = {}^-\sqrt{2}$.

The results obtained as necessary must now be checked with the original equation:

If $x = \sqrt{2}$, then $5 + x^2 = 5 + (\sqrt{2})^2 = 5 + 2 = 7$
If $x = {}^-\sqrt{2}$, then $5 + x^2 = 5 + ({}^-\sqrt{2})^2 = 5 + 2 = 7$

Since both numbers obtained satisfy the given equation, the solution set is $\{{}^-\sqrt{2}, \sqrt{2}\}$.

Example 7-21, with the subsequent discussion, illustrates how field conditions can affect the existence or nonexistence of solutions to a polynomial equation.

**Example 7-21.** If $p(x) = 8x - 2x^2 + x^3$ is a polynomial over $R$, find the solution set in $R$ for the equation $p(x) = 0$.

Assume that a solution exists; then there exists a real number $x$ such that

$$8x - 2x^2 + x^3 = 0$$

from which we obtain

$$x(8 - 2x + x^2) = 0$$

It was pointed out in Sec. 5-1 that a field has no zero divisors. It therefore follows that if a solution exists to the given equation, either $x = 0$ or $8 - 2x + x^2 = 0$. From the latter case we have

$$1 - 2x + x^2 = {}^-7$$

or

$$(1 - x)^2 = {}^-7$$

But if $x$ is a real number, then $(1 - x)^2$ is a nonnegative real number; hence it cannot be equal to the negative number $^-7$. The assumption that a solution to the given equation exists yields, as a necessary condition, $x = 0$. Since the solution set is restricted to $R$, this is the only possible solution.

The result obtained as necessary must now be checked with the original equation:

If $x = 0$, then $8x - 2x^2 + x^3 = 8(0) - 2(0^2) + (0^3) = 0$

The solution set is, then, $\{0\}$, under the above restriction.

In the previous example note that the given polynomial $p(x)$ was expressed as the product of two polynomials; that is, if $q(x) = x$ and $d(x) = 8 - 2x + x^2$, then $p(x) = q(x)d(x)$, and both $q(x)$ and $d(x)$ are polynomials over $R$, the base field for $p(x)$. A necessary condition that $p(x) = 0$ is that either $q(x) = 0$ or $d(x) = 0$. From $q(x) = 0$ we found the solution $x = 0$, but there exists no real number $x$ such that $d(x) = 0$. If $p(x)$ had been given as a polynomial over the field $C$ of complex numbers, then both $q(x)$ and $d(x)$ could have been considered as polynomials over $C$. The solution $x = 0$ (which may be considered as the complex number $0 + 0\mathbf{i}$) still holds. If $d(x) = 0$, we have $(1 - x)^2 = {}^-7$, from which it follows that

$$1 - x = \sqrt{7}\,\mathbf{i} \quad \text{or} \quad 1 - x = {}^-\sqrt{7}\,\mathbf{i}$$

Hence

$$x = 1 - \sqrt{7}\,\mathbf{i} \quad \text{or} \quad x = 1 + \sqrt{7}\,\mathbf{i}$$

Neither $1 - \sqrt{7}\,\mathbf{i}$ nor $1 + \sqrt{7}\,\mathbf{i}$ is a real number, yet by substitution it can be verified that each satisfies the condition $p(x) = 0$. Thus over $R$ the equation $p(x) = 0$ has only one element in its solution set, whereas over $C$ the equation has three solutions. It can also be verified that

$$8 - 2x + x^2 = [(1 - \sqrt{7}\,\mathbf{i}) - x][(1 + \sqrt{7}\,\mathbf{i}) - x]$$

The importance of these observations will become clear shortly, when we consider the implications of the Fundamental Theorem of Algebra.

Since a polynomial defined over a field may be considered as the sum of its monomial terms, it follows, as a consequence of the commutative property of addition, that these terms may be rearranged as addends in any desired order. Frequently it is desirable to have a polynomial arranged in descending, rather than ascending, powers of the variable. This is particularly true in any situation requiring the division of one polynomial by another. It will be more convenient to follow this convention for the remainder of the chapter, although the statements made will hold for all polynomials, with no restrictions on arrangement of terms. Thus we may write

$$d(x) = x^2 - 2x + 8 = [x - (1 - \sqrt{7}\ i)][x - (1 + \sqrt{7}\ i)]$$

It then follows that the polynomial $p(x)$ of Example 7-21 may be written in *factored form* as

$$x^3 - 2x^2 + 8x = x[x - (1 - \sqrt{7}\ i)][x - (1 + \sqrt{7}\ i)]$$

A polynomial of the form $ax + b$ is called a *linear polynomial*. Consequently, we say that the polynomial $p(x)$ can be expressed as the product of three linear polynomials, called *linear factors*. In connection with this observation it should be recalled that $p(x) = 0$ has three solutions over $C$ and, furthermore, that $p(x)$ is of degree 3. **Linear factors**

More generally, it is known that a polynomial of degree $n$, where $n \geqslant 1$, over $C$, can be expressed as the product of $n$ linear factors and that, allowing for possible repetition of some of these factors, the corresponding polynomial equation has $n$ (not necessarily distinct) solutions. One of the fundamental theorems from which these properties of polynomials are derived is the Division Algorithm. The proof of this theorem is beyond the scope of this book.

**Division Algorithm. If $p(x)$ and $d(x)$ are polynomials of degree m and n, respectively, m $\geqslant$ n, then there exist polynomials q(x) and r(x) such that p(x) = q(x) d(x) + r(x), where r(x) is of degree less than n.** **Division Algorithm**

The polynomials $q(x)$ and $r(x)$ are called the *quotient* and *remainder*, respectively, since they can be obtained in the usual manner by formally dividing $p(x)$ by $d(x)$. The following theorem is a special case of the Division Algorithm.

**Theorem 7-6. If $p(x)$ is a polynomial of degree n, n $\geqslant$ 1, and $x - a$ is a linear polynomial over a field F, then there exists an element r $\in$ F and a polynomial q(x) of degree n $-$ 1 over F such that p(x) = (x $-$ a)q(x) + r.**

**Example 7-22.**   Find the quotient and remainder when the polynomial $p(x) = x^3 - 4x^2 - 3x - 10$ is divided by $x - 3$.

The terms are arranged in descending powers of $x$ in each of the polynomials, and the usual division process is used:

$$
\begin{array}{r}
x^2 - \phantom{x} x - 6 \\
x - 3 \overline{\smash{\big)}\ x^3 - 4x^2 - 3x - 10} \\
\underline{x^3 - 3x^2} \phantom{-3x-10} \\
{}^{-}x^2 - 3x \phantom{-10} \\
\underline{{}^{-}x^2 + 3x} \phantom{-10} \\
{}^{-}6x - 10 \\
\underline{{}^{-}6x + 18} \\
{}^{-}28
\end{array}
$$

Thus

$$x^3 - 4x^2 - 3x - 10 = (x - 3)(x^2 - x - 6) + {}^{-}28$$

The quotient is $q(x) = x^2 - x - 6$, and the remainder is $r = {}^{-}28$.

In the preceding example it is of interest to compute $p(x)$ for $x = 3$:

$$p(3) = 3^3 - 4(3)^2 - 3(3) - 10 = {}^{-}28$$

Thus, when $p(x)$ is divided by $x - 3$, the remainder is $p(3)$. This is no accident, as the following theorem will show:

**The Remainder Theorem**

**Theorem 7-7. Remainder Theorem. If a polynomial $p(x)$ of degree $n \geqslant 1$ is divided by $x - a$ until a constant remainder r is obtained, then $p(a) = r$.**

**Proof:**   By Theorem 7-6, $p(x) = (x - a)q(x) + r$, where $q(x)$ is a polynomial. Consequently,

$$
\begin{aligned}
p(a) &= (a - a)q(a) + r \\
&= 0q(a) + r \\
&= r
\end{aligned}
$$

Thus the remainder $r$ is precisely $p(a)$.

From this theorem it follows immediately that the ordered pair $(a,p(a))$ serves as the coordinates of a point on the curve which is the graph of the polynomial function $p(x)$.

If $p(x)$ is a polynomial of degree $n \geqslant 1$, and if $p(a) = 0$ for some

**Zero of a polynomial**

number $a$, then the number $a$ is called a *zero* of the polynomial. Since $p(a)$ is also the remainder upon dividing $p(x)$ by $x - a$, it follows by Theorem 7-7 that if $a$ is a zero of $p(x)$, then $p(x) = (x - a)q(x)$ for some polynomial $q(x)$ and $x - a$ is a factor of $p(x)$. However, if $x - a$ is a factor of $p(x)$, then $p(x) = (x - a)q(x)$ for some polynomial $q(x)$, so that the remainder upon dividing $p(x)$ by $x - a$ is 0, and $a$ is a zero of $p(x)$. Hence we have the following theorem:

**The Factor Theorem**

**Theorem 7-8. Factor Theorem. A number $a$ is a zero of a polynomial $p(x)$ of degree $n \geqslant 1$ if and only if $x - a$ is a factor of $p(x)$.**

**Example 7-23.** Determine whether $x - 3$ is a factor of the polynomial $p(x) = x^6 - 8x^5 + 25x^4 - 40x^3 + 35x^2 - 16x + 3$.

The polynomial $p(x)$ may be divided by $x - 3$ directly by long division; however, by Theorem 7-8, $x - 3$ is a factor of $p(x)$ if and only if 3 is a zero of $p(x)$. Consequently, we need only find $p(3)$ to effect a decision:

$$p(3) = 3^6 - 8(3^5) + 25(3^4) - 40(3^3) + 35(3^2) - 16(3) + 3$$
$$= 729 - 1{,}944 + 2{,}025 - 1{,}080 + 315 - 48 + 3$$
$$= 0$$

Since $p(3) = 0$, 3 is a zero of $p(x)$, and $x - 3$ is a factor of $p(x)$.

Observe that if $p(x)$ is a polynomial over a field $F$ and $a \in F$, then the solution set for the equation $p(x) = a$ is just the set of zeros of the polynomial $p(x) - a$. Because of this relationship between polynomials and polynomial equations, we may direct our attention to finding zeros of polynomials. Whether zeros of a polynomial exist depends to some extent on the base field. The importance of the field $C$ of complex numbers is revealed in the Fundamental Theorem of Algebra. The theorem will be stated without proof, since its proof is beyond the scope of this book.

**Theorem 7-9. Fundamental Theorem of Algebra. Any polynomial of degree n, n ⩾ 1, over the field C of complex numbers has at least one zero.**

Fundamental Theorem of Algebra

By this theorem, a polynomial with complex coefficients, other than a polynomial of degree zero, has at least one zero. If $p(x)$ is a polynomial of degree 1, then it is of the form $ax + b$ for $a, b \in C$, where $a \neq 0$, and since

$$ax + b = a\left(x - \frac{^{-}b}{a}\right)$$

we see that $^{-}b/a$ is a zero of $p(x)$. However, if $n > 1$ and $p(x)$ is a polynomial of degree $n$ over $C$, then Theorem 7-9 guarantees the existence of a zero, say $a$, and by Theorem 7-8, $x - a$ is a factor of $p(x)$; by Theorem 7-6, $p(x) = (x - a)q(x)$ for some polynomial $q(x)$ of degree $n - 1$ over $C$. Again by Theorem 7-9, $q(x)$ has a zero, say $b$, and $x - b$ is a factor of $q(x)$, and hence of $p(x)$. By continuing this process, it can be shown that any polynomial of degree $n \geqslant 1$ over $C$ can be expressed as the product of a complex number and $n$ linear factors, and each of these factors corresponds to a zero of the polynomial. From this argument and the fact that in a field there exist no divisors of zero, Theorem 7-10 follows immediately.

**Theorem 7-10. A polynomial of degree n over the field C of complex numbers has exactly n zeros. (A zero which occurs exactly k times is counted as a zero of multiplicity k.)**

Two other theorems which can be helpful in finding the solution sets of polynomial equations will now be stated without proof. In the discussion following Example 7-21 the complex roots of the polynomial equation of the example were seen to differ only in the sign of the imaginary part. This is in accordance with the following theorem, which is stated without proof.

**Theorem 7-11. If p(x) is a polynomial with real coefficients and a + bi is a zero of p(x), then a − bi is also a root.**

The next theorem, stated without proof, provides a straightforward and fairly simple technique for finding rational roots of certain types of polynomial equations.

**Theorem 7-12. Let c/d be a rational number, where c and d are relatively prime, and let**

$$p(x) = a_n x^n + a_{n-1} x^{n-1} + \cdots + a_2 x^2 + a_1 x + a_0$$

**be a polynomial with integral coefficients. If c/d is a zero of p(x), then c is a divisor of $a_0$, the constant term, and d is a divisor of $a_n$, the leading coefficient.**

This theorem makes it possible to find all rational zeros of any polynomial function by using all integral divisors of $a_0$ and $a_n$ to form all distinct rational numbers which are possible zeros.

**Example 7-24.** Find all the rational zeros of the polynomial

$$p(x) = 7x^4 + 6x^3 - 22x^2 - 18x + 3$$

If $c/d$ is a rational number, reduced to lowest terms, which is a zero of $p(x)$, then $c$ is a divisor of 3, and $d$ is a divisor of 7. Possible values of $c$ are

$$1 \quad ^-1 \quad 3 \quad ^-3$$

Possible values of $d$ are

$$1 \quad ^-1 \quad 7 \quad ^-7$$

Possible rational zeros are

$$1 \quad ^-1 \quad 3 \quad ^-3 \quad \frac{1}{7} \quad \frac{^-1}{7} \quad \frac{3}{7} \quad \frac{^-3}{7}$$

We now check each of these values by substituting for $x$ in $p(x)$:

$$p(1) = 7(1)^4 + 6(1)^3 - 22(1)^2 - 18(1) + 3 = -24$$
$$p(^-1) = 7(^-1)^4 + 6(^-1)^3 - 22(^-1)^2 - 18(^-1) + 3 = 0$$

From the last statement we see that $^-1$ is a zero of $p(x)$, and hence $x + 1$ is a factor of $p(x)$. We divide $p(x)$ by $x + 1$ to obtain

$$p(x) = (x + 1)(7x^3 - x^2 - 21x + 3)$$

Any additional zeros of $p(x)$ will be zeros of the polynomial $q(x) = 7x^3 - x^2 - 21x + 3$. Since zeros may be repeated, we test once more the number $^-1$ by substituting in $q(x)$:

$$q(^-1) = 7(^-1)^3 - (^-1)^2 - 21(^-1) + 3 = 16$$

Since $^-1$ is not a zero, we continue checking $q(x)$ with our list of possible rational zeros:

$$q(3) = 7(3)^3 - (3)^2 - 21(3) + 3 = 120$$
$$q(^-3) = 7(^-3)^3 - (^-3)^2 - 21(^-3) + 3 = ^-132$$
$$q(\tfrac{1}{7}) = 7(\tfrac{1}{7})^3 - (\tfrac{1}{7})^2 - 21(\tfrac{1}{7}) + 3 = 0$$

Since $\tfrac{1}{7}$ is a zero, we divide $q(x)$ by $x - \tfrac{1}{7}$ and obtain,

$$q(x) = 7(x - \tfrac{1}{7})(x^2 - 3)$$

We now focus our attention on the polynomial $x^2 - 3$. A check with the possible rational zeros we have listed will reveal that none of these are zeros of $p(x)$, and we can say that the rational zeros of $p(x)$ are $^-1$ and $\tfrac{1}{7}$.

From the above results we can now express $p(x)$ as

$$p(x) = 7(x + 1)(x - \tfrac{1}{7})(x^2 - 3)$$

We can find the remaining two zeros which are not rational by noting that if $x$ is a zero of $x^2 - 3$, then it is a solution of $x^2 - 3 = 0$, or $x^2 = 3$. Thus it can be shown that $x = \sqrt{3}$ and $x = ^-\sqrt{3}$ are solutions, so that the set of zeros of $p(x)$ is $\{^-1, \tfrac{1}{7}, \sqrt{3}, ^-\sqrt{3}\}$. This procedure is, in this case, better than checking each of the remaining rational numbers which are possible zeros.

The unique zero of the linear function can be found by the use of a finite number of the four field operations performed on the coefficients of the polynomial. The quadratic formula provides a means of finding the two zeros of a quadratic function which calls for a finite number of additions, subtractions, multiplications, divisions, and extraction of square roots performed upon its coefficients.

Algebraic solution of
general polynomial

**Definition 7-1.** An algebraic solution of a general polynomial equation is a solution which can be obtained by only a finite number of additions, subtractions, multiplications, divisions, and extractions of roots performed upon the coefficients of the equation.

Just as for the linear and quadratic polynomial equations, there exist procedures for finding the algebraic solutions of such equations of degrees 3 and 4. It has been established that it is impossible to find algebraic solutions for general polynomial equations of degrees greater than 4.† There are techniques, however, which can be used to find, to any desired degree of precision, the solutions of such equations with numerical coefficients. These procedures are beyond the scope of this book, as we have chosen to restrict our study primarily to linear and quadratic equations.

## EXERCISES

1. Let $p(x) = 3x^3 + 19x^2 - 9x - 5$.

   (a) Find $p(\frac{1}{2})$, $p(\frac{1}{3})$, $p(-\frac{1}{3})$, $p(i)$, $p(-i)$, and $p(-3 + \sqrt{14})$.

   (b) Find the quotient polynomials if $p(x)$ is divided by $x - \frac{1}{3}$ and by $x - i$.

2. Let $p(x) = -6x^3 + 16x^2 - 20x + 8$.

   (a) Find $p(\frac{2}{3})$, $p(-\frac{2}{3})$, $p(1 + i)$, $p(1 - i)$, and $p(\sqrt{2})$.

   (b) Find the quotient polynomials if $p(x)$ is divided by $x - \frac{2}{3}$ and by $x - (1 + i)$

3. Find the solution set in $R$ for $p(x) = 3$ for the following:

   (a) $p(x) = -x^3 + 7x + 9$

   (b) $p(x) = x^4 + 4x^3 + 6x^2 + 4x + 4$

   (c) $p(x) = 5x^5 - 11x^4 + 17x^3 - 23x^2 + 14x + 1$

   (d) $p(x) = 8x^4 - 4x^3 - 26x^2 + 25x - 3$

4. Express $p(x)$ as the product of linear factors over $R$ in the following cases:

   (a) $p(x) = x^4 - 19x^2 + 30x$

   (b) $p(x) = -8x^3 - 22x^2 + 7x + 3$

   (c) $p(x) = -x^3 - 7x^2 - 16x - 12$

   (d) $p(x) = x^4 - 5x^3 + 3x^2 + 9x$

† The mathematicians who were responsible for this significant discovery were Henrik Abel (1802–1829) and Évariste Galois (1811–1832).

**5.** For each of the following form a polynomial over $R$ of lowest degree having the given numbers as zeros:

(a) 1, 2, 3, 4

(b) $^-2, \frac{1}{2}, 5, 0$

(c) $0, 0, ^-1, ^-1, \frac{3}{2}$

(d) $1, ^-1, 2, i, ^-i$

(e) $1, 3, \sqrt{2}, ^-\sqrt{2}$

(f) $i, ^-i, 1 + i, 1 - i$

**6.** For each of the following find the quotient and remainder if $p(x)$ is divided by $d(x)$:

(a) $p(x) = 8x^3 - 4x^2 - 6x - 7, d(x) = x - \frac{1}{2}$

(b) $p(x) = x^4 - 2x^3 + 3x^2 - 4x + 5, d(x) = x + 2$

(c) $p(x) = ^-x^3 - \frac{4}{5}x^2 + \frac{4}{25}x + \frac{37}{25}, d(x) = x - \frac{3}{10}$

(d) $p(x) = x^{20} - 1, d(x) = x - 1$

**7.** (a) Prove that $x - 1$ is a factor of $x^{50} - 1$.

(b) Prove that $x + 1$ is a factor of $x^{50} - 1$.

(c) Prove that $x - i$ is a factor of $x^{30} + 1$.

(d) Prove that $x + i$ is a factor of $x^{30} + 1$.

**8.** What is the smallest integer which is an upper bound to the set of rational zeros of $p(x) = 9 + 6x - x^2 - x^3 + 5x^4$?

**9.** If $0, 1, 2$, and $^-3$ are the zeros of a polynomial of degree 4, show that the product of the zeros is the constant term and that the sum of the zeros is the coefficient of $x^3$.

**10.** Find all the rational zeros of each of the following polynomials; where possible find all the zeros:

(a) $8x^3 - 10x^2 - x - 3$

(b) $^-21x^5 - 20x^4 + 3x^3 + 2x^2$

(c) $^-x^3 - 2x^2 + 11x + 22$

(d) $x^3 - 3x^2 + x - 3$

(e) $x^4 - 5x^3 + 3x^2 + 9x$

(f) $x^3 + 9x^2 + 4x + 36$

(g) $5x^3 + 4x^2 + 8x + 7$

(h) $6x^4 + 5x^3 + 31x^2 + 25x + 5$

(i) $x^4 - x^3 + x^2 - x + 1$

(j) $x^6 - 8$

**11.** Find three consecutive integers whose product is 504.

**12.** Find all numbers which are such that the sum of the number, its square, and its reciprocal is $^-1$.

**13.** A box which is 5 in. high has a base with dimensions 10 by 20 in. A box of the same height but triple the volume is needed. If each base dimension is increased by the same amount, how much should this be in order to build a new box with the desired volume?

**14.** Prove that a polynomial of the third degree over the field $R$ of real numbers has at least one real zero.

**15.** Prove that a polynomial of the fourth degree over the field $R$ of real numbers has either no real zeros, two real zeros, or four real zeros.

**16.** Find a cubic polynomial (of degree 3) with real coefficients which has 2 and $i$ as two of its zeros.

**17.** Find a cubic polynomial with real coefficients which has $^-1$ and $2 - i$ as two of its zeros.

**18.** Find a quadratic polynomial with real coefficients which has 1, 2, and $3 + i$ as three of its zeros.

**19.** Find a quartic polynomial (of degree 4) with real coefficients which has $i$ and $1 - i$ as two of its zeros.

## Invitations to Extended Study

In exercises 1 to 4 assume $F$ to be the field of integers reduced, modulo 5.

**1.** Consider Patterns 1 to 6 of Sec. 7-4.

(a) The terms in the expression $4a + b$ do not appear to have a common factor. Show, however, that in $F$

$$4a + b = 3(3a + 2b)$$

(b) Find an element $c \in F$ such that $a + 4b = c(3a + 2b)$.

(c) From Patterns 1 and 2 we see that

$$4a^2 - 4b^2 = 4(a^2 - b^2) = 4(a + b)(a - b)$$

Show that in $F$, $4a^2 - 4b^2$ may also be factored as the product of $3a + 2b$ and $3a - 2b$.

(d) Is it always true that in $F$ the square of a binomial is a trinomial?

**2.** Let $D = \{a/b \,|\, a, b \in F; b \neq 0\}$. If $b \neq 0$, then the multiplicative inverse of $b$ may be represented by $1/b$, and the fraction $a/b$ may represent the product $a(1/b)$. For example, in $F$, $3(2) = 1$; the multiplicative inverse of 3 is 2, and we may consequently write $\frac{1}{3} = 2$. The fraction $\frac{2}{3}$ can be expressed as an element of $F$ as

$$\tfrac{2}{3} = 2(\tfrac{1}{3}) = 2(2) = 4$$

Express each of the elements of $D$ as an element of $F$.

**3.** Show that the elements 0, 1, and 4 have square roots in $F$, but that the elements 3 and 2 do not.

**4.** Let $p(x) = 3x^2 + 2x + 1$ and $q(x) = x^2 - x - 2$ be polynomials over $F$.

(a) Find the sum and product of $p(x)$ and $q(x)$.

(b) Show that $p(x)$ cannot be factored in $F$. *Hint:* Use the Factor Theorem.

(c) Express $q(x)$ as the product of linear factors. *Hint:* Find the zeros of $q(x)$.

5. Given the cubic polynomial equation with complex coefficients

$$a_3x^3 + a_2x^2 + a_1x + a_0 = 0$$

prove that $a_0a_3 = a_1a_2$ is a necessary and sufficient condition that two roots of the equation are equal but opposite in sign.

6. Prove Theorem 7-11.

7. Prove Theorem 7-12.

8. What is synthetic division, and how may it be used to divide a polynomial by a linear polynomial?

9. What is the euclidean algorithm, and how may it be used to find the greatest common divisor of two or more polynomials?

# CHAPTER 8

# SYSTEMS OF EQUATIONS

## Guidelines for Careful Study

The two previous chapters provided procedures necessary and sufficient for finding the algebraic solutions of equations in one variable. In this chapter we shall develop techniques for finding the algebraic solutions of systems of two equations involving linear and quadratic equations in two variables and systems of three or more linear equations in two or more variables. The following questions can be very helpful as guidelines to careful study of the chapter:

1. What are the field postulates?
2. What are the properties of equality?
3. What is the formula for the linear function?
4. In the general equation of the straight line what represents the slope of the line?
5. What are the coordinates of the $x$ and $y$ intercepts of the straight line which is the graph of $ax + by + c = 0$?
6. How do you find the coordinates of the extremum on the graph of a quadratic function?
7. When is the extremum the highest point (a maximum) of the graph? The lowest point (a minimum)?
8. What is the quadratic formula?
9. What is the discriminant of a quadratic equation?
10. How can the discriminant of a quadratic equation be used to determine the nature of the roots of the equation?
11. What is meant by a system of equations?

**12.** What are the coefficient matrix and augmented matrix of a system of linear equations?

**13.** How do you determine the rank of a matrix?

**14.** When is a system of linear equations said to be inconsistent?

**15.** When is a system of linear equations said to be consistent?

**16.** When does a consistent system of linear equations have a unique solution?

**17.** When the solution of a consistent system of linear equations is not unique, what can be done in the way of finding the solution set?

**18.** What is the graphical technique for finding the solution set of a system of two linear equations in two variables?

**19.** What is the addition technique for solving a system of linear equations?

**20.** How may the pivotal-element technique be used in determining whether a system of linear equations is consistent or inconsistent?

**21.** How may the pivotal-element technique be used to find the solution set of a consistent system of linear equations?

**22.** What is the distinction between an inconsistent system of equations and a system whose graphs have no real points of intersection?

**23.** What are the different techniques suggested by the text for solving systems of equations involving one or more quadratic equations?

## Introduction

In Sec. 6-4 it was established that the equation $ax + by + c = 0$, where $a$, $b$, and $c$ are real numbers and $a$ and $b$ not both zero, represents a straight line. Figures 6-3 to 6-5 illustrate the different positions the graph of such an equation can take. An examination of these graphs will emphasize the fact that there is an infinite number of ordered pairs of real numbers in the solution set of any single linear equation in two variables and with real coefficients. This simply means that a value for one of the variables, say $x$, can be selected arbitrarily. When this value is substituted in the equation, a unique value is determined for the other variable, $y$, such that the ordered pair of values $(x,y)$ denotes the coordinates of a point on the straight line which is the graph of the equation.

In Sec. 6-8 it was found that imposing the single condition that the solution set contain only integers was sufficient to restrict materially the number of ordered pairs in the solution set of a linear equation with integral coefficients. There are still other ways to place restrictions on the solution set of any given linear equation. We shall investigate some of them in this chapter.

Similarly, an examination of typical graphs of the quadratic function, as shown in Figs. 6-8 to 6-11, reveals the fact that there is an infinite number of ordered pairs of real numbers in the solution set of any equation in two variables of the form $y = ax^2 + bx + c$, where $a$, $b$, and $c$ are real numbers and $a \neq 0$. These ordered pairs $(x,y)$ of real numbers are coordinates of points on the parabola which is the graph of the function. Toward the end of the chapter we shall examine the possibility of restricting such solution sets to a finite number of ordered pairs.

The technique used in this chapter to restrict the solution set of any given equation will be to require that it also be the solution set of at least one additional equation. Any set of two or more equations involving the same variables is called a *system of equations*. The *solution set* of such a system consists of those values of the variables which simultaneously satisfy the conditions as specifically expressed by each equation of the system. First we shall examine systems of linear equations, then systems involving one linear equation and one quadratic equation, and finally systems involving two quadratic equations.

**System of equations**

**Solution set**

## 8-1. TWO LINEAR EQUATIONS IN TWO VARIABLES

Consider the two linear equations

$$2x - y = 3$$
$$4x - 2y = 12$$

(8-1)

Careful consideration of these two equations will reveal the fact that their respective graphs (Fig. 8-1) are straight lines with the same slope ($m = 2$) but with different $y$ intercepts. The graph of the first one passes through the point $(0,{}^{-}3)$, and the graph of the second equation passes

FIG. 8-1

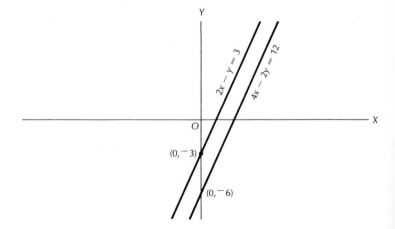

through the point $(0,^-6)$. These two lines are parallel and have no points in common. This is a geometric representation of two linear equations for which the solution set is the *null set*. The equations are said to be *inconsistent*.

**Definition 8-1. An inconsistent system of equations is one for which the solution set is the null set.†**

Inconsistent system
of equations

Next consider the system

$$2x - y = 3$$
$$3x + 2y = 8$$

(8-2)

Examination of the graphs (Fig. 8-2) of these two equations shows that they intersect at the point $(2,1)$. There exists one ordered pair of

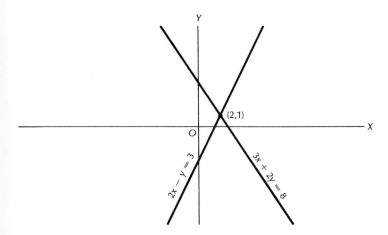

FIG. 8-2

real numbers which is the common solution of the two equations. This is a geometric representation of one type of *consistent* system of equations.

**Definition 8-2. A consistent system of equations is one for which there exists a nonempty solution set.**

Consistent system
of equations

**Definition 8-3. If the solution set of a consistent system of equations contains one and only one element, the equations are said to have a unique solution.**

Unique solution

The procedure employed in Fig. 8-2 presents what is called the *graphical method* for finding the solution set of two linear equations in two variables. There are more general methods, two of which we shall develop subsequently. Before doing this, however, let us examine the

Graphical solution

---

† An equivalent statement of this definition is:
    An inconsistent system of equations is one for which there exists no solution.

one remaining pattern of two equations in two variables. Consider the system

$$2x - y = 3$$
$$4x - 2y = 6$$

(8-3)

Note that the corresponding coefficients and constant terms are proportional. From this it follows that the two equations may be represented by the same straight line (Fig. 8-3). The equations are consistent, since

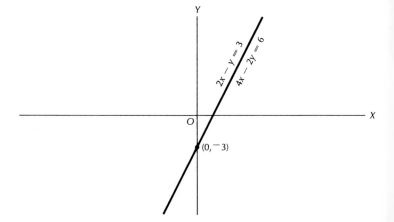

FIG. 8-3

any ordered pair of values which satisfies one equation will satisfy the other equation. The solutions $(x,y)$ for the system may be indicated in the form $(x, 2x - 3)$. Such notation implies that the value of the first variable, $x$, may be assigned arbitrarily, and then the value of the second variable, $y$, will be determined uniquely by the expression $2x - 3$. At times the graph of such a system is considered to be two coincident lines.

## 8-2. ADDITION TECHNIQUE

The general form of two linear equations in two variables $x_1$ and $x_2$ is

$$a_{11}x_1 + a_{12}x_2 = k_1$$
$$a_{21}x_1 + a_{22}x_2 = k_2$$

(8-4)

Normally we shall be interested in such a system where the coefficients and constants $a_{11}$, $a_{12}$, $a_{21}$, $a_{22}$, $k_1$, and $k_2$ are real numbers. The two variables are here distinguished from each other by the subscripts 1 and 2. The first subscript on each coefficient indicates the equation in which it occurs, and the second subscript indicates the variable with which it is associated. For example, $a_{12}$, read "a one two," is recognized as being the coefficient of variable $x_2$, read "x two," in the first equation.

The variable $x_2$ may be eliminated from the two equations by multiplying the first equation by $a_{22}$ and the second equation by $^-a_{12}$ to obtain

$$a_{11}a_{22}x_1 + a_{22}a_{12}x_2 = k_1a_{22}$$
$$^-a_{12}a_{21}x_1 - a_{22}a_{12}x_2 = ^-k_2a_{12}$$

Now we add the two equations to get

$$(a_{11}a_{22} - a_{12}a_{21})x_1 = k_1a_{22} - k_2a_{12} \tag{8-5}$$

A similar process, with $^-a_{21}$ as a multiplier for the first equation and $a_{11}$ for the second, will produce

$$(a_{11}a_{22} - a_{12}a_{21})x_2 = k_2a_{11} - k_1a_{21} \tag{8-6}$$

There are two cases to consider.

**Case 1:** $a_{11}a_{22} - a_{12}a_{21} \neq 0$. Under this condition Eqs. (8-5) and (8-6) may be solved to obtain

$$x_1 = \frac{k_1a_{22} - k_2a_{12}}{a_{11}a_{22} - a_{12}a_{21}}$$

$$x_2 = \frac{k_2a_{11} - k_1a_{21}}{a_{11}a_{22} - a_{12}a_{21}}$$

Substitution of these values obtained for $x_1$ and $x_2$ in the original Eqs. (8-4) will establish the fact that they constitute the solution set of the system, and the system has a unique solution.

**Case 2:** $a_{11}a_{22} - a_{12}a_{21} = 0$. Under this condition Eqs. (8-5) and (8-6) become

$$0x_1 = k_1a_{22} - k_2a_{12}$$
$$0x_2 = k_2a_{11} - k_1a_{21}$$

If the right-hand members of both these equations are zero, the equations become $0x_1 = 0$ and $0x_2 = 0$. Any pair of values for $x_1$ and $x_2$ would be a solution of these two equations. Thus any pair of values which will satisfy either of the two equations of the original system will satisfy the other equation, and the system is a consistent system with a nonunique solution set. If $k_1a_{22} - k_2a_{12} \neq 0$ or $k_2a_{11} - k_1a_{21} \neq 0$, then there exist no values of $x_1$ and $x_2$ which will satisfy both equations. Since the solution set of the system is the null set, it is an inconsistent system of equations.

**Example 8-1.**  The addition technique, with the indicated multipliers, applied to system (8-2) will yield the solution set in the following manner:

| *Multipliers* | | *Multipliers* | |
|---|---|---|---|
| 2 | $4x - 2y = \ \ 6$ | $^-3$ | $^-6x + 3y = \ ^-9$ |
| 1 | $3x + 2y = \ \ 8$ | 2 | $6x + 4y = 16$ |
| | $7x \quad\quad = 14$ | | $7y = \ \ 7$ |
| | $x \quad\quad = \ \ 2$ | | $y = \ \ 1$ |

The same technique applied to system (8-3) yields $0x = 0$ and $0y = 0$. Thus any ordered pair of numbers which will satisfy one of the two equations also will satisfy the other. Similarly, the same technique applied to system (8-1) yields $0x = 6$ and $0y = 12$. Since there are no values for $x$ and $y$ which will satisfy these last two equalities, there exists no solution, and the system is inconsistent.

Instead of applying the addition technique twice, as was done in finding the solution set of system (8-2), the usual procedure is to apply it one time and then use the *equivalent system* to obtain the solution set.

**Equivalent systems**

**Definition 8-4. Two or more systems of equations are said to be equivalent systems if and only if they have the same solution set.**

It is not difficult to verify that the system

$$2x - y = \ \ 3$$
$$7x \quad\quad = 14$$

is equivalent to system (8-2). The equations of system (8-2) may be written in the form

$$2x - \ y - 3 = 0$$
$$3x + 2y - 8 = 0$$

Using the same multipliers as in the previous application of the addition technique, we obtain from the left members of these two equations an equality which is true for *all values of x and y:*
$$2(2x - y - 3) + (3x + 2y - 8) = 7x - 14$$

Since this relation holds for all values of $x$ and $y$, it should be evident that any pair of values $(x,y)$ which will satisfy any two of the three equations $2x - y - 3 = 0$, $3x + 2y - 8 = 0$, and $7x - 14 = 0$ will also satisfy the third equation. This is the condition which makes the two systems equivalent.

## EXERCISES

In Exercises 1 to 8 plot the graph of each equation of the system. For consistent systems use the addition technique to find the solution set.

**1.** $5x - 2y = 11$
$3x + 4y = {}^-9$

**2.** $2x + 7y = 14$
$4x + 14y = 26$

**3.** $x - 4y = 8$
$\frac{1}{2}x + 2y = 4$

**4.** $x - 4y = 8$
$\frac{1}{2}x + 2y = 4$

**5.** $0.3x + 0.2y = 2$
$1.2x + 0.8y = 6$

**6.** $7x + 5y = 9$
$\frac{7}{3}x + \frac{5}{3}y = 3$

**7.** $0.1x + 0.2y = 2$
$0.3x - 0.4y = 1$

**8.** $\frac{1}{2}x - \frac{2}{3}y = {}^-2$
$\frac{3}{2}x + \frac{4}{3}y = 14$

In Exercises 9 to 12 find the values of $x$ and $y$ by first solving for $1/x$ and $1/y$.

**9.** $\dfrac{2}{x} - \dfrac{6}{y} = {}^-4$

$\dfrac{1}{x} + \dfrac{1}{y} = \dfrac{1}{2}$

**10.** $\dfrac{3}{x} + \dfrac{2}{y} = 2$

$\dfrac{1}{x} - \dfrac{1}{y} = \dfrac{{}^-1}{6}$

**11.** $\dfrac{4}{x} + \dfrac{1}{y} = 11$

$\dfrac{2}{x} + \dfrac{3}{y} = 13$

**12.** $\dfrac{5}{x} - \dfrac{6}{y} = {}^-10$

$\dfrac{10}{x} + \dfrac{9}{y} = 50$

**13.** An office manager has $220 in his budget for the purchase of first-class and airmail postage stamps. He estimates that he will need twice as many first-class as airmail stamps. If he purchases stamps in accordance with this estimate, how many of each type will he buy?

**14.** The ten digit of a given base-ten numeral is two less than the units digit. If the digits are reversed, and the new numeral is considered as written in base seven, the two numerals represent the same number. What is the numeral?

**15.** On a recent telephone bill the charge for local service exceeded that for long distance by 17 cents. The 10 percent Federal Tax on the total service amounted to $1.57. What were the respective charges for local and long-distance services?

**16.** In a certain state the total gasoline tax on 1 gal of gasoline is one-half the base charge per gallon. The total cost for 107 gal of gasoline was $35.31. What is the base charge and the total tax on 1 gal of gasoline?

**17.** Find the formula for the linear function whose graph passes through the points $(2,9)$ and $({}^-1,6)$.

**18.** Find the formula for the linear function whose graph has an $x$ intercept of 2 and a $y$ intercept of $^-3$.

**19.** Two boys live $3\frac{1}{2}$ miles apart. They wish to select a place between their homes to meet. One boy has a bicycle, and the other boy has to walk. The second boy plans to start immediately and figures that he can walk at the rate of 2 mph. The first boy figures he can travel at an average speed of 6 mph on his bicycle. If the boy with the bicycle cannot start until 15 min later, how far from each boy's home should they plan to meet?

**20.** An earthquake shock travels as a wave along the earth's surface. The formula which expresses the time $t$, in seconds, required for the shock to travel from a center of disturbance to an observation station is expressed in the form

$$t = f + \frac{d}{v}$$

where

$f$ = a delay factor, in seconds
$d$ = the number of miles traveled
$v$ = the speed of travel, in miles per second

It took the shock of a particular quake 3 min 51 sec to reach an observation station 542 miles away and 2 min 4 sec to reach one 285 miles away. Correct to the nearest tenth, determine the delay factor in seconds and the speed in miles per second of the shock.

**21.** If two resistances of $r_1$ ohms and $r_2$ ohms are each combined in parallel, their combined resistance of $r$ ohms is given by the formula

$$\frac{1}{r} = \frac{1}{r_1} + \frac{1}{r_2}$$

Find the two resistances whose combined effect is 4 ohms if one is twice the other.

## 8-3. RANK OF A MATRIX

In Chap. 4 the concept of matrix was introduced in the context of the ring postulates. In this section our concern is with matrices, not as elements of an algebraic system, but as efficient aids in the analysis and solution of systems of linear equations. In this case, just as in the previous one, a matrix is merely a rectangular array of elements and has no numerical value. However, with each matrix there is associated a number, called its *rank*, which is of considerable significance, especially in the study of systems of linear equations.

Before defining what is meant by the rank of a matrix, a technique by means of which it may be computed will be described. This particular technique is called a *pivotal transformation*. Each such transformation will reduce a given matrix by one row and one column. The process of successive pivotal transformations is continued until the original matrix has been transformed into either a zero matrix or a nonzero matrix with only one row or only one column. The procedure is as follows:

Pivotal transformation

1. Let $M = (a_{ij})$ be a given matrix with at least two rows and two columns. Select any nonzero element of $M$ as the *pivotal element*, and call it $a_{pq}$.

Pivotal element

2. Block out the $p$th row and the $q$th column of $M$ as the row and column to be eliminated by the transformation.
3. Each remaining element $a_{ij}$, for $i \neq p$ and $j \neq q$, is to be replaced by the expression $a_{ij}a_{pq} - a_{iq}a_{pj}$. Note:

   (a) The factors of the first product are the element to be replaced, $a_{ij}$, and the pivotal element $a_{pq}$.
   (b) The factors of the second product are $a_{iq}$ (same row, $i$, as the element to be replaced and the same column, $q$, as the pivotal element) and $a_{pj}$ (same row, $p$, as the pivotal element and the same column, $j$, as the element to be replaced).
   (c) The second product is *always* subtracted from the first product.

4. Form the new matrix, using the new elements in the order obtained.

**Example 8-2.**   Consider the matrix

$$M = \begin{pmatrix} 2 & 3 & 1 & {}^{-}2 \\ {}^{-}1 & 4 & 6 & 5 \\ 3 & 2 & 0 & {}^{-}4 \end{pmatrix}$$

1. Select 1 of the first row and third column to be the pivotal element, $a_{pq}$, for $p = 1$ and $q = 3$. $a_{13}$ is the pivotal element.
2. Block out the first row and third column as the row and column to be eliminated by the pivotal transformation.
3. The elements $a_{ij}$ to be replaced are $a_{21} = {}^{-}1$, $a_{22} = 4$, $a_{24} = 5$, $a_{31} = 3$, $a_{32} = 2$, and $a_{34} = {}^{-}4$. The element $a_{21} = {}^{-}1$ is to be replaced by

   $$a_{21}a_{13} - a_{23}a_{11} = {}^{-}1(1) - 6(2) = {}^{-}13$$

   Similarly, the replacements for the remaining elements are

   For 4: $4(1) - 6(3) = {}^{-}14$
   For 5: $5(1) - 6({}^{-}2) = 17$

For 3: $3(1) - 0(2) = 3$

For 2: $2(1) - 0(3) = 2$

For $^-4$: $^-4(1) - 0(^-2) = ^-4$

**4.** One pivotal transformation has transformed the original $3 \times 4$ matrix into the $2 \times 3$ matrix

$$\begin{pmatrix} ^-13 & ^-14 & 17 \\ 3 & 2 & ^-4 \end{pmatrix}$$

There is a simple but effective check which may be used in the execution of any pivotal transformation. The matrix of the example is repeated here with an explanation of the method of obtaining and using a check column.

*Check*

$$\begin{pmatrix} 2 & 3 & 1 & ^-2 \\ ^-1 & 4 & 6 & 5 \\ 3 & 2 & 0 & ^-4 \end{pmatrix} \begin{matrix} 4 \\ 14 \\ 1 \end{matrix}$$

The elements of this first check column are obtained as the sum of the elements in each respective row:

$$4 = 2 + 3 + 1 + {}^-2$$
$$14 = {}^-1 + 4 + 6 + 5$$
$$1 = 3 + 2 + 0 + {}^-4$$

In effecting the pivotal transformation the elements of the check column are treated in the same manner as the elements of the matrix. 14 is replaced by $14(1) - 6(4) = {}^-10$, and 1 is replaced by $1(1) - 0(4) = 1$. Thus the new matrix with its check column is

*Check*

$$\begin{pmatrix} ^-13 & ^-14 & 17 \\ 3 & 2 & ^-4 \end{pmatrix} \begin{matrix} ^-10 \\ 1 \end{matrix}$$

The elements of the new check column must be the sum of the elements in its corresponding row. $^-10 = {}^-13 + {}^-14 + 17$ and $1 = 3 + 2 + {}^-4$. If there is any discrepancy here, an error has been made somewhere in the computation. Attention is called to the fact that this is not an absolute check. For example, in the illustration 3, 2, $^-4$ is the proper orientation of the elements of the second row of the new matrix. It should be obvious that the erroneous results 2, 3, $^-4$ would yield the same sum, 1.

**Rank of a matrix**

**Definition 8-5. An m $\times$ n matrix is of rank r if and only if the following conditions hold:**

1. r pivotal transformations reduce it to a zero matrix.
2. r − 1 pivotal transformations reduce it, for m ⩽ n, to a nonzero matrix of one row or, for m > n, to a nonzero matrix of one column.†

Recall that if a matrix has the same number of rows as columns ($m = n$), it is called a *square matrix*. If the rank $r = n$, the matrix is said to be *nonsingular;* otherwise the square matrix is said to be *singular.*

**Singular, nonsingular matrix**

**Example 8-3.** One pivotal transformation transformed the matrix M of Example 8-2 into

$$\left(\begin{array}{c:c:c} ^-13 & ^-14 & 17 \\ \hdashline 3 & 2 & ^-4 \end{array}\right)\begin{array}{c} ^-10 \\ \hdashline 1 \end{array}$$

If, in this new matrix, we select 2 as the pivotal element, $^-13$ and 17 will be replaced by $^-13(2) - {}^-14(3) = 16$ and $17(2) - {}^-14(^-4) = {}^-22$, respectively. The element $^-10$ of the check column is replaced by $^-10(2) - {}^-14(1) = {}^-6$. Since $16 + {}^-22 = {}^-6$, the check is established. Thus two pivotal transformations have transformed the original matrix M into the nonzero matrix of one row

$$(^-22 \quad 16)$$

It therefore follows that M is of rank 3.

There are three other transformations which are useful in finding the rank of a matrix or in dealing with systems of equations:

**Elementary Row Transformations**

**Elementary row transformations**

E₁  Interchange any two rows.
E₂  Multiply any row by a nonzero number.
E₃  Multiply any row by a nonzero number and add it to another row.

It should be fairly evident that transformations E₁ and E₂ will not change the rank of a matrix in any way whatsoever. Although the proof that E₃ does not affect the rank of a matrix‡ is not too difficult, it will be accepted without proof here.

† This definition can be shown to be equivalent to the traditional definition. See F. L. Wren, Neo-sylvestor Contractions and the Solution of Systems of Linear Equations, *Bulletin of the American Mathematical Society,* **43:** 826–827 (1937).

‡ Franz E. Hohn, "Elementary Matrix Algebra," p. 91, The Macmillan Company, New York, 1958.

**Example 8-4.** Determine the rank of the following matrices:

$$(0 \quad 0 \quad 0 \quad 0) \quad \text{and} \quad \begin{pmatrix} 0 \\ 0 \\ 0 \end{pmatrix}$$

In each of these zero matrices, zero pivotal transformations are required to reduce each matrix to a zero matrix, so the rank is zero.

**Example 8-5.** Determine the rank of the following matrices:

$$(2 \quad 1 \quad 0 \quad 5 \quad 6) \quad \text{and} \quad \begin{pmatrix} 0 \\ 4 \end{pmatrix}$$

Zero pivotal transformations are required to reduce the first matrix to a nonzero matrix of one row and the second matrix to a nonzero matrix of one column. In each case $r - 1 = 0$. Hence the rank of each matrix is 1.

**Example 8-6.** Determine the rank of the matrix

$$\begin{pmatrix} 1 & 2 & 3 \\ 3 & -1 & 2 \\ 2 & 4 & 5 \end{pmatrix}$$

*Check*

$$\begin{pmatrix} 1 & 2 & 3 \\ 3 & -1 & 2 \\ 2 & 4 & 5 \end{pmatrix} \begin{matrix} 6 \\ 4 \\ 11 \end{matrix}$$

With 1 as the pivotal element, this matrix transforms to

*Check*

$$\begin{pmatrix} -7 & -7 \\ 0 & -1 \end{pmatrix} \begin{matrix} -14 \\ -1 \end{matrix}$$

In this matrix, if one so desires, elementary transformation $E_2$ may be used to get a simpler matrix of the same rank:

*Check*

A second pivotal transformation, as illustrated, produces the matrix

(1)

In this example $m = n$, and 2 pivotal transformations have reduced the matrix to a nonzero matrix of one row. Since $r - 1 = 2$, the rank of the original matrix is 3. It is a nonsingular matrix.

This illustration may be extended to the case of an $m \times n$ matrix for $m < n$ by simply annexing any number of columns to the original matrix. It should be evident that, independently of the elements obtained to replace the elements of the attached columns, the same transformation used here would transform this $m \times n$ matrix into a nonzero matrix of one row. Hence its rank would be 3.

This matrix can be used to advantage to illustrate the fact that the elementary row transformations do not affect the rank of a matrix:

**1.** Multiply row 1 by $^-3$ and add to row 2 to get

$$\begin{pmatrix} 1 & 2 & 3 \\ 0 & ^-7 & ^-7 \\ 2 & 4 & 5 \end{pmatrix} \quad (\text{By } \mathbf{E}_3)$$

**2.** Multiply row 1 by $^-2$ and add to row 3 to get

$$\begin{pmatrix} 1 & 2 & 3 \\ 0 & ^-7 & ^-7 \\ 0 & 0 & ^-1 \end{pmatrix} \quad (\text{By } \mathbf{E}_3)$$

**3.** Multiply row 2 by $^-1/7$ and row 3 by $^-1$ to get

$$\begin{array}{ccc} & Check & \\ \begin{pmatrix} 1 & 2 & 3 \\ 0 & 1 & 1 \\ 0 & 0 & 1 \end{pmatrix} & \begin{matrix} 6 \\ 2 \\ 1 \end{matrix} & (\text{By } \mathbf{E}_2) \end{array}$$

**4.** Use the 1 in row 1 and column 1 as the pivotal element to get

$$\begin{array}{cc} Check & \\ \begin{pmatrix} 1 & 1 \\ 0 & 1 \end{pmatrix} & \begin{matrix} 2 \\ 1 \end{matrix} \end{array}$$

which has already been obtained as a matrix with the same rank as the original matrix.

If rows 1 and 2 of the original matrix are interchanged, we have the matrix

$$\begin{pmatrix} 3 & ^-1 & 2 \\ 1 & 2 & 3 \\ 2 & 4 & 5 \end{pmatrix}$$

The same uses of transformations $E_3$ and $E_2$ will give

$$\begin{pmatrix} 0 & 1 & 1 \\ 1 & 2 & 3 \\ 0 & 0 & 1 \end{pmatrix} \begin{matrix} Check \\ 2 \\ 6 \\ 1 \end{matrix}$$

In this case we use the 1 in row 2 and column 1 as the pivotal element to get the same result as before, the matrix

$$\begin{pmatrix} 1 & 1 \\ 0 & 1 \end{pmatrix} \begin{matrix} Check \\ 2 \\ 1 \end{matrix}$$

**Example 8-7.**   Determine the rank of the matrix

$$\begin{pmatrix} 1 & 4 & 2 & ^-1 & 3 \\ 2 & 1 & 4 & 0 & 6 \\ 3 & 5 & 6 & ^-1 & 9 \\ 4 & 9 & 8 & ^-2 & 12 \end{pmatrix}$$

$$\begin{pmatrix} 1 & 4 & 2 & ^-1 & 3 \\ 2 & 1 & 4 & 0 & 6 \\ 3 & 5 & 6 & ^-1 & 9 \\ 4 & 9 & 8 & ^-2 & 12 \end{pmatrix} \begin{matrix} Check \\ 9 \\ 13 \\ 22 \\ 31 \end{matrix}$$

Choose the 1 of the second row and column as the pivotal element to get

$$\begin{pmatrix} ^-7 & ^-14 & ^-1 & ^-21 \\ ^-7 & ^-14 & ^-1 & ^-21 \\ ^-14 & ^-28 & ^-2 & ^-42 \end{pmatrix} \begin{matrix} Check \\ ^-43 \\ ^-43 \\ ^-86 \end{matrix}$$

In the resulting matrix choose $^-1$ in the first row and third column as the pivotal element to get

$$\begin{pmatrix} 0 & 0 & 0 \\ 0 & 0 & 0 \end{pmatrix} \begin{matrix} Check \\ 0 \\ 0 \end{matrix}$$

In this case two pivotal transformations have reduced the matrix to a zero matrix. Hence the rank of the original matrix is 2.

It should be evident that if any one of the columns were to be deleted from the given matrix, the new matrix would be an $m \times n$ matrix with $m = n$. If neither the second nor fourth columns were deleted, then the same transformations would reduce the new matrix to a zero matrix. If either of these two columns should be deleted, then there would be two other pivotal transformations which would produce a zero matrix. The square matrix would be a singular matrix.

**Example 8-8.** Determine the rank of the matrix

$$
\begin{pmatrix}
4 & 1 & 2 \\
1 & 5 & 3 \\
2 & 1 & 4 \\
3 & 0 & 1 \\
-13 & -4 & -7
\end{pmatrix}
$$

$$
\begin{array}{ccc|c}
 & & & Check \\
4 & 1 & 2 & 7 \\
1 & 5 & 3 & 9 \\
2 & 1 & 4 & 7 \\
\hline
3 & 0 & 1 & 4 \\
\hline
-13 & -4 & -7 & -24
\end{array}
$$

Choose the 1 in the fourth row and third column as the pivotal element to get

$$
\begin{array}{c|c|c}
 & & Check \\
-2 & 1 & -1 \\
\hline
-8 & 5 & -3 \\
-10 & 1 & -9 \\
8 & -4 & 4
\end{array}
$$

Using the 1 in the first row and second column, we get

$$
\begin{array}{cc}
 & Check \\
2 & 2 \\
-8 & -8 \\
0 & 0
\end{array}
$$

Here two pivotal transformations have reduced the $m \times n$ matrix with $m > n$ to a nonzero matrix of one column. Hence the rank is 3.

Note that if the two transformations had reduced the original matrix to the zero matrix

$$\begin{pmatrix} 0 \\ 0 \\ 0 \end{pmatrix}$$

then the rank would have been 2.

EXERCISES

1. What is the nature of the elements of a matrix whose rank is zero?
2. What is the nature of the elements of a matrix of one row or one column whose rank is 1?

Determine the rank of each of the matrices in Exercises 3 to 15.

3. $\begin{pmatrix} 2 & 3 & 1 & 4 \\ 1 & 2 & 0 & 3 \end{pmatrix}$    4. $\begin{pmatrix} ^-4 & 3 & 8 & 5/6 \\ ^-2 & 3/2 & 4 & 5/12 \end{pmatrix}$    5. $\begin{pmatrix} 2 & 1 \\ 0 & 1/2 \\ 1 & 2 \end{pmatrix}$

6. $\begin{pmatrix} 1 & 3 & 4 \\ 2/3 & 3 & 8/3 \\ ^-2 & ^-6 & ^-8 \\ 1/2 & 3/2 & 2 \end{pmatrix}$    7. $\begin{pmatrix} 1 & 2 & 3 \\ ^-1 & 3 & ^-2 \\ 4 & 0 & 7 \end{pmatrix}$

8. $\begin{pmatrix} 1 & 0 & 4 & 5 & ^-3 \\ 2 & 2 & 8 & 10 & ^-6 \\ 3 & 2 & 12 & 15 & ^-9 \end{pmatrix}$

9. $\begin{pmatrix} 1 & ^-1 & 4 & 3 & ^-5 \\ 2 & 4 & ^-1 & ^-2 & 3 \\ 3 & 3 & 1 & 2 & 2 \end{pmatrix}$

10. $\begin{pmatrix} 4 & ^-1 & 3 & 12 \\ 8 & ^-2 & 6 & 24 \\ 2 & ^-1/2 & 3/2 & 6 \\ 4/3 & ^-1/3 & 1 & 4 \end{pmatrix}$    11. $\begin{pmatrix} 1 & 1 & 1 & 1 \\ 2 & 3 & 0 & 1 \\ 3 & 4 & ^-1 & 3 \\ 12 & 16 & 1 & 1 \end{pmatrix}$

12. $\begin{pmatrix} 2 & 0 & 1 & 1 & ^-3 \\ 1 & 1 & ^-1 & 2 & 1 \\ 3 & 1 & 1 & 0 & 2 \\ 6 & 2 & 1 & 3 & 0 \end{pmatrix}$    13. $\begin{pmatrix} 4 & 5 & 6 \\ 1 & 0 & 1 \\ 2 & 1 & 0 \\ ^-3 & 2 & 4 \end{pmatrix}$

14. $\begin{pmatrix} 1 & 0 & 1 & 2 \\ 3 & 1 & 0 & 1 \\ 4 & 1 & 1 & 3 \\ ^-1 & ^-1 & 2 & 3 \\ 1 & 1 & 3 & 7 \end{pmatrix}$

**15.**
$$\begin{pmatrix} 2 & ^-1 & ^-2 & 3 \\ 4 & ^-2 & ^-4 & 6 \\ 1 & ^-1/2 & ^-1 & 3/2 \\ 2/3 & ^-1/3 & ^-2/3 & 1 \end{pmatrix}$$

**16.** Which, if any, of the matrices in Exercises 3 to 15 are nonsingular, and which, if any, are singular?

In Exercises 17 to 19 determine the value, or values, of $x$ which will make each matrix a singular matrix:

**17.**
$$\begin{pmatrix} 1 & 2 & ^-1 \\ 2 & 3 & x \\ x & 2 & ^-3 \end{pmatrix}$$
**18.**
$$\begin{pmatrix} x & 4 & 3 \\ ^-1 & 1 & 2 \\ 1 & 2 & x \end{pmatrix}$$

**19.**
$$\begin{pmatrix} 1 & 2 & 0 & ^-3 \\ 1 & 1 & x & 2 \\ 3 & 5 & x & ^-5 \\ x & 1 & 1 & 0 \end{pmatrix}$$

## 8-4 USING THE PIVOTAL-ELEMENT TECHNIQUE

It becomes quite evident upon examination that the values obtained for $x_1$ and $x_2$ in the solution set of system (8-4) depend solely upon the coefficients and constant terms in the two equations. Also, the solution set for system (8-2) would consist of the ordered pair (2,1), regardless of whether the variables were $x$ and $y$, or $r$ and $s$, or any other set of two symbols. Matrix notation affords a convenient method for dealing with only the coefficients and constants of any number of linear equations involving any number of variables. For example, system (8-2) is completely represented by the matrix

$$\begin{pmatrix} 2 & ^-1 & 3 \\ 3 & 2 & 8 \end{pmatrix}$$

whose elements, by rows, are the coefficients and constant term of each respective equation. Such a matrix for any system of linear equations is called the *augmented matrix* of the system. The submatrix† of the augmented matrix obtained by deleting the column of constants is called the *coefficient matrix*. For system (8-2) it is

**Augmented matrix**

**Coefficient matrix**

$$\begin{pmatrix} 2 & ^-1 \\ 3 & 2 \end{pmatrix}$$

The relation between the ranks of these two matrices is of fundamental

† A submatrix of a given matrix is the array which remains when one or more rows and/or columns are deleted from the original matrix.

**Submatrix**

importance in the analysis and solution of systems of linear equations. Let us investigate this significance. Since the augmented matrix always has the same number of rows as the coefficient matrix and one more column, its rank can never be less than that of the coefficient matrix. Furthermore, since the difference in the number of pivotal transformations needed to determine the ranks of the two matrices is at most one, the rank of the augmented matrix can never exceed that of the coefficient matrix by more than 1. In other words, if the rank of the coefficient matrix is $r$, then the rank of the augmented matrix is always either $r$ or $r + 1$.

The pivotal-element technique, used in finding the rank of a matrix, may also be used as a simple technique for finding the solution sets of systems of linear equations. This method, applied to the augmented matrix of any system, not only determines simultaneously the ranks of both the augmented matrix and the coefficient matrix, but also effects the same transformation on the system of equations as that of eliminating one of the variables by the addition technique discussed in Sec. 8-2. The procedure consists of transforming the augmented matrix by selecting *any nonzero element of the coefficient matrix* as the pivotal element. By so choosing the pivotal element, the transformation is performed on both matrices simultaneously. For this reason the ranks of the two matrices are determined by the same sequence of transformations. The net effect of any one transformation on the system of equations is to eliminate the variable whose coefficients are found in the blocked-out column. For example, consider the augmented matrices of systems (8-7) to (8-9) which are, respectively, systems (8-1) to (8-3), discussed previously. For the system

$$2x - y = 3$$
$$4x - 2y = 12 \qquad\qquad (8\text{-}7)$$

the augmented matrix, with its check column, is

| $x$ | $y$ | | Check |
|---|---|---|---|
| 2 | $^-1$ | 3 | 4 |
| 4 | $^-2$ | 12 | 14 |

It is helpful to use the variable with which the coefficients are associated as an identifying label for each column of the coefficient matrix. With $^-1$ as the pivotal element, the matrix is transformed to

| $x$ | | Check |
|---|---|---|
| (0 | $^-6$) | $^-6$ |

One pivotal transformation has reduced the coefficient matrix to a zero matrix and the augmented matrix to a nonzero matrix of one row. From Definition 8-5, the rank of the coefficient matrix is 1 and that of the augmented matrix is 2. This resultant matrix represents the equation $0x = {}^-6$. Since there exists no value of $x$ which can be multiplied by 0 to yield $^-6$, there exists no solution for the system. In this case *the coefficient matrix and the augmented matrix are of different ranks, and the system of equations is inconsistent.*

**Inconsistent systems**

The augmented matrix for the system

$$2x - y = 3$$
$$3x + 2y = 8 \qquad\qquad (8\text{-}8)$$

is

$$
\begin{array}{ccc}
x & y & \text{Check} \\
\end{array}
$$

$$
\left(
\begin{array}{cc|c}
2 & ^-1 & 3 \\
3 & 2 & 8
\end{array}
\right)
\begin{array}{c}
4 \\
13
\end{array}
$$

With $^-1$ as the pivotal element, this matrix is transformed into

$$
\begin{array}{cc}
x & \text{Check} \\
(^-7 & ^-14) \quad ^-21
\end{array}
$$

One pivotal transformation has reduced each matrix to a nonzero matrix of one row, so each matrix is of rank 2. From the resultant equation we have $x = 2$. We may substitute this value in either of the two equations of the system to find that $y = 1$. Substitution of these values in the other equation establishes that $x = 2$, $y = 1$ is the unique solution set of the system. In this case *the coefficient matrix and the augmented matrix have the same rank, and the system is consistent. Since the rank is the same as the number of variables, the solution set is unique.*

**Unique solution**

The augmented matrix for the system

$$2x - y = 3$$
$$4x - 2y = 6 \qquad\qquad (8\text{-}9)$$

is

$$
\begin{array}{ccc}
x & y & \text{Check} \\
\end{array}
$$

$$
\left(
\begin{array}{cc|c}
2 & ^-1 & 3 \\
4 & ^-2 & 6
\end{array}
\right)
\begin{array}{c}
4 \\
8
\end{array}
$$

In this case the resultant matrix is

x      *Check*

(0    0)

One pivotal transformation has reduced each matrix to a zero matrix, so each matrix is of rank 1. The resultant equation is $0x = 0$, which is satisfied by any value arbitrarily assigned to x. It follows that either equation may be solved for one of the variables in terms of the other. Any set of values determined by an arbitrary assignment of a value to this variable will satisfy both equations. In this case *the coefficient matrix and the augmented matrix have the same rank, so the system is consistent. The rank is less than the number of variables, so the solution set is not unique.*

**Nonunique solution**

There still remains one basic pattern of a consistent system of linear equations in two variables. This is the case where there are more equations than variables in the system. For illustration purposes we shall consider systems (8-10) to (8-12), with three equations in two variables.

If the equation $6x - 3y = 9$ is adjoined to the consistent system (8-9), we obtain the system

$$2x - y = 3$$
$$4x - 2y = 6 \qquad\qquad (8\text{-}10)$$
$$6x - 3y = 9$$

for which the augmented matrix is

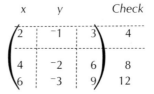

With $^{-}1$ as the pivotal element, the matrix is transformed into

x      *Check*

$$\begin{pmatrix} 0 & 0 \\ 0 & 0 \end{pmatrix} \quad \begin{matrix} 0 \\ 0 \end{matrix}$$

The coefficient matrix and the augmented matrix have the same rank, which is 1. The equations are consistent; in fact, each of the equations may be expressed in the form $2x - y = 3$. The graph of the system is essentially that of Fig. 8-3. The only difference is that for this system the line would be considered as representing three coincident lines. Any one of the equations may be solved for one of the variables in terms of the other variable. This relation will determine ordered pairs of the solution set of the system.

If the equation $3x + 2y = 8$ is adjoined to the system (8-9), we obtain the system

$$2x - y = 3$$
$$4x - 2y = 6 \qquad\qquad (8\text{-}11)$$
$$3x + 2y = 8$$

for which the augmented matrix is

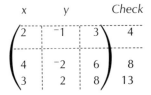

With $^-1$ as the pivotal element, this matrix is transformed into

$$\begin{array}{cc} x & \quad Check \\ \begin{pmatrix} 0 & 0 \\ ^-7 & ^-14 \end{pmatrix} & \begin{matrix} 0 \\ ^-21 \end{matrix} \end{array}$$

One transformation has reduced the coefficient matrix to

$$\begin{pmatrix} 0 \\ ^-7 \end{pmatrix}$$

a nonzero matrix of one column, so its rank is 2. One more transformation, with either $^-7$ or $^-14$ as the pivotal element, will reduce the augmented matrix to a zero matrix, so its rank is 2. The two matrices have the same rank, so the system is consistent. Since the rank is the same as the number of variables the solution set is unique. It consists of the pair of values $x = 2$ and $y = 1$ determined from the reduced equation $^-7x = ^-14$ and any one of the three given equations. The graph of the system is essentially that of Fig. 8-2. The only difference would be that the line labeled $2x - y = 3$ would be considered as the graph not only of this equation, but also of the equation $4x - 2y = 6$. In other words, the line representing $3x + 2y = 8$ intersects the two coincident lines representing $2x - y = 3$ and $4x - 2y = 6$ at the point $(2,1)$.

If the equation $5x + y = 11$ is adjoined to consistent system (8-8), we have the system

$$2x - y = 3$$
$$3x + 2y = 8 \qquad\qquad (8\text{-}12)$$
$$5x + y = 11$$

for which the augmented matrix is

$$
\begin{array}{ccc}
x & y & \textit{Check} \\
\end{array}
$$

$$
\left(\begin{array}{ccc|c}
2 & ^-1 & 3 & 4 \\
\hline
3 & 2 & 8 & 13 \\
5 & 1 & 11 & 17
\end{array}\right)
$$

With $^-1$ as the pivotal element, this matrix is transformed into

$$
\begin{array}{cc}
x & \textit{Check} \\
\end{array}
$$

$$
\left(\begin{array}{cc}
^-7 & ^-14 \\
^-7 & ^-14
\end{array}\right)\;
\begin{array}{c} ^-21 \\ ^-21 \end{array}
$$

The coefficient matrix is of rank 2, since one transformation has reduced it to the nonzero matrix of one column

$$
\left(\begin{array}{c} ^-7 \\ ^-7 \end{array}\right)
$$

The augmented matrix is also of rank 2, since one more transformation will reduce it to a zero matrix. The equations are consistent and have the unique solution set $x = 2$ and $y = 1$. The graph of the system consists of three lines which intersect in a common point, as shown in Fig. 8-4.

**FIG. 8-4**

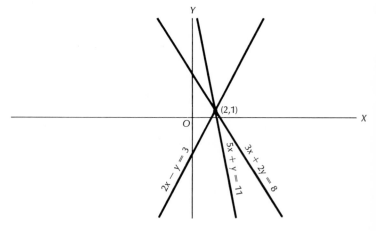

For systems of three linear equations in two unknowns there also exist three types of inconsistency which are illustrative of the general situation for $m$ equations in $n$ variables where $m > n$. As illustrations of these three types of inconsistency, consider systems (8-13) to (8-15).

If the equation $6x - 3y = 15$ is adjoined to the inconsistent system (8-7), we have the system

$$2x - y = 3$$
$$4x - 2y = 12 \qquad\qquad (8\text{-}13)$$
$$6x - 3y = 15$$

for which the augmented matrix is

| x | y | Check | |
|---|---|---|---|
| 2 | $^-1$ | 3 | 4 |
| 4 | $^-2$ | 12 | 14 |
| 6 | $^-3$ | 15 | 18 |

With $^-1$ as the pivotal element, this matrix transforms into

x    Check

$$\begin{pmatrix} 0 & ^-6 \\ 0 & ^-6 \end{pmatrix} \begin{matrix} ^-6 \\ ^-6 \end{matrix}$$

The coefficient matrix is of rank 1 and the augmented matrix is of rank 2 (why?). The equations are inconsistent. Each row of the final matrix represents the equation $0x = ^-6$, for which no solution exists. There exists no solution set for the system. A careful examination of the equations reveals that their graphs are three straight lines with a common slope but with different $y$ intercepts. They are three parallel lines and have no point of intersection (Fig. 8-5).

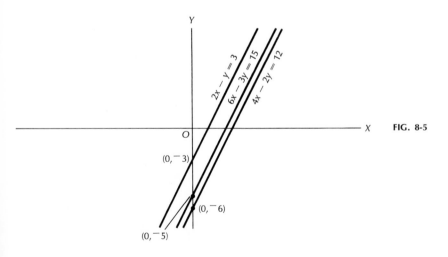

FIG. 8-5

If the equation $3x + 2y = 8$ is adjoined to system (8-7), we have the system

$$2x - y = 3$$
$$4x - 2y = 12 \qquad\qquad (8\text{-}14)$$
$$3x + 2y = 8$$

for which the augmented matrix is

$$
\begin{array}{ccc}
x & y & \textit{Check}
\end{array}
$$

$$
\left(
\begin{array}{c:c:c}
2 & ^-1 & 3 \\
\hdashline
4 & ^-2 & 12 \\
3 & 2 & 8
\end{array}
\right)
\begin{array}{c}
4 \\
14 \\
13
\end{array}
$$

With $^-1$ as the pivotal element, we obtain

$$
\begin{array}{cc}
x & \textit{Check}
\end{array}
$$

$$
\begin{pmatrix}
0 & ^-6 \\
^-7 & ^-14
\end{pmatrix}
\begin{array}{c}
^-6 \\
^-21
\end{array}
$$

The coefficient matrix is of rank 2, and the augmented matrix is of rank 3 (why?). The equations are inconsistent. There exists no solution set for the system. The equation represented by the first row of the reduced matrix is $0x = ^-6$, which is that of system (8-7). The equation represented by the second row is $^-7x = ^-14$, or the resultant equation of system (8-8). Thus the graphs of the first and second equation are the parallel lines of Fig. 8-1, and the graphs of the first and third equations are the intersecting lines of Fig. 8-2. If the second and third equations are considered together, they will be found to represent two lines which intersect in the point $(20/7, \, ^-2/7)$. The graph of the system therefore consists of two parallel lines intersected by a third line (Fig. 8-6).

FIG. 8-6

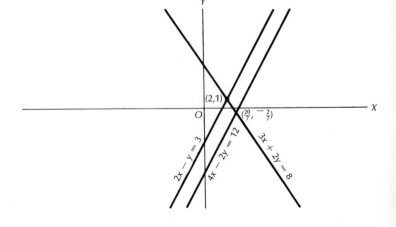

The remaining pattern of an inconsistent system of equations is represented by

$$2x - y = 3$$
$$3x + 2y = 8$$
$$x - 4y = 12$$

(8-15)

where the augmented matrix is

| x | y | 3 | Check |
|---|---|---|---|

$$\begin{pmatrix} 2 & ^-1 & 3 \\ 3 & 2 & 8 \\ 1 & ^-4 & 12 \end{pmatrix} \begin{matrix} 4 \\ 13 \\ 9 \end{matrix}$$

With $^-1$ as the pivotal element, this matrix transforms into

| x | | Check |
|---|---|---|

$$\begin{pmatrix} ^-7 & ^-14 \\ 7 & 0 \end{pmatrix} \begin{matrix} ^-21 \\ 7 \end{matrix}$$

The coefficient matrix is of rank 2 and the augmented matrix of rank 3 (why?). The equations are inconsistent. There exists no solution set for the system. The equations represented by the final matrix, each considered with $2x - y = 3$, lead to the solution set $x = 2$, $y = 1$ for the first two equations and $x = 0$, $y = ^-3$ for the first and third equations. Similarly, the last two equations have the solution set $x = 4$, $y = ^-2$. The graphs are three straight lines which intersect in pairs at the three points $(2,1)$, $(0,^-3)$, and $(4,^-2)$ (see Fig. 8-7).

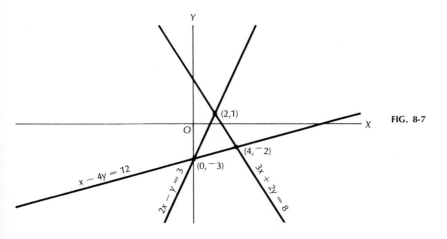

FIG. 8-7

## 8-5. *m* LINEAR EQUATIONS IN *n* VARIABLES

The detailed discussion of systems of linear equations in two variables gives a picture of the various basic types of relations which can exist for any number of equations in any number of variables. In the case of two variables the picture is made clearer by supporting graphs of lines in the plane. Analogous geometric interpretations of systems of equations in three variables would be in terms of planes and lines in three dimensions. Just as $ax + by + c = 0$, where $a$, $b$, and $c$ are real and $a$, and $b$ are not both zero, represents a line in two-dimensional space, so $ax + by + cz + d = 0$, with $a$, $b$, $c$, and $d$ real and $a$, $b$, and $c$ not all zero, represents a plane in a space of three dimensions. Similar interpretations exist in geometries of still higher dimensions for systems of $m$ equations in $n$ variables.

The theorems which cover all possible cases of a system of $m$ linear equations in $n$ variables will be stated without proof. The technique used will be that of the pivotal-element method.† While there are other methods for dealing with systems of linear equations (see Exercises 2 and 6, pages 287–288), that presented here is one of the more efficient, since it reduces the amount of computation necessary and also provides an effective check. Examples will be given for each case, and for consistent systems the technique for finding the solution set will be shown. Remember that the pivotal element for each reduction can be chosen *only* from the coefficient matrix, and it must be a nonzero element.

**Inconsistent systems of equations**

**Theorem 8-1.** **A system of m linear equations in n variables is inconsistent if the coefficient matrix and the augmented matrix have different ranks.**

**Example 8-9.** Inconsistent systems of equations: **m < n.**

$$2x - 3y - 2z + w = 4$$
$$x + 2y + z - 2w = {}^-5$$
$$9x - 10y - 7z + 2w = 20$$

The augmented matrix of this system with its check column is

---

† For a discussion of the general case with supporting proofs of the necessary theorems see Wren, *op. cit.*, pp. 823–834. For a more extended discussion of such systems see also J. Houston Banks and F. Lynwood Wren, "Elements of Algebra," pp. 241–263, Allyn and Bacon, Inc., Boston, 1962.

$$\begin{array}{ccccc}
x & y & z & w & Check \\
\end{array}$$

$$\left(\begin{array}{ccccc|c}
2 & {}^-3 & {}^-2 & 1 & 4 & 2 \\
1 & 2 & 1 & {}^-2 & {}^-5 & {}^-3 \\
9 & {}^-10 & {}^-7 & 2 & 20 & 14
\end{array}\right)$$

If we select as the pivotal element the coefficient of $z$ in the second equation, this will have the effect of eliminating $z$ and give the resultant system, whose augmented matrix is

$$\begin{array}{cccc}
x & y & w & Check \\
\end{array}$$

$$\left(\begin{array}{cc|cc|c}
4 & 1 & {}^-3 & {}^-6 & {}^-4 \\
16 & 4 & {}^-12 & {}^-15 & {}^-7
\end{array}\right)$$

Choosing as the pivotal element the coefficient of $y$ in the first equation, we get

$$\begin{array}{ccc}
x & w & Check \\
(0 & 0 & 9) \quad 9
\end{array}$$

Since two pivotal transformations have reduced the coefficient matrix to a zero matrix, it is of rank 2. The same two transformations reduced the augmented matrix to a nonzero matrix of one row, so it is of rank 3. The two matrices have different ranks, so the system of equations is inconsistent. There exists no solution set for the system. This is evident from the equation $0x + 0w = 9$, which is represented by the final reduced matrix.

**m = n.**   System (8-7), discussed previously, is an example of this case. It should be evident that there is no essential difference between the test for this case and that for $m < n$.

**m > n.**   The three examples furnished by systems (8-13) to (8-15) illustrate the different possibilities of this case.

**Example 8-10.**   Use Theorem 8-1 to show that it is impossible to find a quadratic function whose graph will pass through the points $(1, {}^-2)$, $(2,3)$, $(3,8)$, and $(4, {}^-3)$.

The formula for the quadratic function is $y = ax^2 + bx + c$, with $a \neq 0$. The conditions that the graph of this function pass through each of the given points can be found by substituting these coordinates in the formula. These four conditions are

$(1,^-2):\quad a + b + c = ^-2$
$(2,3):\quad 4a + 2b + c = 3$
$(3,8):\quad 9a + 3b + c = 8$
$(4,^-3): 16a + 4b + c = ^-3$

Here we have a system of four linear equations in the variables $a, b,$ and $c$. The augmented matrix of the system is

$$
\begin{array}{cccc}
a & b & c & \quad Check
\end{array}
$$

$$
\left(\begin{array}{ccc|c}
1 & 1 & 1 & ^-2 \\
4 & 2 & 1 & 3 \\
9 & 3 & 1 & 8 \\
16 & 4 & 1 & ^-3
\end{array}\right)
\begin{array}{c}
1 \\
10 \\
21 \\
18
\end{array}
$$

The suggested first pivotal transformation gives

$$
\begin{array}{ccc}
b & c & \quad Check
\end{array}
$$

$$
\left(\begin{array}{cc|c}
^-2 & ^-3 & 11 \\
^-6 & ^-8 & 26 \\
^-12 & ^-15 & 29
\end{array}\right)
\begin{array}{c}
6 \\
12 \\
2
\end{array}
$$

A second pivotal transformation with $^-2$ as the pivotal element gives

$$
\begin{array}{cc}
c & \quad Check
\end{array}
$$

$$
\left(\begin{array}{c|c}
^-2 & 14 \\
^-6 & 74
\end{array}\right)
\begin{array}{c}
12 \\
68
\end{array}
$$

Observe that at this point two pivotal transformations have reduced the coefficient matrix to a nonzero matrix of one column, so it is of rank 3. One more transformation reduces the augmented matrix to the nonzero matrix of one column, $(^-64)$. The augmented matrix is therefore of rank 4. The equations are inconsistent, so there are no values of $a, b,$ and $c$ which will satisfy the four equations of the system. This is also evident from the inconsistent condition imposed by the reduced matrix, $^-2c = 14$ and $^-6c = 74$. It thus follows that there exists no quadratic function whose graph will pass through the four given points.

**Consistent systems of equations**

**Theorem 8-2. A system of m linear equations in n variables is consistent if the coefficient matrix and augmented matrix have the same rank r. If r = n, the system has a unique solution set. If r< n, then it is possible to solve for certain r of the variables uniquely in terms of the remaining n − r variables. These values will also satisfy the remaining m − r equations.**

**Example 8-11.** First show that each system of equations is consistent, and then find the solution set.

**m < n.**

$$3x_1 - 2x_2 + x_3 + 2x_4 = 0$$
$$6x_1 - 4x_2 - 2x_3 - x_4 = {}^-1$$
$$9x_1 - 6x_2 - x_3 + x_4 = {}^-1$$

The augmented matrix for this system is

| $x_1$ | $x_2$ | $x_3$ | $x_4$ | | Check |
|---|---|---|---|---|---|
| 3 | $^-2$ | 1 | 2 | 0 | 4 |
| 6 | $^-4$ | $^-2$ | $^-1$ | $^-1$ | $^-2$ |
| 9 | $^-6$ | $^-1$ | 1 | $^-1$ | 2 |

A first reduction gives

| $x_1$ | $x_3$ | $x_4$ | | Check |
|---|---|---|---|---|
| 0 | 8 | 10 | 2 | 20 |
| 0 | 8 | 10 | 2 | 20 |

A second reduction gives

| $x_1$ | $x_4$ | Check |
|---|---|---|
| (0 | 0 | 0) | 0 |

The coefficient matrix and augmented matrix have the same rank, 2, so the equations are consistent. Since the rank is less than 4, which is the number of variables, the solution set is not unique. It is possible to solve for some two of the variables in terms of the remaining $4 - 2$, or 2, variables.

From the first reduced matrix we have

$$8x_3 + 10x_4 = 2$$

or

$$x_3 = \frac{-5}{4}x_4 + \frac{1}{4}$$

If this value is substituted in any one of the three given equations, we can obtain

$$x_1 = \frac{2}{3}x_2 - \frac{1}{4}x_4 - \frac{1}{12}$$

These values will satisfy all three of the given equations independently of the values of the variables $x_2$ and $x_4$. This fact can be verified by substituting in the original equations and finding that the variables all cancel out.

The set of ordered quadruples $(x_1, x_2, x_3, x_4)$ in which

$$x_1 = \frac{2}{3} x_2 - \frac{1}{4} x_4 - \frac{1}{12}$$

$$x_3 = \frac{^-5}{4} x_4 + \frac{1}{4}$$

**Complete solution**

is called the *complete solution* of the system. This is because any values selected for $x_2$ and $x_4$ will determine values of $x_1$ and $x_3$ such that the equations will be satisfied. Any such specific quadruple of values is

**Particular solution**

called a *particular solution* of the system.

Note that we might have solved for $x_4$ in terms of $x_3$ or for $x_2$ instead of $x_1$. Note also that we cannot solve the system for $x_1$ and $x_2$ in terms of $x_3$ and $x_4$. Why? This is why the phrase "certain $r$ of the variables" occurs in the statement of the theorem.

**m = n.**   Use Theorem 8-2 to find the equation of the quadratic function whose graph passes through the points $(2, ^-1)$, $(^-1, 2)$, and $(3, 2)$.

The formula for the quadratic function is $y = ax^2 + bx + c$, with $a \neq 0$. The conditions that its graph pass through the three given points are

$(2, ^-1)$:   $4a + 2b + c = ^-1$
$(^-1, 2)$:   $a - b + c = 2$
$(3, 2)$:   $9a + 3b + c = 2$

This is a system of three equations in three variables whose augmented matrix is

$$
\begin{array}{ccccc}
a & b & c & & Check \\
\left(\begin{array}{ccc|c} 
4 & 2 & 1 & ^-1 \\
1 & ^-1 & 1 & 2 \\
\hline
9 & 3 & 1 & 2
\end{array}\right) & \begin{array}{c} 6 \\ 3 \\ \\ 15 \end{array}
\end{array}
$$

A first transformation gives

$$
\begin{array}{cccc}
a & b & & Check \\
\left(\begin{array}{cc|c}
^-5 & ^-1 & ^-3 \\
\hline
^-8 & ^-4 & 0
\end{array}\right) & \begin{array}{c} ^-9 \\ \\ ^-12 \end{array}
\end{array}
$$

A second transformation gives

$$\begin{array}{cc} a & Check \\ (^-12 & ^-12)\quad ^-24 \end{array}$$

The coefficient matrix and the augmented matrix of the system have the same rank, 3, and this is the number of variables. The system is consistent and has a unique solution.

The final matrix of one row and two columns represents the equation $^-12a = ^-12$, or $a = 1$. If this value is substituted for $a$ in either of the two equations in $a$ and $b$ represented by the immediately preceding matrix, we find $b = ^-2$. These values of $a$ and $b$ substituted in any one of the three original equations give $c = ^-1$. Substitution in the remaining equations will establish $a = 1$, $b = ^-2$, $c = ^-1$ as the unique solution of the system of equations.

It therefore follows that the unique quadratic function whose graph passes through the points $(2,^-1)$, $(^-1,2)$, and $(3,2)$ is $y = x^2 - 2x - 1$.

**m > n.** The three cases of consistent systems of linear equations of equations of this type are represented by systems (8-10) to (8-12).

## EXERCISES

**1.** A system of linear equations whose constant terms are all zeros is called a *system of homogeneous linear equations*. Why will such a system always be a consistent system?

*Homogeneous system*

**2.** If a system of homogeneous linear equations has a unique solution set, what can be said about the elements of this set?

In Exercises 3 to 8 first test to see whether the system is consistent or inconsistent. If it is consistent, find the solution set and draw the graph.

**3.** $\quad x + y = 4$
$\quad 3x - 2y = ^-3$

**4.** $\quad 2x + 3y = 5$
$\quad 10x + 15y = 8$

**5.** $3x - 2y = 5$
$\quad 6x - 4y = 10$

**6.** $0.2x - 0.04y = 0.6$
$\quad 3x - 0.6y = 9$

**7.** $0.5x + 1.5y = 7$
$\quad 2.5x - \quad y = 1$

**8.** $\frac{2}{3}x - \frac{1}{2}y = \frac{3}{4}$
$\quad \frac{1}{2}x - \frac{3}{8}y = \frac{1}{4}$

In Exercises 9 to 24 use the pivotal-element technique to determine whether each system of equations is consistent or inconsistent and to find the solution set of each consistent system.

**9.** $3x + y + 2z = 11$
$\quad x - 2y + z = 0$
$\quad 2x + y - 3z = ^-5$

**10.** $\quad x_1 + x_2 + x_3 + x_4 = 0$
$\quad 2x_1 - x_2 + 3x_3 + x_4 = 7$
$\quad 3x_1 \quad\quad + 4x_3 + 2x_4 = 7$
$\quad 5x_1 + 2x_2 + 6x_3 + 4x_4 = 7$

**11.** $3x_1 - 2x_2 + \phantom{0}x_3 = 5$
$\phantom{0}2x_1 - \phantom{0}x_2 - \phantom{0}3x_3 = 4$
$^-3x_1 + \phantom{0}x_2 + 10x_3 = 2$

**12.** $2r + 3s + \phantom{0}t = 5$
$\phantom{00}r - \phantom{0}s + 2t = 0$

**13.** $x + 2y = 1$
$3x - \phantom{0}y = 17$
$4x + 3y = 14$
$2x + 7y = ^-4$

**14.** $x + \phantom{0}y + \phantom{0}z = 2$
$2x + 3y + 2z = 3$
$x + 2y + \phantom{0}z = 1$
$4x + 7y + 4z = 7$

**15.** $3x_1 - 2x_2 - \phantom{0}x_3 + 4x_4 = ^-1$
$\phantom{0}x_1 + 4x_2 + 3x_3 - \phantom{0}x_4 = 2$
$5x_1 + 6x_2 + 5x_3 + 2x_4 = 0$

**16.** $3x + \phantom{0}y + 2z = 0$
$x - \phantom{0}y + 3z = 0$
$4x + 2y - \phantom{0}z = 0$

**17.** $2r - s + 3t - \phantom{0}u + \phantom{0}v = 0$
$3r + s + 5t + 4u + 6v = 24$
$^-r + s - 2t + \phantom{0}u + \phantom{0}v = 6$

**18.** $2x_1 - \phantom{0}x_2 + \phantom{0}x_3 + 3x_4 = 5$
$\phantom{0}x_1 + 2x_2 + 3x_3 - 2x_4 = 0$
$3x_1 + \phantom{0}x_2 - \phantom{0}x_3 - 4x_4 = ^-2$
$6x_1 + 4x_2 - \phantom{0}x_3 - 2x_4 = 4$
$\phantom{0}2x_2 - 4x_3 + \phantom{0}x_4 = 8$

**19.** $2r + \phantom{00}s - \phantom{0}t = 0$
$\phantom{0}r - \phantom{0}2s + 3t = 7$
$\phantom{0}s - \phantom{0}t = ^-2$
$5r + 11s - 6t = ^-7$

**20.** $x - 3y + 3z + \phantom{00}u - \phantom{00}v = 6$
$2x + \phantom{0}y - 4z - \phantom{0}2u + \phantom{0}3v = ^-4$
$2y + \phantom{0}z - \phantom{0}3u + \phantom{0}2v = ^-5$
$2x + 9y \phantom{00000} - 14u + 11v = ^-24$
$3x - 7y + 10z \phantom{00000} - \phantom{0}v = 13$

**21.** $3u + 2v = 5$
$2u - \phantom{0}v = 1$
$\phantom{0}u + \phantom{0}v = 2$
$6u + 2v = 9$

**22.** $4x - 3y + 2z + \phantom{0}u = 4$
$2x + \phantom{0}y - 4z - 2u = ^-3$
$5x \phantom{00000} + 3z + 3u = 11$
$x - 2y - 5z - 4u = 2$

**23.** $x_1 + \phantom{0}x_2 - 2x_3 \phantom{000000} = 0$
$2x_1 - 3x_2 - 2x_3 - 3x_4 = 4$
$4x_1 - \phantom{0}x_2 \phantom{00000} - \phantom{0}x_4 = 4$
$x_1 + 6x_2 + 5x_3 + 6x_4 = ^-4$
$3x_1 - 7x_2 - 5x_3 - 7x_4 = 8$

**24.** $3r - 3s + 4t - \phantom{0}u + 3v = 7$
$r + \phantom{0}s - \phantom{0}t + 2u - 4v = ^-1$
$2r \phantom{00000} + 3t \phantom{00000} - \phantom{0}v = 4$
$6r - \phantom{0}s + 6t + \phantom{0}u - 2v = 3$

Use Theorems 8-1 and 8-2 as aids in solving Exercises 25 to 36.

**25.** (a) Find the equation of the straight line through the three points $(1, ^-2)$, $(2, 3)$, and $(3, 8)$.

(b) Show that any pair of these three points are sufficient to find the equation of the line.

(c) Show that it is impossible to find a quadratic function whose graph will contain the three points of part (a).

**26.** (a) Show that it is impossible to find the equation of a quadratic function whose graph will pass through the three points $(1, ^-3)$, $(^-1, 1)$, and $(4, ^-9)$.

(b) Show that these points are points of the line $y = ^-2x - 1$.

**27.** Find the formula for the quadratic function whose graph passes through the three points $(4,^-3)$, $(^-1,2)$, and $(3,1)$.

**28.** Select any three points on the graph of the linear function $y = 3x - 2$ and show that it is impossible to find a quadratic function whose graph will pass through these three points.

**29.** From plane geometry we know that three points not on the same line uniquely determine a circle. The general equation of a circle is $x^2 + y^2 + ax + by + c = 0$. Find the equation of the specific circle determined by the three points $(3,1)$, $(1,4)$, and $(5,^-1)$.

**30.** (a) Show that it is impossible to pass a circle through the three points $(0,3)$, $(1,4)$, and $(^-1,2)$.

(b) Show that these points are points of the line $y = x + 3$.

**31.** In three-space a point is located by an ordered triple $(x,y,z)$ of real numbers, and the general equation of a plane is

$$ax + by + cz + d = 0$$

where $a$, $b$, $c$, and $d$ are real and $a$, $b$, and $c$ are not all zero. From geometry, we know that three points not on the same line uniquely determine a plane. Find the equation of the plane determined by the three points $(1,1,1)$, $(1,3,2)$, and $(^-1,0,1)$.

**32.** In three-space two planes intersect in a line. Show that the planes represented by the equations of the given system all pass through the line determined by the first two equations

$$
\begin{aligned}
2x + 3y - z &= 5 \\
x - y + 3z &= 5 \\
4x + y + 5z &= 21 \\
2x + 13y - 15z &= {}^-17 \\
x + 4y - 4z &= {}^-3
\end{aligned}
$$

**33.** Find the equations of two planes which intersect at the line which is determined by the two points $(1,2,1)$ and $(3,^-4,5)$.

**34.** Find the equations of three other planes which intersect at the line of Exercise 33. Use Theorem 8-2 to prove that your answer is correct.

**35.** A man has a total of $50,000 in four different investments which bear interest at the respective rates of 4.5, 5, 4, and 5.5 percent, respectively. His yearly income from the four investments is $2,515. The amount invested at 5.5 percent is $2,000 more than the sum of the amounts invested at the other three rates. The amount invested at 4.5 percent is $4,000 less than the sum of the amounts invested at 4 and 5 percent, respectively. How much money does he have in each investment?

**36.** The combined resistance $r$ ohms of three resistances of $r_1$, $r_2$, and $r_3$ ohms is given by $1/r = 1/r_1 + 1/r_2 + 1/r_3$ if connected in parallel, and $r = r_1 + r_2 + r_3$ if they are connected in series. The combined effect of the three resistances is known to be 13 ohms in series and $1\frac{1}{3}$ ohms in parallel. Furthermore, the parallel combination of two of the resistances has the same effect as one-half the third resistance. What is the amount of each resistance?

Exercises 37 to 42 are based on the geometric configuration of the four points $(2,3)$, $(^-2,1)$, $(1,0)$, and $(0,^-3)$, all of which lie in the same plane.

**37.** Find the equation of the straight line through the points $(2,3)$, $(1,0)$, and $(0,^-3)$.

**38.** Find the equations of the remaining straight lines determined in the configuration.

**39.** Which set of three points is not sufficient to determine a circle? Why? (See Exercise 29 for the general equation of a circle.)

**40.** Find the equations of all circles which are determined by sets of three points of the configuration.

**41.** Which of the straight lines of Exercises 37 and 38 is not a common chord of two circles of the configuration? Why?

**42.** Identify for each of the remaining straight lines of Exercises 37 and 38 the two circles of which it is the common chord.

## 8-6.  INCONSISTENCY AND INTERSECTION

**Cartesian frame of reference**

In a cartesian frame of reference the ordered pair $(x,y)$, where the domain of each variable is the set of all real numbers, may be used to structure a one-to-one correspondence between the points of the plane and the set of all ordered pairs of real numbers. When there is a formula which explicitly relates the values of $y$ to those for $x$ as the independent variable, there are no longer two arbitrary choices of values. There remains only one such choice, that for the variable $x$. Values for $x$ may be assigned arbitrarily, and then the corresponding values for $y$ will be determined by the formula. If the coefficients of the formula are real numbers, the ordered pairs of values determined will be coordinates of points of a curve lying in the plane. For example, $y = mx + k$, where $m$ and $k$ are real numbers, will determine a real value for $y$ associated with each arbitrarily chosen real value $x$ to give a point on a straight line. Similarly, $y = ax^2 + bx + c$, with $a$, $b$, and $c$ real and $a \neq 0$, yields a real value for $y$ for each arbitrarily chosen real value of $x$ to locate a point on a parabola. When two such formulas are considered simultaneously, there may be no longer any arbitrary choices, for a real value of $x$ must yield a real value for $y$ which, together with the $x$, satisfies both equations and locates a point which is on both curves.

From this discussion we see that an equation in two variables is a condition placed on the relation between the values of the variables and has the net effect of removing one degree of freedom in the arbitrary selection of values for one of the variables involved. Two such conditions imposed simultaneously may result in an inconsistent situation. This simply means that it is quite possible that the condition imposed by one equation may be inconsistent with that imposed by the other equation. In this case there are no values of the variables which will satisfy both conditions simultaneously. There exists no solution for the system of equations, so the solution set is the null set. Geometrically, the curves which are the graphs of an inconsistent system of equations certainly can have no points in common and therefore cannot intersect. It is not true, however, that two nonintersecting curves necessarily represent the graphs of an inconsistent system of equations. The question of consistency or inconsistency can be answered only within the context determined jointly by the number field in which the solution set is sought and the nature of the condition on the independent variable $x$ which results from the requirement that the two equations must yield the same value for the dependent variable $y$. Typical cases will be discussed in Examples 8-12 to 8-15.

**Example 8-12.** The simplest case in which nonintersection of graphs is synonymous with inconsistency of solution is that of two parallel lines. This was observed in a specific case in Sec. 8-1 and Fig. 8-1. In general, for $k_1 \neq k_2$,

$$y = mx + k_1$$
$$y = mx + k_2$$

are two linear functions whose graphs have the same slope $m$ but different $y$ intercepts, $k_1$ and $k_2$. Their graphs will be two parallel lines. The condition on $x$ that these two formulas yield the same value for $y$ is $mx + k_1 = mx + k_2$, which requires that $k_1 - k_2 = 0$. Since $k_1 \neq k_2$, there exist no numbers, real or complex, for which the equality is true. It thus follows that the two equations impose inconsistent conditions on the variables $x$ and $y$.

Similarly, for $c_1 \neq c_2$

$$y = ax^2 + c_1$$
$$y = ax^2 + c_2$$
$$a \neq 0$$

represent two quadratic functions whose graphs are parabolas of identical characteristics, except that their extrema are at different positions on the $y$ axis (see Fig. 6-9). These two curves will not intersect. The condition on $x$ that these two formulas yield the same value for $y$ is $ax^2 +$

$c_1 = ax^2 + c_2$, or $c_1 - c_2 = 0$. In this case also, inconsistency and non-intersection are synonymous, as there exist no numbers, real or complex, for which this equality is true.

The simplest illustration of the synonymity of consistency of equations and intersection of their graphs was illustrated in Sec. 8-1 and Figs. 8-2 and 8-3. Further cases will now be considered. Observe that in some of the illustrations consistency or inconsistency cannot be determined by intersection or nonintersection of graphs.

**Example 8-13.** Consider the two quadratic functions

$$y = ax^2 + b_1x + c_1 \qquad a \neq 0$$
$$y = ax^2 + b_2x + c_2$$

Note that the coefficients of $x^2$ are equal. For the illustration we shall assume $b_1 \neq b_2$. The relation between $c_1$ and $c_2$ is immaterial; they may or may not be equal. Here the condition on $x$ that the two formulas yield the same value for $y$ is

$$ax^2 + b_1x + c_1 = ax^2 + b_2x + c_2$$

This simplifies to the linear condition

$$(b_1 - b_2)x = c_2 - c_1$$

Since $b_1 - b_2 \neq 0$, we find that for the two formulas to give the same value of $y$ we must have

$$x = \frac{c_2 - c_1}{b_1 - b_2}$$

If this value is substituted in either equation, a unique value is obtained for $y$. The conclusion follows that the system is consistent with a unique solution. Since the coefficient and constant terms are all real, it also follows that this unique solution is an ordered pair of real numbers and the graphs of the two functions intersect in one and only one point. Figure 8-8 illustrates this case for the two functions

$$y = x^2 + 4x + 1$$
$$y = x^2 + 6x + 3$$

To obtain the same value for $y$ we must have

$$x^2 + 6x + 3 = x^2 + 4x + 1$$
$$2x = {}^-2$$
$$x = {}^-1$$

Either equation gives $y = {}^-2$ to correspond to $x = {}^-1$. The solution set

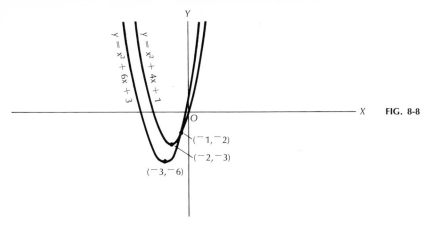

FIG. 8-8

for the system consists of the one ordered pair $(^-1,^-2)$, which indicates that the parabolas intersect at the point $(^-1,^-2)$.

**Example 8-14.**   Consider the two equations

$$y = ax^2 + bx + c \qquad a \neq 0$$
$$y = mx + k$$

where the coefficients are all real numbers. The graphs are, respectively, a parabola and a straight line. The condition that the two equations yield the same value for $y$ is

$$ax^2 + bx + c = mx + k$$

which may be written as the resultant quadratic equation

$$ax^2 + (b - m)x + (c - k) = 0$$

From the Fundamental Theorem of Algebra (Theorem 7-9) we know that there exist two not necessarily distinct roots $x_1$ and $x_2$ of this equation. For each of these values of $x$ there is determined a unique $y$ to give the solution set $\{(x_1,y_1), (x_2,y_2)\}$ of the system.

Since the coefficients of the resultant quadratic equation are real, the roots will be real if and only if the discriminant is nonnegative. Under this condition the system will be consistent, and the graphs of the two functions will intersect at two real and distinct points if the discriminant is positive, or two real coincident points if the discriminant is zero (in the latter case the two curves are tangent). If the discriminant is negative, the roots will not be real, and the curves will have no points of intersection. If, in addition, the conditions of the problem are such that the solution is restricted to the field of real numbers, the system is inconsistent. Thus over the field of real numbers there is a definite relation between consistency of solution and intersection of graphs. Over the field of complex numbers, however, such a system is always consistent, and there is no relation whatsoever between consistency of solution and intersection of graphs.

FIG. 8-9

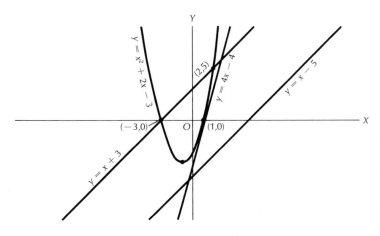

The three possible situations of this case are illustrated in Fig. 8-9. In the system

$$y = x^2 + 2x - 3$$
$$y = x + 3$$

the condition on $x$ is

$$x^2 + 2x - 3 = x + 3$$

which simplifies to

$$x^2 + x - 6 = 0$$

The discriminant is $1^2 - 4(1)(^-6) = 1 + 24 = 25$, so the roots are real and unequal. They are, in fact, $x = ^-3$ or $2$. The solution set of the system is $\{(^-3,0), (2,5)\}$, and the graphs intersect at two distinct points.
    In the system

$$y = x^2 + 2x - 3$$
$$y = 4x - 4$$

the condition on $x$ is

$$x^2 + 2x - 3 = 4x - 4$$

or

$$x^2 - 2x + 1 = 0$$

The discriminant is $(^-2)^2 - 4(1)(1) = 0$, and the roots are real and equal. These two equal values of x are 1 and 1. Hence the solution set for the system is $\{(1,0)\}$, and the straight line is tangent to the parabola at the point $(1,0)$.

In the system

$$y = x^2 + 2x - 3$$
$$y = x - 5$$

the condition on x is

$$x^2 + 2x - 3 = x - 5$$

or

$$x^2 + x + 2 = 0$$

and the discriminant is $1^2 - 4(1)(2) = ^-7$. The roots of the resultant equation are not real, so the solution set for the system does not represent points of the plane. The graphs do not intersect. The solution set is

$$\left\{ \frac{^-1}{2} + \frac{\sqrt{7}}{2}i, \frac{^-11}{2} + \frac{\sqrt{7}}{2}i, \frac{^-1}{2} - \frac{\sqrt{7}}{2}i, \frac{^-11}{2} - \frac{\sqrt{7}}{2}i \right\}$$

As in case of the linear and quadratic functions of Example 8-14, the two quadratic functions

$$y = a_1x^2 + b_1x + c_1 \qquad a_1 \neq 0$$
$$y = a_2x^2 + b_2x + c_2 \qquad a_2 \neq 0$$

where $a_1 \neq a_2$ leads to a resultant quadratic equation in x. The value of the discriminant will determine whether the solution set is real or not, and whether the two curves will intersect in two distinct points, be tangent to each other, or have no points in common. The condition on x that the two curves $y = x^2$ and $y = ^-x^2$ have a point in common is $x^2 = ^-x^2$. It should be evident that $x = 0$ is the only value of x satisfying this condition. In Fig. 6-8 the two curves are seen to be tangent to each other at the point $(0,0)$.

**Example 8-15.** The graphs of two quadratic equations may have at most four and as few as no points in common. Some of these possible situations are illustrated by the three systems of this example. First consider the two equations

$$y = x^2$$
$$y^2 = x$$

From the Substitution Rule (see page 25) we determine the condition on x necessary and sufficient that both equations give the same value for $y$ to be the fourth-degree equation

$$x^4 - x = 0$$

which may be written in the form

$$x(x - 1)(x^2 + x + 1) = 0$$

The roots of this equation are

$$x = 0, \ 1, \ \frac{-1}{2} + \frac{\sqrt{3}}{2}\,i, \ \frac{-1}{2} - \frac{\sqrt{3}}{2}\,i$$

The solution set of the system is then

$$\left\{ (0,0), \ (1,1), \ \left(\frac{-1}{2} + \frac{\sqrt{3}}{2}\,i, \ \frac{-1}{2} - \frac{\sqrt{3}}{2}\,i\right), \ \left(\frac{-1}{2} - \frac{\sqrt{3}}{2}\,i, \ \frac{-1}{2} + \frac{\sqrt{3}}{2}\,i\right) \right\}$$

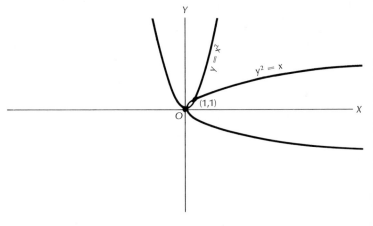

FIG. 8-10

The two curves thus have two points in common (Fig. 8-10).

For the two equations

$$y = x^2 + 4$$
$$y^2 = x$$

the condition on $x$ is the fourth-degree equation

$$x^4 + 8x^2 - x + 16 = 0$$

Although not as simple as in the case of a quadratic equation, there is a discriminant technique which can be used to determine the nature of the roots of fourth-degree equations.† Application of the technique to this equation reveals that the equation has no real roots. The solution

† L. E. Dickson, "First Course in the Theory of Equations," pp. 50–54, John Wiley & Sons, Inc., New York, 1922.

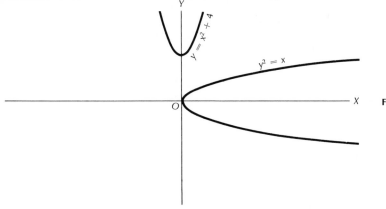

FIG. 8-11

set of the given system of two quadratics consists of four ordered pairs of imaginary values. The curves have no points of intersection (Fig. 8-11).

Next consider the two equations

$$y = x^2$$
$$x = y^2 - 4y + 2$$

The condition on $x$ is

$$x^4 - 4x^2 - x + 2 = 0$$

which may be written in the form

$$(x + 1)(x - 2)(x^2 + x - 1) = 0$$

The roots are

$$x = {}^-1,\ 2,\ \frac{{}^-1 + \sqrt{5}}{2},\ \frac{{}^-1 - \sqrt{5}}{2}$$

The solution set of the system is

$$\left\{ ({}^-1,1), (2,4),\ \left( \frac{{}^-1 + \sqrt{5}}{2}, \frac{3 - \sqrt{5}}{2} \right),\ \left( \frac{{}^-1 - \sqrt{5}}{2}, \frac{3 + \sqrt{5}}{2} \right) \right\}$$

The curves intersect at four distinct points (Fig. 8-12). The pairs of irrational values are represented in the figure by approximate values listed here in the same order in which they occur above: (0.62,0.37) and (⁻1.62,2.62).

These examples have been presented to illustrate some of the more significant possibilities of consistency of solution and intersection of graphs for systems of two equations in two variables. It should be evident that the only way to arrive at answers concerning such equa-

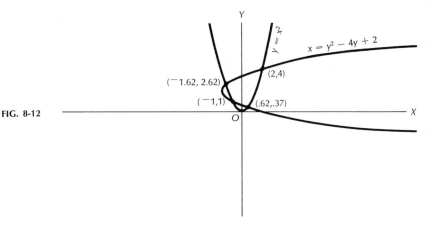

FIG. 8-12

tions is to orient one's thinking in the context of the desired number field as one examines the condition on the independent variable that the two equations must yield the same value for the dependent variable.

## 8-7. SYSTEMS OF EQUATIONS INVOLVING QUADRATICS

In the previous section the solution sets of a few systems of equations involving quadratic equations were obtained by first finding the condition on the independent variable $x$ which resulted from requiring that the two equations of the system yield the same value for the dependent variable $y$. The net effect of this technique was that we arrived at a solution set of a given system of equations by substituting for $y$ in one equation its value in terms of $x$ as determined by the other equation. The **Substitution process**  Substitution Rule (see page 25) provides the authority for the use of this technique in solving equations.

For a system consisting of one quadratic equation and one linear equation in two variables, the solution set may be obtained by this process:

1. Solve the linear equation for one variable, say $y$, in terms of the other variable $x$.
2. In the quadratic equation replace $y$ by its equivalent expression in terms of $x$. The resultant equation will be either a linear or a quadratic equation in $x$.
3. Solve the resultant equation.
4. Substitute each value obtained for $x$ in the linear equation to obtain the associated value for $y$ in the solution set of the system.
5. Substitute each ordered pair of values in the quadratic equation to verify that it belongs to the solution set of the system.

**Example 8-16.**   Find the solution set of

$$xy = 12$$
$$2x + 3y = 17$$

**1.** $y = \dfrac{17 - 2x}{3}$

**2.** $x\dfrac{17 - 2x}{3} = 12$

or

$$2x^2 - 17x + 36 = 0$$

**3.** Using the quadratic formula,

$$x = \frac{17 \pm \sqrt{289 - 288}}{4}$$

$$x = \frac{17 \pm 1}{4}$$

$$x = \tfrac{9}{2} \quad \text{or} \quad x = 4$$

**4.** For $x = 4$

$$y = \frac{17 - 2(4)}{3} = \frac{17 - 8}{3} = 3$$

For $x = \tfrac{9}{2}$

$$y = \frac{17 - 2(\frac{9}{2})}{3} = \frac{17 - 9}{3} = \frac{8}{3}$$

The ordered pairs are $(4,3)$ and $(\tfrac{9}{2},\tfrac{8}{3})$.
**5.** The ordered pair $(4,3)$ is a solution, since $4(3) = 12$. The ordered
pair $(\tfrac{9}{2},\tfrac{8}{3})$ is a solution, since $\tfrac{9}{2}(\tfrac{8}{3}) = \tfrac{72}{6} = 12$.
The solution set of the system is $\{(4,3), (\tfrac{9}{2},\tfrac{8}{3})\}$.

At times the solution of a system of two quadratic equations can be
reduced to that of the solution of a linear equation and one quadratic.
The system of Example 8-13 furnished one illustration of such a situation. Another important case is that of the intersection of two circles.
From the definition of a circle and the distance formula, the equation for a circle with center at point $(h,k)$ and radius $r$ is (Fig. 8-13)

$$(x - h)^2 + (y - k)^2 = r^2$$

which may be written in simple form as

$$x^2 + y^2 + ax + by + c = 0$$

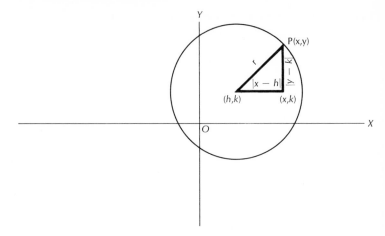

FIG. 8-13

where

$$a = {}^-2h \qquad b = {}^-2k \qquad c = h^2 + k^2 - r^2$$

The intersection of two circles will then be determined by the solution set of a system of two such equations. The addition technique can be used to reduce the problem of solving such a system to that of finding the solution set of a linear equation and one of the given equations.

**Example 8-17.**   Find the points of intersection of the two circles

$$x^2 + y^2 + 2x - y - 5 = 0$$
$$x^2 + y^2 - 2x - 9y + 15 = 0$$

Multiply the second equation by $^-1$ and add it to the first equation to get

$$4x + 8y - 20 = 0$$

or

$$x + 2y - 5 = 0$$

If this equation is solved for x in terms of y, and the resulting value is substituted in the first of the two given equations, the resultant equation is

$$y^2 - 5y + 6 = 0$$

The roots of this equation are $y = 2$ or $3$. The linear equation then pairs $x = 1$ with $y = 2$ and $x = {}^-1$ with $y = 3$. Substitution in the second of the two original equations verifies that the solution set of the system is $\{(1,2), ({}^-1,3)\}$. The two circles intersect at the two points $(1,2)$ and $({}^-1,3)$.

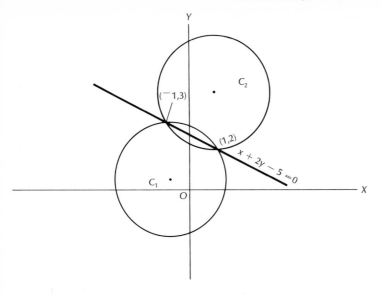

FIG. 8-14

In Fig. 8-14 the circle with $C_1$ as center represents the first equation of the system, and the circle with center $C_2$ represents the second. The linear equation $x + 2y - 5 = 0$, which results from using the addition technique to combine the two equations, is the equation of the common secant, or *radical axis*, of the two circles. It should be evident from this discussion that any two circles will intersect at two distinct points, be tangent, or not intersect at all.

**Radical axis of two circles**

Frequently the addition technique, or merely the Term Replacement Rule (see page 10), can reduce a rather complicated-looking system of equations to simple systems of equations whose solution will be solutions of the original system. The addition technique is particularly effective if it will eliminate the constant term and at the same time give a quadratic expression which is easily factored.

**Example 8-18.** Find the solution set for the system of equations

$$x^2 + xy - 2y^2 = 8$$
$$xy - y^2 = 8$$

Multiplying the second equation by ⁻1 and adding to the first one, we obtain

$$x^2 - y^2 = 0$$

which may be written in factored form as

$$(x - y)(x + y) = 0$$

Since there are no zero divisors, we have

$$x - y = 0 \quad \text{or} \quad x + y = 0$$

As a result of the previous discussion, it follows that if there exist solutions for the original system, they are to be found by pairing $y = x$ or $y = {}^-x$ with either of two given equations. Using the second equation, we get

$$xy - y^2 = 8 \qquad\qquad \text{or} \qquad xy - y^2 = 8$$
$$y = x \qquad\qquad\qquad\qquad\quad y = {}^-x$$

We substitute in the first equation to get

$$x^2 - x^2 = 8$$
$$0 = 8$$

This is an impossible condition, so this system is inconsistent. There are no solutions of the original system for which $y = x$.

We substitute in the first equation to get

$${}^-x^2 - x^2 = 8$$
$${}^-2x^2 = 8$$
$$x^2 = {}^-4$$
$$x = \pm 2i$$

From the linear equation, we get $y = \mp 2i$.

Substitution in the two original equations will establish that the solution set of system is $\{(2i, {}^-2i), ({}^-2i, 2i)\}$. The corresponding curves do not intersect.

**Example 8-19.**  Find the solution set for the system of equations

$$3x^2 - 2xy + 2y^2 = 23$$
$$2y^2 = 2xy - 4$$

In the first equation we replace the term $2y^2$ by its equivalent term $2xy - 4$ and then simplify to obtain

$$x^2 = 9$$

whence

$$x = \pm 3$$

Substitution in the second equation gives:

For $x = 3$

$$2y^2 = 6y - 4$$
$$y^2 - 3y + 2 = 0$$
$$(y - 1)(y - 2) = 0$$
$$y = 1 \text{ or } 2$$

For $x = {}^-3$

$$2y^2 = {}^-6y - 4$$
$$y^2 + 3y + 2 = 0$$
$$(y + 1)(y + 2) = 0$$
$$y = {}^-1 \text{ or } {}^-2$$

Substitution in the first equation will verify that the solution set for the system is $\{(3,1), (3,2), (^-3,^-1), (^-3.^-2)\}$. The two curves will intersect at four distinct points.

Finally, if the two equations are of the form $ax^2 + by^2 = c$, they are said to be *linear in the squares of the variables*, and are readily solved by the addition technique.

**Example 8-20.** Find the solution set of the system

$$4x^2 + 25y^2 = 100$$
$$x^2 + \phantom{2}y^2 = 16$$

We multiply the second equation by $^-4$ and add it to the first equation we get

$$21y^2 = 36$$

$$y = \pm \frac{6}{21} \sqrt{21}$$

From the second equation we get

$$x = \pm \frac{10}{7} \sqrt{7}$$

Substitution in the first equation verifies that the solution set of the system is

$$\left\{ \left(\frac{10}{7} \sqrt{7}, \frac{6}{21} \sqrt{21}\right), \left(\frac{10}{7} \sqrt{7}, \frac{^-6}{21} \sqrt{21}\right), \left(\frac{^-10}{7} \sqrt{7}, \frac{6}{21} \sqrt{21}\right), \right.$$
$$\left. \left(\frac{^-10}{7} \sqrt{7}, \frac{^-6}{21} \sqrt{21}\right) \right\}$$

The two curves, which are, respectively, a circle and an ellipse, will intersect at four distinct points.

Normally we might expect a system of one linear equation and one quadratic equation to have two solutions, real or imaginary, and a system of two quadratic equations to have four solutions, real or imaginary. However, the discussions of this section and the previous one have pointed out that this is not necessarily the case. Each system must be examined carefully on its own merits.

EXERCISES

1. Why do two equations representing concentric circles with unequal radii constitute an inconsistent system of equations?

In Exercises 2 to 13 first find a resultant quadratic equation in $x$, and then use the discriminant to determine whether the parabola and straight line represented by the equations will intersect in two distinct points, be tangent, or not intersect.

**2.** $y = x^2$
$y = 2x + 3$

**3.** $y = x^2 + 4$
$y = {}^-2x + 3$

**4.** $y = x^2 - 1$
$y = {}^-3x - 6$

**5.** $y = {}^-2x^2 + 4$
$y = 3x + 7$

**6.** $y = {}^-x^2$
$y = {}^-4x + 4$

**7.** $y = 3x^2 - 2$
$y = x + 1$

**8.**   $y = x^2 - 4x + 3$
$2x - y = 6$

**9.**   $y = 2x^2 - x + 4$
$3x + 2y = 4$

**10.**   $y = 2x^2 - 6x + 5$
$5x - 2y = 3$

**11.**   $y = {}^-x^2 - 2x + 1$
$4x + y = 2$

**12.**   $y = {}^-3x^2 + 2x - 7$
$x - 3y = 4$

**13.**   $y = x^2 + 3x + 2$
$2x + y = 3$

**14 to 25.** Construct the graphs and find the solution set over C for each system in Exercises 2 to 13.

In Exercises 26 to 31 each equation represents a circle. First find the equation of the radical axis of the two circles. Pair this equation with one of the two given equations to form an equivalent system. Use the discriminant of the resulting equation of this equivalent system to determine whether the two circles will intersect in two distinct points, be tangent, or have no points in common.

**26.** $x^2 + y^2 \qquad = 25$
$x^2 + y^2 - 16x - 12y = {}^-75$

**27.** $x^2 + y^2 \qquad = 4$
$x^2 + y^2 + 6x + 6y = {}^-14$

**28.** $x^2 + y^2 + \ 4x - 6y = 3$
$x^2 + y^2 - 12x - 2y = {}^-33$

**29.** $x^2 + y^2 - 14x - 14y = {}^-80$
$x^2 + y^2 - \ 4x - \ 4y = 0$

**30.** $x^2 + y^2 - 6x - \ 6y = {}^-13$
$x^2 + y^2 + 2x + 10y = 59$

**31.** $x^2 + y^2 \qquad = 25$
$x^2 + y^2 - 6x + 8y = 25$

**32 to 37.** Find the solution set of each system in Exercises 26 to 31.

**38 to 43.** Construct the graphs for each system of Exercises 26 to 31.
*Hint:* First write each equation in the form

$$(x - h)^2 + (y - k)^2 = r^2$$

In Exercises 44 to 51 find the solution set of each system of equations.

**44.** $x^2 + 3x + y^2 = 2$
$x^2 + 3x + y \ = 0$

**45.**   $x^2 - 2xy + 5y^2 = 20$
$3x^2 + 4xy + 5y^2 = 20$

**46.** $x^2 + y^2 = 25$
$x^2 + y^2 = 64$

**47.** $5x^2 - 6xy - 4y^2 = 7$
$3x^2 - 5xy - \ y^2 = 7$

**48.** $2x^2 + 2xy - 3y^2 = 4$
$x^2 + 3xy = 6$

**49.** $x^2 + y^2 - 2y = 4$
$(x + 2)^2 + (y - 1)^2 = 1$

**50.** $x^2 - 4xy = 45$
$xy - y^2 = {}^-6$

**51.** $x^2 + 2xy - y^2 = 7$
$x^2 - 3xy + y^2 = {}^-5$

**52.** Find two real numbers whose sum is 7 and the sum of whose squares is 25.

**53.** What relation exists between the sides of a rectangle if its area is equal to one-half the square of its diagonal?

**54.** The product, difference, and difference of the squares of two numbers are all equal. What are the numbers?

**55.** Find two real numbers whose difference is 6 and are such that the sum of their squares is 16.

**56.** Would it make any difference in the answer to Exercise 55 if the word "real" were replaced by the word "complex"?

**57.** Would it make any difference in the answer to Exercise 52 if the word "real" were replaced by the word "complex"?

**58.** When a certain two-digit number is represented by a numeral written in base four, the sum of its digits is 3. If a new numeral is constructed in base five to represent the same number the digit in the ones position will be the square of the digit in the base position of the old numeral, and the digit in the base position will be the one digit of the old numeral. What is the numeral in base four?

**59.** The sum of two numbers is equal to their product, and the difference between their reciprocals is 2. What are the two numbers?

**60.** The product of two numbers is 21 less than the sum of their squares. The difference of their squares is 9. What are the numbers?

## Invitations to Extended Study

**1.** Look up the definition of a determinant, the sum and product of two determinants, and properties for dealing with determinants.

**2.** What is Cramer's rule for solving systems of $n$ linear equations in $n$ variables? Prove that it does give the solution set of such a system.

**3.** What is the definition of the rank of a matrix in terms of the determinants of the matrix?

**4.** Prove that the definition of the rank of a matrix used in this chapter is equivalent to the definition in terms of the determinants of the matrix.

**5.** Prove that the pivotal-element technique of finding the solution set of a system of $n$ linear equations in $n$ variables is equivalent to Cramer's rule.

**Synthetic elimination**

6. What is a triangular matrix? Show how a system of $m$ linear equations in $n$ unknowns may be solved by converting the augmented matrix to an equivalent triangular form. This technique is sometimes referred to as the *method of synthetic elimination*.

7. Use the principles of determinant theory to prove the validity of the use of the check column in the pivotal-element method of solving systems of equations.

8. What is meant by a fundamental system of a given system of linear homogeneous equations? Construct three examples of different types to illustrate such a system.

9. How may systems of quadratic equations in two variables be used to extract the square roots of complex numbers?

10. What is a general technique which may be used to find the solution set of a system of two equations in two variables when each term in each equation is of the second degree?

11. When is an equation in two variables said to be *symmetrical* in the variables? What is a general method for finding the solution set of a system of two such quadratic equations?

12. What is the complete geometric interpretation of the possibilities of solution of systems of three linear equations in three variables? Summarize your answers in the context of the ranks of the coefficient and augmented matrices of the systems of equations.

# CHAPTER 9

# THE CONCEPT OF INEQUALITY

## Guidelines for Careful Study

In Chap. 5 the concept of an ordered field was introduced as one of the important structures which the field of rational numbers has in common with the field of real numbers, and which distinguishes each of them from the field of complex numbers. Underlying this concept was the still more fundamental one of inequality. The two inequality relations, *less than* and *greater than,* are relations which are neither reflexive nor symmetric. They are, however, each characterized by the transitive, additive, and, with certain significant qualifications, multiplicative properties.

*The two inequality relations*

In this chapter some of the more basic theorems concerning the use of the inequality relations will be developed. Also, the chapter will be concerned with techniques for dealing with inequalities in two variables. The following questions can be very helpful as guidelines for careful study of the chapter.

1. What is the Principle of Trichotomy for real numbers?
2. What are the basic properties of equality?
3. What is a real-number line?
4. What is a closed interval on the number line? An open interval?
5. What is meant by the absolute value of a real number?
6. What is the Term-replacement Rule?
7. What is proposition replacement?
8. What is the Substitution Rule?

9. What is the Rule of Disjunction?
10. When is the product or quotient of two real numbers positive?
11. When is the product or quotient of two real numbers negative?
12. What is the formula for a linear function?
13. What is the general equation of a straight line?
14. What is the procedure for drawing the graph of a linear function or of the equation of a straight line?
15. What is the general formula of the quadratic function?
16. What is the procedure for drawing the graph of a quadratic function?
17. What is the general equation of a circle?
18. What is the procedure for drawing the graph of the equation of a circle?
19. What is the transitive property for the inequality relations? The additive property? The multiplicative property?
20. What are strict inequalities? Mixed inequalities?
21. When are two inequalities said to be equivalent?
22. What is the solution set for an inequality in one variable?
23. What is the procedure for drawing the graph of the solution set of an inequality in one variable?
24. What is the procedure for drawing the graph of an inequality in two variables?
25. What is the graphical procedure for indicating the solution set of a system of two inequalities in two variables?
26. What is a conditional inequality?
27. What is an inconsistent inequality?
28. What is an absolute (identical) inequality?
29. When are two or more inequalities said to be consistent?

## Introduction

**Principle of Trichotomy**

The *Principle of Trichotomy* states that between any pair of real numbers *exactly one* of three relations holds. These three relations are frequently stated in one of five equivalent forms:

1. For any two real numbers $a$ and $b$ it is true that $a = b$; or there exists a positive real number $c$ such that $a = b + c$; or there exists a positive real number $d$ such that $a + d = b$.
2. For any two real numbers $a$ and $b$ it is true that $a = b$; or $a$ is greater than $b (a > b)$; or $a$ is less than $b (a < b)$.
3. For any two real numbers $a$ and $b$ it is true that $a - b = 0$; or $a - b > 0$; or $a - b < 0$.
4. For any real number $a$ it is true that $a = 0$; or $a > 0$; or $a < 0$.
5. For any real number $a$ it is true that $a = 0$; or $a > 0$; or $^-a > 0$.

The equivalence of statements 1 and 2 follows from the definition of an inequality:

**Definition 9-1. For a and b two real numbers, a > b if and only if there exists a positive real number c such that a = b + c.**

Definition of an inequality

A similar definition relates $a < b$ to $a + d = b$, where $d$ is a positive real number.

To argue the equivalence of statements 1 and 3, first note that the equivalence of $a - b = 0$ and $a = b$ is an immediate consequence of the additive property of equality and the properties of real numbers. Next, if $a - b > 0$, then it follows from the definition of the concept of "greater than" and the properties of real numbers that there exists a positive real number $c$ such that $a - b = 0 + c = c$ or $a = b + c$. Conversely, if $a = b + h$ for some positive real number $h$, then it follows from the properties of real numbers that $a - b = h = 0 + h$ or $a - b > 0$. A similar argument establishes the equivalence of $a + d = b$ for some positive real number $d$ and $a - b < 0$. Thus the equivalence of statements 1 and 3 is established.

EQUIVALENT FORMS OF EXPRESSION TABLE 9-1

| Negative Form | Positive Form |
|---|---|
| $a \neq b$<br>a is not equal to b | $a \gtreqless b$<br>a is either greater than or less than b |
| $a \not< b$<br>a is not less than b | $a \geq b$<br>a is either greater than or equal to b |
| $a \not> b$<br>a is not greater than b | $a \leq b$<br>a is either less than or equal to b |
| $a \not\leq b$<br>a is neither less than nor equal to b | $a > b$<br>a is greater than b |
| $a \not\geq b$<br>a is neither greater than nor equal to b | $a < b$<br>a is less than b |
| $a \not\lessgtr b$<br>a is neither greater than nor less than b | $a = b$<br>a is equal to b |

Equivalence of statements 2 and 4 follows from Theorem 9-2 (Exercise 29). The equivalence of statements 4 and 5 evidently depends entirely on the proof that $a < 0$ and $^-a > 0$ are equivalent inequalities,

**Equivalent inequalities**

where by *equivalent inequalities* we mean two inequalities each of which implies the other within the domain of definition of the variables. The proof of this equivalence is left as an exercise (Exercise 30). On the basis of statements 4 and 5, the positive real numbers are identified with those greater than zero and the negative real numbers with those less than zero. This completes the chain of equivalence for the five statements. As a consequence, any one of these statements will be referred to as the Principle of Trichotomy.

Statements concerning inequalities may be expressed in either of two equivalent forms, one positive in nature and the other negative. Each of these forms is denoted by a corresponding symbol. These equivalent statements, together with their respective symbols, are listed in Table 9-1 in a parallel vertical array.

While the positive manner of expression is more generally used, there are occasions in which the given conditions are best stated in the negative form.

## 9-1. INEQUALITY AND THE NUMBER LINE

It is well known that there exists a one-to-one correspondence between the set of all points of a line and the set of all real numbers. Such

**Real-number line**

a *number line* is represented in Fig. 9-1, with the interval from $^-4$ to

**FIG. 9-1**

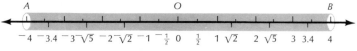

The real–number line

$^+4$ specifically indicated on it. On such a line the distance between two points is always represented by a nonnegative real number. For example, associated with each point there is a numeral which indicates the number of units of distance this particular point is from the origin, or reference point. Whether the sign of the numeral is positive or negative has nothing to do with distance; rather, it simply indicates the direction of the point with reference to the origin. For example, in Fig. 9-1 the points $A$ and $B$ are each 4 units from the point $O$, but the point $A$ is to the left of this reference point, while $B$ is to the right. In such a one-to-one correspondence it is frequently the custom to identify a point by the number with which it is associated. The origin might then be designated as the *zero point*, the point $A$ as the "point $^-4$," and the point

*B* as the "point 4." In this context the Principle of Trichotomy is subject to still another helpful interpretation:

**Trichotomy on the number line. For any two real numbers a and b exactly one of the following conditions holds:**

1. **They represent the same point (a = b).**
2. **The point represented by a is to the left of the point represented by b (a < b).**
3. **The point represented by a is to the right of the point represented by b (a > b).**

Within the described convention of the real-number line, the fact that a point *x* lies within the open interval $(^-4,4)$ may be indicated by either of the two equivalent notations $^-4 < x < 4$ or $|x| < 4$. From the definition of absolute value, the *strict inequality* $|x| < 4$ is read "the absolute, or numerical, value of *x* is strictly less than 4," and it is to be understood to imply that the variable *x* can be assigned any numerical value larger than $^-4$ but smaller than $^+4$. Thus it has exactly the same meaning as the strict inequality $^-4 < x < 4$. Similarly, the *mixed inequality* $|x| \leq 4$ is read "the absolute, or numerical, value of *x* is less than or equal to 4." It is equivalent to the mixed inequality $^-4 \leq x \leq 4$, and each indicates that the variable *x* may be assigned any value between, and including, $^-4$ and $^+4$ or, equivalently, that the point *x* is on the real number line within the closed interval $[^-4,4]$.

As is evident in the previous illustrations, the solution set over the field of real numbers of either a strict or mixed inequality is normally an infinite set. For this reason it is frequently desirable to represent the solution set of an inequality or a system of inequalities by an appropriate graph. The solution set for the strict inequalities $|x| < 4$ or $^-4 < x < 4$ is indicated in Fig. 9-1 by a shaded bar along the segment $\overline{AB}$. Since the points *A* and *B* are circled, the graph represents the open interval, which does not contain its end points. The circles would have been omitted to indicate the closed interval $|x| \leq 4$.

## 9-2. FUNDAMENTAL PROPERTIES OF INEQUALITY

By definition, the concepts $a > b$ and $a < b$ are identified with the existence of positive real numbers *c* and *d* such that $a = b + c$ and $a + d = b$, respectively. It should be immediately evident that neither of the strict inequalities is either reflexive or symmetric. The point has been made previously that both types of inequalities are characterized by transitive, additive, and multiplicative properties. These facts will be established by proving appropriate theorems for the strict inequalities. The cases for the mixed inequalities will be stated as corollaries, and the proofs will be left as exercises. Since any theorem stated for $a < b$ is also a theorem for $b > a$, it follows that the argument for a theorem stated for one of the strict inequalities is analogous to the corresponding theorem stated for the other.

**Transitive property**

**Theorem 9-1.  For real numbers a, b, and c, if a $<$ b and b $<$ c, then a $<$ c.**

*Hypothesis: a, b, c are real numbers, a $<$ b, and b $<$ c*
*Conclusion: a $<$ c*

### Proof:

| Statement | Reason |
|---|---|
| 1. $a$, $b$, and $c$ are real numbers | 1. Why? |
| 2. $a < b$ and $b < c$ | 2. Why? |
| 3. There exist positive real numbers $h$ and $k$ such that $a + h = b$ and $b + k = c$ | 3. Why? |
| 4. $(a + h) + k = c$ | 4. 3; substitution |
| 5. $a + (h + k) = (a + h) + k$ | 5. Why? |
| 6. $a + (h + k) = c$ | 6. 4, 5; transitive property of equality |
| 7. $h + k > 0$ | 7. Why? |
| 8. $a < c$ | 8. Why? |

**Corollary.  For real numbers a, b, and c, if a $\leq$ b and b $\leq$ c, then a $\leq$ c.**

**Additive property**

The additive property for inequalities is essentially the same as that for equality. This is established in the following theorem:

**Theorem 9-2.  For real numbers a and b, if a $<$ b, then a $+$ c $<$ b $+$ c for any real number c.**

*Hypothesis: a, b, and c are real numbers and a $<$ b*
*Conclusion: a $+$ c $<$ b $+$ c*

### Proof:

| Statement | Reason |
|---|---|
| 1. $a$, $b$, and $c$ are real numbers | 1. Why? |
| 2. $a < b$ | 2. Why? |
| 3. There exists a positive real number $h$ such that $a + h = b$ | 3. Why? |
| 4. $(a + h) + c = b + c$ | 4. 3; additive property of equality |
| 5. $(a + c) + h = (a + h) + c$ | 5. Why? |
| 6. $(a + c) + h = b + c$ | 6. Why? |
| 7. $a + c < b + c$ | 7. Why? |

**Corollary.**  For real numbers a and b, if a ⩽ b, then a + c ⩽ b + c for any real number c.

The analogy between the multiplicative property for equality and that for inequality is not as close as it is for addition. There are, in fact, two multiplicative properties for inequality, as established in Theorems 9-3 and 9-4.

**Theorem 9-3.**  For real numbers a, b, and c, with c > 0, if a < b, then ac < bc.    **Positive multiplier**

*Hypothesis:* a, b, and c are real numbers, a < b, and c > 0
*Conclusion:* ac < bc

## Proof:

| *Statement* | *Reason* |
|---|---|
| 1. a, b, and c are real numbers, a < b, and c > 0 | 1. Hypothesis |
| 2. There exists a real number $k > 0$ such that $a + k = b$ | 2. Definition |
| 3. $(a + k)c = bc$ | 3. Why? |
| 4. $ac + kc = bc$ | 4. Why? |
| 5. $kc > 0$ | 5. Product of positive numbers is positive |
| 6. $ac < bc$ | 6. Why? |

**Corollary.**  For real numbers a, b, and c, with c > 0, if a ⩽ b, then ac ⩽ bc.    **Negative multiplier**

**Theorem 9-4.**  For real numbers a, b, and c, with c < 0, if a < b, then ac > bc.

*Hypothesis:* a, b, and c are real numbers, a < b, and c < 0
*Conclusion:* ac > bc

## Proof:

| *Statement* | *Reason* |
|---|---|
| 1. a, b, and c are real numbers, a < b, and c < 0 | 1. Why? |
| 2. There exists a real number $k > 0$ such that $a + k = b$ | 2. Why? |
| 3. $ac + kc = bc$ | 3. Why? |
| 4. $ac = bc + {}^-kc$ | 4. Why? |
| 5. ${}^-kc > 0$ | 5. Why? |
| 6. $ac > bc$ | 6. Why? |

**Corollary.**  For real numbers a, b, and c, with c < 0, if a ⩽ b, then ac ⩾ bc.

The proofs of the following theorem and its corollary are very similar to the arguments for Theorem 9-2 and its corollary. They are left as exercises (Exercises 5 and 6).

**Theorem 9-5. For real numbers a, b, c, and d, if $a < b$ and $c < d$, then $a + c < b + d$.**

**Corollary. For real numbers a, b, c, and d, if $a \leq b$ and $c \leq d$, then $a + c \leq b + d$.**

## EXERCISES

1. Prove the corollary to Theorem 9-1.
2. Prove the corollary to Theorem 9-2.
3. Prove the corollary to Theorem 9-3.
4. Prove the corollary to Theorem 9-4.
5. Prove Theorem 9-5.
6. Prove the corollary to Theorem 9-5.
7 to 11. Restate each of the Theorems 9-1 to 9-5 for the relation "is greater than." Prove each theorem.
12 to 16. Restate the corollaries for Theorems 9-1 to 9-5 for the mixed inequality $\geq$. Prove each new corollary.
17. Prove this theorem:

    If $a$ is a real number, then $a^2 \geq 0$; furthermore, $a^2 = 0$ if and only if $a = 0$.
18. Prove that any nonzero real number and its multiplicative inverse are either both positive or both negative.
19. Construct a counterexample to disprove the conjecture that if $a < b$ and $c < d$, then $ac < bd$.
20. Given the two rational numbers $a/b$ and $c/d$, where $a$, $b$, $c$, and $d$ are integers, with $b > 0$ and $d > 0$, prove that $a/b < c/d$ if and only if $ad < bc$.
21. Prove this theorem:

    If $a$ and $b$ are any two real numbers such that $a < b$, then $a < (a + b)/2 < b$.
22. Prove this converse of Theorem 9-2:

    For real numbers $a$, $b$, and $c$, if $a + c < b + c$, then $a < b$.
23. Incorporate Theorem 9-2 and its converse, Exercise 22, into a theorem using "if and only if."
24. Construct a counterexample to show that the converse of Theorem 9-5 is not necessarily true.
25. Prove this converse of Theorem 9-3:

    For real numbers $a$, $b$, and $c$, with $c > 0$, if $ac < bc$, then $a < b$.
26. State and prove the converse of Theorem 9-4.
27. Incorporate Theorem 9-3 and its converse, Exercise 25, into a theorem using "if and only if."

28. Incorporate Theorem 9-4 and its converse, Exercise 26, into a theorem using "if and only if."
29. Use Theorem 9-2 to prove the equivalence of statements 2 and 4 on page 290.
30. Prove this theorem:
    If $a$ is a negative real number, then its additive inverse is positive, and conversely.
31. Prove this theorem:
    If the real number $a$ lies within the interval $(^-1,0)$, then $a < {}^-a^2 < a^3$.
32. Prove this theorem:
    If the real number $a$ lies within the interval $(0,1)$, then $a^3 < a^2 < a$.
33. Prove this theorem:
    If $a$ and $b$ are two positive real numbers, then $a^2 > b^2$ if and only if $a > b$.

## 9-3. INEQUALITIES IN ONE AND TWO VARIABLES

The discussion in Sec. 9-1 suggests that for $a > 0$ the inequalities $|x| < a$ and $^-a < x < a$ are equivalent forms for expressing the open interval $(^-a,a)$ of the real-number line, and $|x| \leq a$ and $^-a \leq x \leq a$ are equivalent forms for the closed interval $[^-a,a]$. Now that the basic properties of inequalities have been established, it is possible to determine similar equivalent forms for expressing any interval of the number line, whether it is open or closed. Also, it is possible to deal with one or more inequalities in a manner quite analogous to that used in working with equations. Here we shall be concerned only with inequalities in one or two variables. Such inequalities involving only first powers of the variables are called *linear inequalities*.

**Linear inequalities**

**Example 9-1.** Given the interval $2 < x < 8$, express this same interval in an equivalent form using absolute values.

The use of absolute values requires that the left end point of an interval be numerically equal but opposite in sign to the right end point. This transformation can be accomplished on the given inequality by using Theorem 9-2. First we find the average of the two end-point values: $(2 + 8)/2 = 5$. Using the additive inverse of this number, we obtain the following sequence of equivalent statements:

$2 < x < 8$
$2 < x$ and $x < 8$
$2 - 5 < x - 5$ and $x - 5 < 8 - 5$
$^-3 < x - 5$ and $x - 5 < 3$
$^-3 < x - 5 < 3$

Hence $2 < x < 8$ is equivalent to $|x - 5| < 3$.

It should be evident that the reverse process of that in the example would convert $|x - 5| < 3$ into the equivalent form $2 < x < 8$.

**Example 9-2.**   For what values of $x$ is $3x + 5 \leqslant x - 7$?

To solve an inequality of this type it is first desirable to convert it into an equivalent inequality, with the variable alone on one side. Although not necessary, it is usually desirable to collect the coefficients of the variable so that its resultant coefficient will be positive. By the corollary to Theorem 9-2, we may add $^-x - 5$ to both sides of the given mixed inequality to obtain

$$2x \leqslant {}^-12$$

To find the solution set we now multiply each side by $\frac{1}{2}$. The corollary to Theorem 9-3 gives

$$x \leqslant {}^-6$$

**Example 9-3.**   Find the solution set of the inequality $x^2 + x - 6 > 0$.

An equivalent form of the inequality is

$$(x + 3)(x - 2) > 0$$

Since the product of two real numbers is positive if and only if both numbers are of the same sign, it follows that there are two conditions either of which must be satisfied by the values of $x$ for which the inequality is true:

$$x + 3 > 0 \text{ and } x - 2 > 0 \qquad \text{or} \qquad x + 3 < 0 \text{ and } x - 2 < 0$$

These two inequalities must be satisfied for the same values of $x$. From the first inequality we obtain $x > {}^-3$, and from the second we obtain $x > 2$.

Of these two possibilities, only $x > 2$ guarantees that both inequalities are satisfied. This may be checked by using any such number, say $x = 4$, for which we have $7(2) = 14$ or $4^2 + 4 - 6 = 14$ and $14 > 0$.

These two inequalities must be satisfied for the same values of $x$. From the first inequality we obtain $x < {}^-3$, and from the second we obtain $x < 2$.

Of these two possibilities, only $x < {}^-3$ guarantees that both inequalities are satisfied. This may be checked by using any such number, say $x = {}^-6$, for which we have $^-3(^-8) = 24$ or $(-6)^2 - {}^-6 - 6 = 24$ and $24 > 0$.

The solution set is therefore given by $x > 2$ or $x < {}^-3$.

In most cases, as in the previous example, the solution set of an inequality is an infinite set. For this reason it is usually helpful to use a

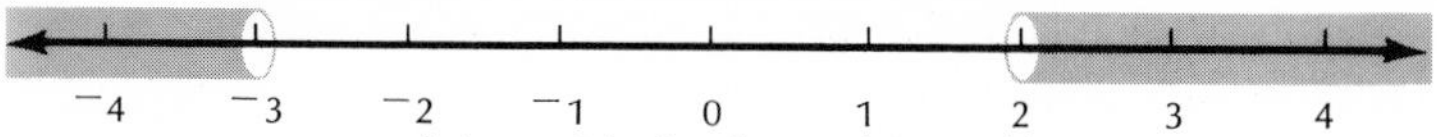

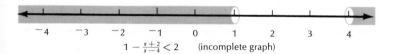

$x^2 + x - 6 > 0$    (incomplete graph)

FIG. 9-2

graph to represent the solution set. Figure 9-2 shows the graph for the solution set of the inequality of Example 9-3. The shaded portion along the number line indicates the graph.

**Example 9-4.**   Solve the inequality

$$1 - \frac{x + 2}{x - 4} < 2$$

To solve an inequality of this type it is first desirable to clear of fractions. This can be accomplished here by multiplying both sides of the inequality by $x - 4$. Theorems 9-3 and 9-4 tell us that it is necessary to consider two distinct cases, $x - 4 > 0$ and $x - 4 < 0$ (why is it not necessary to consider the case $x - 4 = 0$?).

Assume $x - 4 > 0$, or equivalently, $x > 4$. Multiply the given inequality by $x - 4$ to get, from Theorem 9-3,

$$(x - 4) - (x + 2) < 2(x - 4)$$
$$^{-}6 < 2x - 8$$
$$2 < 2x$$
$$1 < x$$

An analysis of this situation reveals that the two conditions on the variable $x$, $x > 4$ and $x > 1$, are consistent if and only if $x > 4$. This can be checked by using $x = 5$, which gives the true inequality $^{-}6 < 2$.

Assume $x - 4 < 0$, or equivalently, $x < 4$. Multiply the given inequality by $x - 4$ to get, from Theorem 9-4,

$$(x - 4) - (x + 2) > 2(x - 4)$$
$$^{-}6 > 2x - 8$$
$$2 > 2x$$
$$1 > x$$

An analysis of this situation reveals that the two conditions on the variable $x$, $x < 4$ and $x < 1$, are consistent if and only if $x < 1$. This can be checked by using $x = 0$, which gives the true inequality $\frac{3}{2} < 2$.

$1 - \frac{x+2}{x-4} < 2$    (incomplete graph)

FIG. 9-3

Figure 9-3 shows the graph of this solution set.

In Example 9-3 the inequalities $x > ^{-}3$ and $x < 2$, respectively, were seen to contribute nothing to the solution of the problem. This is because any value of $x$ which satisfies the condition $x > 2$ is automatically a value such that $x > {}^-3$. Similarly, any value of $x$ which is such that $x < {}^-3$ is automatically a value which satisfies the inequality $x < 2$. Inequalities such as $x > {}^-3$ and $x < 2$ in Example 9-3, which are automatically satisfied by the conditions imposed by other inequalities in the same context, are called *redundant inequalities*. In Example 9-4 the inequalities $x > 1$ and $x < 4$, respectively, are similarly redundant.

**Redundant inequalities**

**Example 9-5.**   Find the solution set for the inequality

$$\frac{x - 1}{x - 4} \leqslant 0$$

In a mixed inequality we first examine the strict inequality. The quotient of two real numbers is negative if and only if the two numbers are of opposite signs. Thus we have:

$$x - 1 < 0 \text{ and } x - 4 > 0 \qquad \text{or} \qquad x - 1 > 0 \text{ and } x - 4 < 0$$

This implies $x < 1$ and $x > 4$. These two inequalities impose inconsistent conditions on the variable $x$. There are no real numbers which are simultaneously less than 1 and greater than 4.

This implies $x > 1$ and $x < 4$. Thus any value of $x$ in the open interval $(1,4)$ will satisfy the inequality. This can be checked by selecting some number, say 2, from the interval. For this value we have

$$\frac{2 - 1}{2 - 4} = \frac{1}{{}^-2}$$

or

$$\frac{{}^-1}{2} < 0$$

It is evident that in the given mixed inequality the equality requires $x = 1$. Hence the solution set is the infinite set of the interval $[1,4)$. This is shown in the graph of Fig. 9-4. The fact that the right end point is

FIG. 9-4

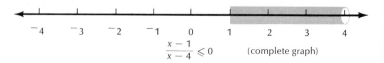

$$\frac{x - 1}{x - 4} \leqslant 0 \qquad \text{(complete graph)}$$

circled and the left one is not indicates that the interval is closed at the left end but not at the right end. An equivalent form for indicating this solution set is $1 \leqslant x < 4$.

In Example 9-5 one set of conditions on the variable was found to be inconsistent. This, of course, meant that there were no values which could be selected from the set of real numbers and assigned to the variable so that both inequalities would be satisfied simultaneously. It is also possible that there are inequalities for which there exist no real values which can be assigned to the variable or variables to make them hold. For example, from the definition of absolute value, we know that there exists no real number $a$ such that $|a| < 0$; also, since the sum of two real numbers is a real number, it follows from Exercise 17 of Sec. 9-2 that there are no real numbers $x$ and $y$ such that $(x + y)^2 < 0$ or $x^2 + y^2 < 0$. Such an inequality is called an *inconsistent inequality*. If any given inequality reduces to any such condition as these or any other relation that cannot exist within any specified field, the inequality is, for that field, an inconsistent inequality and one for which no solution exists.

**Inconsistent inequality**

**Example 9-6.**   Find the solution set for the inequality

$$\frac{4x + 1}{4} + 3 < x - 1$$

Multiplication by 4 gives

$$4x + 1 + 12 < 4x - 4$$

Addition of $^-4x$ to both sides gives

$$13 < {}^-4$$

which is an impossible relation. The given inequality is inconsistent, and there exists no solution.

A *mixed linear inequality in two variables*, $x$ and $y$, is one which can be expressed in the form $ax + by \geq c$, where each of the variables occurs to the first degree only. The graph of the solution set of such an inequality is a half plane† and its edge, or boundary line. The edge of the half plane will be the straight line which is the graph of the equality, and the half plane will be the graph of the strict inequality. The technique for graphing such inequalities consists of first plotting the graph of the linear function represented by the equality, and then shading that portion of the plane which contains the points whose coordinates satisfy the strict inequality.

**Mixed linear inequality**

**Half plane**

**Example 9-7.**   Plot the graph for the inequality $y > 2x - 1$.

† A straight line drawn in a plane will divide the plane into two *half planes*. The line is in neither half plane, but is the edge of each.

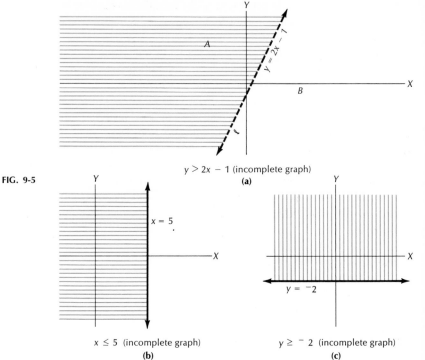

y > 2x − 1 (incomplete graph)

**FIG. 9-5**

(a)

x ≤ 5 (incomplete graph)

(b)

y ≥ ⁻2 (incomplete graph)

(c)

The straight line of Fig. 9-5a, which is the graph of the linear function $y = 2x - 1$, divides the plane into two half planes, A and B. The shaded portion A, *without the line,* is the graph of the given strict inequality. This can be checked by selecting any point within this portion of the plane and substituting its coordinates in the formula for the inequality. For example, the coordinates of the origin give the true inequality $0 > {}^-1$. The dotted line $\ell$ is excluded from the graph.

The graph of the mixed inequality $y \geqslant 2x - 1$ is the closed half plane which is the union of A and the line which is the graph of $y = 2x - 1$. In this case the line $\ell$ would be solid.

**Example 9-8.** Plot the graph for the inequality $x \leqslant 5$. The straight line of Fig. 9-5b, which is the graph of the equation $x = 5$, separates the plane into two half planes. The set of points on the line and to the left of the line represents the closed half plane which is the graph of the inequality $x \leqslant 5$.

**Example 9-9.** Plot the graph for the inequality $y \geqslant {}^-2$. The straight line of Figure 9-5c, which is the graph of the equation $y = {}^-2$, separates the plane into two half planes. The set of points on the line and above the line represents the closed half plane which is the graph of the inequality $y \geq {}^-2$.

Analogous techniques will provide the graph for any inequality involving one or two variables.

**Example 9-10.** Plot the graph of the inequality $y < x^2 - 2x - 3$.

In Fig. 9-6 the parabola is the graph of the quadratic function $y = x^2 - 2x - 3$. It divides the plane into three disjoint sets of points: those on the curve, those in the portion of the plane marked $A$, and those

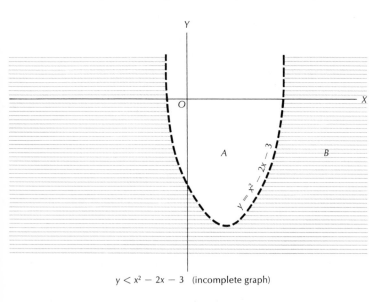

FIG. 9-6

$y < x^2 - 2x - 3$ (incomplete graph)

in the portion of the plane marked $B$, which is shaded to indicate the solution set of the given inequality. Since the given inequality is strict, the parabola is not included. The graph of the mixed inequality $y \leq x^2 - 2x - 3$ would be the union of the set of points $B$ and the set of points of the curve. The point $(5,1)$ can serve as a check point. Its coordinates give $1 < 5^2 - 2(5) - 3$, or $1 < 12$, which is a true inequality.

**Example 9-11.** The curve of Fig. 9-7 is a circle with center at the origin and radius of 5 units. Its equation is $x^2 + y^2 = 25$, and it separates the plane into three sets of points: $C$, the set of all points on the curve; $I$, the set of all points interior to the curve; and $E$, the set of all points exterior to the curve. These inequalities are represented in the figure as indicated:

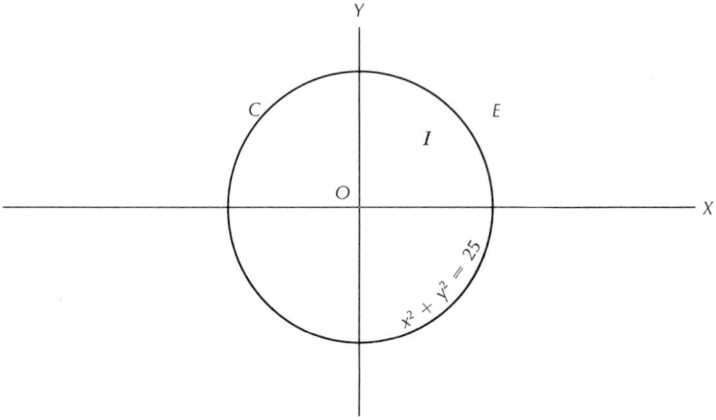

FIG. 9-7

1. $x^2 + y^2 < 25$, the set $I$
2. $x^2 + y^2 \leq 25$, the union of sets $I$ and $C$
3. $x^2 + y^2 > 25$, the set $E$
4. $x^2 + y^2 \geq 25$, the union of sets $E$ and $C$

EXERCISES

In Exercises 1 to 12 convert each statement into its equivalent interval form without using absolute values.

| | | |
|---|---|---|
| 1. $\lvert x \rvert < 2$ | 2. $\lvert a \rvert \leq 6$ | 3. $\lvert s \rvert \geq 8$ |
| 4. $\lvert y \rvert > 1$ | 5. $\lvert x - 2 \rvert > 5$ | 6. $\lvert y + 4 \rvert \geq 1$ |
| 7. $\lvert a - 1 \rvert \leq 1$ | 8. $\lvert s + 3 \rvert < 2$ | 9. $\lvert z \rvert < 0$ |
| 10. $\lvert a \rvert > 0$ | 11. $\lvert x + 2 \rvert < 0$ | 12. $\lvert y - 3 \rvert > 0$ |

In Exercises 13 to 24 convert each expressed interval into its equivalent form using absolute values.

| | | |
|---|---|---|
| 13. $^-4 \leq a \leq 4$ | 14. $3 \leq x \leq 7$ | 15. $^-5 > x > ^-9$ |
| 16. $5 > x > ^-5$ | 17. $2 \geq r \geq ^-3$ | 18. $1 < y < 9$ |
| 19. $(1,3)$ | 20. $[^-1,1]$ | 21. $[^-4,6]$ |
| 22. $(^-3,^-1)$ | 23. $(0,7)$ | 24. $[^-5,0]$ |

Solve the inequalities of Exercises 25 to 30.

25. $3x - 1 \leq 2x + 7$

26. $\dfrac{2x + 5}{6} - 1 > \dfrac{x - 3}{2}$

27. $\dfrac{9x - 1}{3} - 2 > 3x + 2$

28. $^-3x + \tfrac{1}{2} \geq 2x - \tfrac{1}{3}$

29. $x^2 - 7x + 4 < x^2 + 5x - 20$

30. $\dfrac{2x - 1}{2} + \dfrac{x + 2}{4} > \dfrac{5x + 1}{4}$

Solve the inequalities of Exercises 31 to 40 and graph each solution set.

**31.** $x^2 - 3x + 2 \geqslant 0$

**32.** $x^2 - 5x - 6 < 0$

**33.** $x^2 - 3x - 10 \leqslant 0$

**34.** $x^2 - 6x + 9 < 0$

**35.** $2x^2 + x - 6 > 0$

**36.** $6x^2 - 11x - 10 \geqslant 0$

**37.** $\dfrac{x + 1}{x - 2} > 0$

**38.** $\dfrac{x - 4}{x - 3} < 0$

**39.** $\dfrac{x + 5}{x - 1} \leqslant 0$

**40.** $\dfrac{2x - 3}{x + 6} \geqslant 0$

Graph the solution set for the inequalities of Exercises 41 to 56.

**41.** $y \geqslant 2x - 3$

**42.** $y \geqslant 3x + 2$

**43.** $2x - y > 3$

**44.** $x - \frac{1}{2}y < 2$

**45.** $3x + y \geqslant 5x + 3y - 1$

**46.** $\dfrac{2x - y - 1}{4} \leqslant \dfrac{3x + y + 1}{2}$

**47.** $y > x^2$

**48.** $y \leqslant {}^-x^2$

**49.** $y \leqslant x^2 - 2x + 3$

**50.** $y \geqslant {}^-x^2 + x + 2$

**51.** $y < {}^-2x^2 - 4x + 3$

**52.** ${}^-y < {}^-x^2 + 5x - 6$

**53.** $x^2 + y^2 < 9$

**54.** $x^2 + y^2 \leqslant 16$

**55.** $x^2 + y^2 \geqslant 36$

**56.** $x^2 + y^2 > 1$

## 9-4. ABSOLUTE (IDENTICAL) INEQUALITIES

In the previous sections we have been concerned with conditional inequalities, some of which were inconsistent. Just as $|a| < 0$ is, by definition, an inequality which does not hold for any real number, so $|a| \geqslant 0$ is true for *all* real numbers and $|a| > 0$ is true for all nonzero real numbers. Similarly, the inequalities $(x + y)^2 \geqslant 0$, $(x - y)^2 \geqslant 0$, and $x^2 + y^2 \geqslant 0$ hold for all real numbers $x$ and $y$; also, $x^2 + y^2 > 0$ holds for all nonzero real numbers $x$ and $y$. Such inequalities are called *absolute, or identical, inequalities.*

**Definition 9-2. An absolute (identical) inequality is an inequality which is true for all values within the domain of definition of the variables involved.**

Absolute inequality

The technique for establishing that a given inequality is an absolute inequality usually consists of two distinct parts. The first part might be called an *analysis.* Here we assume the given inequality to be absolute, and by using the properties of the domain of definition of the variables and the appropriate theorems, we attempt to derive equivalent inequalities. This process is continued until we recognize one of the derived inequalities as one which is absolute. This completes the analysis, and we are now ready to tackle the second part, or *proof* of the inequality. This part of the problem consists of starting with the recognized absolute inequality and reversing the steps of the analysis in an attempt to derive the desired inequality. Each step, both in the analysis and in the

Analysis and proof

proof, must be based on a valid property of the domain of definition of the variables.

**Example 9-12.**  Show that the inequality

$$\frac{9x - 1}{3} - 2 < 3x + 2$$

is true for all real values of x. In other words, prove that the given inequality is absolute over the field of real numbers.

**Analysis:**

| Statement | Reason |
|---|---|
| 1. $\dfrac{9x - 1}{3} - 2 < 3x + 2$ | 1. Assumed for all real values of x |
| 2. $(9x - 1) - 6 < 3(3x + 2)$ | 2. Theorem 9-3 |
| 3. $9x - 7 < 9x + 6$ | 3. Why? |
| 4. $^-7 < 6$ | 4. Theorem 9-2 |

Through the use of well-known properties of the field of real numbers, we have shown that if the given inequality is assumed to be absolute, it is necessary that $^-7 < 6$ for all real numbers, which is obviously true.

It is very important to recognize that *the inequality has not yet been proved to be absolute*. The question still remains. We have discovered a possible way to prove it. Since, for the inequality to be absolute, it is *necessary* that $^-7 < 6$ for all real numbers, we can investigate to see whether this known absolute inequality is *sufficient* to establish that the given inequality is also absolute.

**Proof:**

| Statement | Reason |
|---|---|
| 1. $^-7 < 6$ | 1. Known to be an absolute inequality |
| 2. $9x - 7 < 9x + 6$ | 2. Theorem 9-2 |
| 3. $(9x - 1) - 6 < 3(3x + 2)$ | 3. Why? |
| 4. $\dfrac{(9x - 1) - 6}{3} < 3x + 2$ | 4. Theorem 9-3, since $\frac{1}{3} > 0$ |
| 5. $\dfrac{9x - 1}{3} - 2 < 3x + 2$ | 5. Why? |

The proof is now complete.

**Example 9-13.** Show that the inequality

$$x^2y + xy^2 \leqslant x^3 + y^3$$

holds for all real numbers x and y such that $x + y > 0$.

**Analysis.** The domain of definition of the variables involved has been restricted to all real numbers whose sum is a positive real number. This does not mean that either x or y must be positive, but it does mean that they cannot both be negative and, furthermore, that if they are not both positive, the number with the larger absolute value must be positive.

| Statement | Reason |
|---|---|
| 1. $x^2y + xy^2 \leqslant x^3 + y^3$ | 1. Assumed to be absolute for $x + y > 0$ |
| 2. $(x + y)xy$ $\leqslant (x + y)(x^2 - xy + y^2)$ | 2. Factoring |
| 3. $xy \leqslant x^2 - xy + y^2$ | 3. Theorem 9-3, since $1/(x + y) > 0$ |
| 4. $0 \leqslant (x^2 - xy + y^2) - xy$ | 4. Theorem 9-2 |
| 5. $0 \leqslant x^2 - 2xy + y^2$ | 5. Why? |
| 6. $0 \leqslant (x - y)^2$ | 6. Why? |

Since x and y are real numbers, this last inequality is recognized as being absolute.

**Proof:**

| Statement | Reason |
|---|---|
| 1. $0 \leqslant (x - y)^2$ | 1. Known absolute inequality |
| 2. $0 \leqslant x^2 - 2xy + y^2$ | 2. Why? |
| 3. $xy \leqslant x^2 - xy + y^2$ | 3. Theorem 9-2 |
| 4. $(x + y)xy$ $\leqslant (x + y)(x^2 - xy + y^2)$ | 4. Theorem 9-3, since $x + y > 0$ |
| 5. $x^2y + xy^2 \leqslant x^3 + y^3$ | 5. Why? |

The proof is now complete.

Since each step of the analysis is reversible, the proof could be written in the more compact form shown below. The reader should supply the reasons which justify the steps of this argument.

1. $x^2y + xy^2 \leqslant x^3 + y^3 \leftrightarrow (x + y)xy \leqslant (x + y)(x^2 - xy + y^2)$
2. $(x + y)xy \leqslant (x + y)(x^2 - xy + y^2) \leftrightarrow xy \leqslant x^2 - xy + y^2$
3. $xy \leqslant x^2 - xy + y^2 \leftrightarrow 0 \leqslant x^2 - 2xy + y^2$

4. $0 \leqslant x^2 - 2xy + y^2 \leftrightarrow 0 \leqslant (x - y)^2$

5. $x^2y + xy^2 \leqslant x^3 + y^3 \leftrightarrow 0 \leqslant (x - y)^2$

## EXERCISES

In these exercises the domain of each variable is the set of all real numbers unless otherwise restricted. Prove that each inequality is absolute.

**1.** $\dfrac{2x + 3}{5} - 1 < \dfrac{2x}{5} + 2$

**2.** $\dfrac{9x + 13}{6} > \dfrac{5}{3} + \dfrac{3x - 1}{2}$

**3.** $a^2 + b^2 \geqslant 2ab$

**4.** $\dfrac{a^2 + b^2}{2} - \dfrac{10a^2}{3} \leqslant \dfrac{10b^2}{3}$

**5.** $\dfrac{a + b}{2} \geqslant \sqrt{ab}$, for $ab \geqslant 0$

**6.** $\dfrac{x^2}{y} + \dfrac{y^2}{x} \geqslant x + y$ for $x > 0$ and $y > 0$

**7.** $x^2 + y^2 + 1 > 2(xy + x - y)$

**8.** $\dfrac{2ab}{a + b} \leqslant \sqrt{ab}$ for $ab > 0$

**9.** $(x - y)^2 \geqslant x(2y - 3x)$

**10.** $s + \dfrac{1}{s} \geqslant 2$ for $s > 0$

## 9-5. SYSTEMS OF INEQUALITIES IN TWO VARIABLES

The solution set of a system of inequalities in two variables may be the empty set or a nonempty set which may or may not be finite. Most generally, it will be an infinite set and will be determined as the intersection of the respective solution sets of the different inequalities of the system. Normally, the simplest and most effective technique for obtaining and identifying this intersection set is to graph the solution set of each inequality separately and in different patterns of shading. The solution set of the system is then identified by selecting that portion of the plane which shows all patterns of shading.

**Example 9-14.**   Find the solution set of the system

$y > 2x + 3$

$y < 2x - 5$

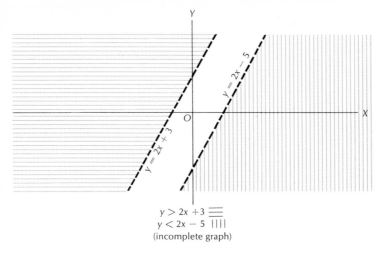

FIG. 9-8

$$y > 2x + 3 \equiv$$
$$y < 2x - 5 \;\; ||||$$
(incomplete graph)

In Fig. 9-8 the incomplete graph of this system is shown. The solution set of $y > 2x + 3$ is the half plane which is shaded by horizontal lines, and that of $y < 2x - 5$ is the half plane shaded by vertical lines. The fact that there is no portion of the plane cross-hatched, or showing the two patterns of shading overlapped, means that the solution set of the system is the empty set.

If the system had consisted of the mixed inequalities

$$y \geqslant 2x + 3$$
$$y \leqslant 2x - 5$$

the graph of each solution set would have included the respective boundaries of the half planes. This would have made no difference in the solution set of the system.

**Example 9-15.**   Find the solution set of the system

$$y \geqslant |x|$$
$$y \leqslant {}^-|x|$$

Figure 9-9 shows the graph of this system. The incomplete graph of $y \geqslant |x|$ is the graph of the line $y = |x|$, together with the portion of the plane shaded by horizontal lines. The incomplete graph of $y \leqslant {}^-|x|$ is the graph of the line $y = {}^-|x|$, together with the portion of the plane shaded by vertical lines. The origin is the only point common to both sets. The solution set is the finite set $\{(0,0)\}$.

If the system had been the two strict inequalities $y > |x|$ and $y < {}^-|x|$, what would have been the solution set?

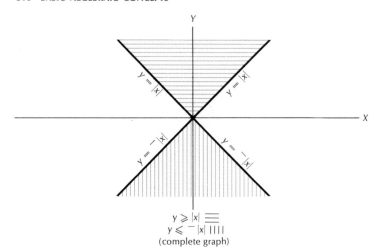

FIG. 9-9

$y \geqslant |x| \equiv$
$y \leqslant {}^-|x| |||$
(complete graph)

**Example 9-16.**   Find the solution set of the system

$y > x^2$
$y < x + 3$
$y < {}^-x + 3$

In Fig. 9-10 the complete graph of this system is shown. The solution set of $y < {}^-x + 3$ is the half plane indicated by horizontal shading, that of $y < x + 3$ is the half plane indicated by vertical shading, and that of

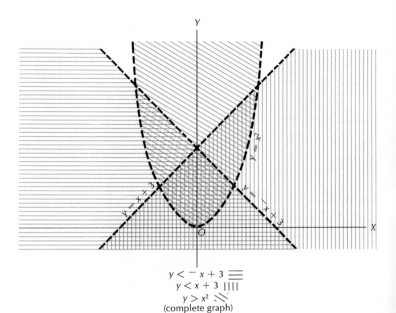

FIG. 9-10

$y < {}^-x + 3 \equiv$
$y < x + 3 \; |||$
$y > x^2$
(complete graph)

$y > x^2$ is that portion of the plane indicated by diagonal shading. That portion of the plane cross-hatched with all three patterns is the complete graph of the solution set of the given system of inequalities. The solution set of the system is an infinite set bounded by, but excluding, the two straight lines and the parabola.

In problems of this type, where more than two inequalities are involved, it is usually best to use scratch paper to determine what portion of the plane is to be shaded. After this has been done, the shading can be solid.

The most effective check in problems of this type is to select some point in the region of the determined solution set. The coordinates of this point should make each inequality a true inequality. For example, the point (0,1) is in the shaded region representing the solution set of the given system. Using these coordinates, we obtain the true inequalities $1 > 0$, $1 < 3$, and $1 < 3$ for the given inequalities.

## EXERCISES

Use the graphing technique to find the solution set of each system of inequalities. In each case state whether the graph of the solution set is complete or incomplete.

**1.** $y > x + 2$
 $y < {}^{-}x$

**2.** $y > x$
 $y < x - 1$

**3.** $y \geqslant x^2 - 3$
 $y \leqslant x$

**4.** $y \geqslant x^2$
 $y \leqslant {}^{-}x^2$

**5.** $y \geqslant x^2 + 2x - 3$
 $y < x + 2$

**6.** $y < x$
 $y > x^2 - 1$

**7.** $x^2 + y^2 \leqslant 16$
 $y \leqslant {}^{-}|x|$

**8.** $x^2 + y^2 < 9$
 $y \geqslant 2x - 2$

**9.** $y < |x - 2|$
 $y > {}^{-}|x - 2|$

**10.** $y \leqslant |x + 1|$
 $y \geqslant {}^{-}|x + 1|$

**11.** $y < x^2$
 $x^2 + y^2 < 4$

**12.** $y \leqslant \sqrt{x^2}$
 $y > 0$

**13.** $x - y \geqslant 1$
 $y - x \geqslant 1$

**14.** $2y - x \geqslant 3$
 $3x - y \leqslant 1$

**15.** $x \leqslant 0$
 $y \geqslant 0$
 $4x + y \leqslant 8$

**16.** $y - x < 2$
 $2x + y < 6$
 $y > {}^{-}x$

**17.** $x < 0$
 $y > 0$
 $2x + 3y < 6$
 $y - x < 7$

**18.** $3y - 7x \geqslant {}^{-}15$
 $2x + 3y \leqslant 15$
 $y - x \leqslant 5$
 $y + x \geqslant 2$

## 9-6. SIMPLE LINEAR PROGRAMMING

One of the most important of the many applications of inequalities

Linear programming

is to the solution of problems in *linear programming*. Such problems, which occur frequently in business and industry, require finding maximum or minimum values for linear functions in two or more variables

Constraints

within the domain of certain limits determined by prescribed *constraints*. Usually, these constraints are expressed in the form of linear inequalities involving the variables.

The discussion here will be restricted to the simplest type of problems in linear programming, namely, those involving only two vari-

Extrema

ables. We shall therefore be seeking *extrema* (maximum or minimum values) in a plane for functions of the form $ax + by + c$, where $a$, $b$, and $c$ are real numbers and $a$ and $b$ cannot be zero. The constraints will be linear inequalities involving one or both of the variables $x$ and $y$.

In Sec. 9-3 it was stressed that the graph of any strict inequality in

Open and closed half planes

two variables is an *open half plane* (a half plane without its edge), and the graph of any mixed inequality in two variables is a *closed half plane* (a half plane together with its edge). In Sec. 9-5 systems of inequalities were discussed, and the graph of such a system was found to be, in general, a geometric figure. If each inequality in a system is linear, then the boundary of the graph consists of straight lines, rays, or segments. Such a graph may be considered as the intersection of half planes. If an inequality is nonlinear, then the corresponding boundary of its graph may be curved. Any geometric set which includes each of

Closed and open sets

its bounding lines or curves is said to be *closed*, and any such set which excludes each of its bounding lines or curves is said to be *open*. Otherwise, the set is said to be neither closed nor open.

An important concept in the study of linear programming is that of convexity.

Convex set

**Definition 9-3. A set of points is said to be convex if it has the property that when any two points A and B are elements of the set, it is also true that each point of the straight-line segment AB is also an element of the set.**

Examples of sets which are convex and sets which are not convex are illustrated in Fig. 9-11. A heavy line indicates that portion of a boundary which is included in the set, and a dotted line indicates that part of a boundary which is excluded from the set. Figure 9-11a is an example of a closed set which is convex; Fig. 9-11b is an example of an open set which is convex; Fig. 9-11c is neither open nor closed, and it is an example of a set which is not convex. Whether the set is closed or open has nothing to do with convexity. It is important to note that a half plane, whether open or closed, is, by virtue of its definition, a

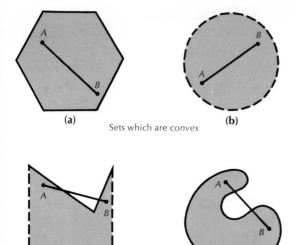

**(a)**

Sets which are *convex*

**(b)**

FIG. 9-11

**(c)**

Sets which are *not convex*

**(d)**

convex set of points. An important property of convex sets is expressed in the following theorem:

**Theorem 9-6. The intersection of two convex sets is also a convex set.**

**Proof.** Let $C_1$ and $C_2$ be the two given convex sets and $A$ and $B$ two points of the intersection set $C_1 \cap C_2$. $A$ and $B$ are therefore points common to $C_1$ and $C_2$. Since $C_1$ and $C_2$ are convex sets, it follows, by Definition 9-3, that each point of the line segment $\overline{AB}$ is a point common to $C_1$ and $C_2$. Therefore each point of $\overline{AB}$ is an element of $C_1 \cap C_2$. It follows, then, that $C_1 \cap C_2$ is a convex set.

**Corollary. The intersection of two half planes (whether closed or open) is a convex set.**

**Definition 9-4. The intersection of a finite number of closed half planes is called a convex polygonal set of points.**

*Convex polygonal set*

The intersection of closed half planes may be an infinite region (not entirely enclosed by boundary lines as in Fig. 9-12) or a finite region† (entirely enclosed by boundary lines, as in Fig. 9-13). When this intersection is a finite region, its boundary will be a convex polygon whose vertices will be points of intersection of pairs of edges of the intersect-

† The fact that a finite region of the plane is entirely enclosed by boundary lines does not imply that it contains only a finite number of points.

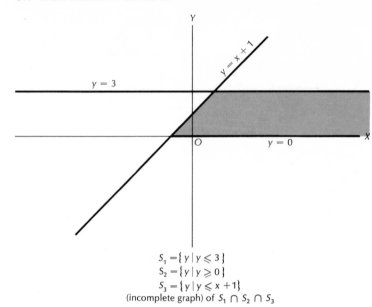

FIG. 9-12

$$S_1 = \{\, y \mid y \leqslant 3 \,\}$$
$$S_2 = \{\, y \mid y \geqslant 0 \,\}$$
$$S_3 = \{\, y \mid y \leqslant x + 1 \,\}$$
(incomplete graph) of $S_1 \cap S_2 \cap S_3$

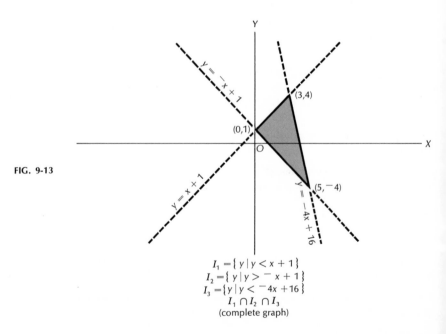

FIG. 9-13

$$I_1 = \{\, y \mid y < x + 1 \,\}$$
$$I_2 = \{\, y \mid y > {}^- x + 1 \,\}$$
$$I_3 = \{\, y \mid y < {}^- 4x + 16 \,\}$$
$$I_1 \cap I_2 \cap I_3$$
(complete graph)

ing half planes. These vertices will be called the *corner points* of the finite convex polygonal set of points. An important property of such sets is stated in Theorem 9-7, which we shall accept without proof here.†

**Theorem 9-7. If the function represented by ax + by + c, where a, b, and c are real numbers and a and b not both zero, is defined over a finite convex polygonal set, then it takes on its maximum and minimum values at the corner points of the set.**

This theorem provides the needed authority and suggests the procedural outline for attacking linear programming problems. The suggested pattern of attack for two-variable problems, the type of concern in this text, may be outlined in these steps:

1. Determine the constraints of the problem and express them as inequalities involving either one or both of the variables.
2. Simplify the system and discard any redundant inequalities found to exist. Summarize the constraints.
3. Graph the convex polygonal set which is the intersection of the half planes determined by the several inequalities.
4. Find the corner points of this intersection set.
5. Construct the linear function to be maximized or minimized.
6. Test the coordinates of each of the corner points and select those which provide the desired solution of the problem.

**Example 9-17.** A candy maker has contracted to provide a dealer with a mixed order of 200 lb of candy per week. Each order is to have a mixture of cream centers, hard centers, and nut centers. There must be at least 60 lb of cream centers and at least 40 lb of nut centers. No order is to contain more than 120 lb of either cream centers or hard centers. His profit is 25 cents/lb on nut centers, 40 cents/lb on hard centers, and 50 cents/lb on cream centers. How much of each kind of candy should he produce for maximum profit? What would this profit be per 200 lb?

**1.** Let

$$x = \text{lb of cream centers}$$
$$y = \text{lb of hard centers}$$
$$200 - x - y = \text{lb of nut centers}$$

Since negative values are inadmissible for indicating the number of

† For a proof of this theorem see John G. Kemeny, J. Laurie Snell, and Gerald L. Thompson, "Finite Mathematics," pp. 254–257, Prentice-Hall, Inc., Englewood Cliffs, N.J., 1957.

pounds of each kind of candy to be produced, the following constraints are identifiable.

$$x \geq 0 \qquad\qquad x \geq 60 \qquad x \leq 120$$
$$y \geq 0 \qquad\qquad y \leq 120$$
$$200 - x - y \geq 0 \qquad 200 - x - y \geq 40$$

**2.** Careful examination of $200 - x - y \geq 40$ and its equivalent form $x + y \leq 160$, together with $x \geq 60$, identifies $200 - x - y \geq 0$, $x \geq 0$, and $y \leq 120$ as redundant inequalities to be discarded. To summarize the constraints,

$$x \geq 60$$
$$x \leq 120$$
$$y \geq 0$$
$$x + y \leq 160$$

**3.** Figure 9-14 is the graph of the intersection of the convex polygonal sets determined by the given inequalities.

**FIG. 9-14**

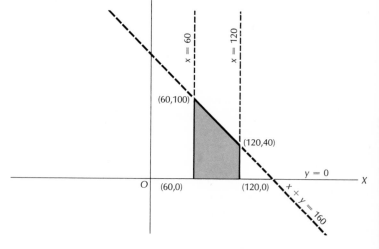

**4.** The corner points of the intersection set are (60,0), (120,0), (60,100), and (120,40).

**5.** If $p(x,y)$ represents the profit function, then

$$p(x,y) = 0.25(200 - x - y) + 0.40y + 0.50x$$

or

$$p(x,y) = 0.25x + 0.15y + 50$$

**6.** The values of $p(x,y)$ at each corner point are, in dollars:

(60,0):    $0.25(60) + 0.15(0) + 50 = 65$
(120,0):   $0.25(120) + 0.15(0) + 50 = 80$
(60,100):  $0.25(60) + 0.15(100) + 50 = 80$
(120,40):  $0.25(120) + 0.15(40) + 50 = 86$

For a maximum profit of $86 per 200 lb of candy the candy maker should produce 120 lb of cream centers, 40 lb of hard centers, and 40 lb of nut centers.

## EXERCISES

1. An automobile dealer wishes to stock new cars in three different price ranges. His lot capacity for storing and displaying cars limits to 80 the number of cars he can accommodate. He has already contracted for the sale of five cars in the highest price range $H$, and from past experience, he has limited his expectation of sales in this area to no more than 15 cars. He has also established 35 cars as the maximum sales potential in the medium price range $M$, and 40 cars as the minimum number to be sold in the lowest price range $L$. He estimates his profit per car to be $1,800 in price range $H$, $1,200 in price range $M$, and $600 in price range $L$. What combinations of sales will give him his maximum profit on 80 cars? What will this profit be?

2. A manufacturer produces two models, $M_1$ and $M_2$, of a certain type of tool. In the manufacture of each model two different machines, $A$ and $B$, are used. Neither machine may be operated more than 12 hr each day. On model $M_1$ machine $A$ is used for 1 hr and machine $B$ is used for $1\frac{1}{2}$ hr. On model $M_2$ machine $A$ is used for 2 hr and machine $B$ is used for 1 hr. The profit on model $M_1$ is $3.50 per unit, and on model $M_2$ it is $2 per unit. How many units of each model should be produced per day for the maximum profit?

3. Would it have made any difference in the manufacturing pattern of Exercise 2 if the profit had been  $2.00 on model $M_1$ and $3.50 on model $M_2$?

4. A manufacturer produces two grades, $G_1$ and $G_2$, of a certain type of product. The table shows the weekly use for each machine in hours per unit of each grade and the maximum number of hours.

|       | $G_1$ | $G_2$ | Max |
|-------|-------|-------|-----|
| $M_1$ | 2     | 1     | 32  |
| $M_2$ | 2     | 3     | 40  |
| $M_3$ | 1     | 2     | 26  |

The manufacturer estimates his profit to be $15 per unit of grade $G_1$ and $25 per unit of grade $G_2$. How many units of each grade should be produced per week for a maximum profit?

5. A change in the cost of materials occurred in such a way that the producer of Exercise 4 revised his estimate of profit to $20 per unit of each grade. Did this necessitate a revision in the number of units of each grade to be produced for a maximum profit?

6. A gardener wants to mix three ingredients, $A$, $B$, and $C$, for use in a fertilizer. Ingredient $A$ contains 6 percent nitrogen, 7 percent phosphoric acid, and 10 percent calcium; ingredient $B$ contains 9 percent nitrogen, 4 percent phosphoric acid, and 7 percent calcium; ingredient $C$ contains 7 percent nitrogen, 8 percent phosphoric acid, and 5 percent calcium. He desires that the fertilizer contain at most 7.5 percent nitrogen, 6.7 percent phosphoric acid, and 6.7 percent calcium. The cost per pound of each ingredient is $A$, 20 cents; $B$, 12 cents; and $C$, 10 cents. How much of each type of ingredient should the gardener use to mix 100 lb of fertilizer at minimum cost? What would be the cost per pound?

7. What would be the most expensive mixture the gardener of Exercise 6 might use for his fertilizer? What would be the cost per pound?

8. A farmer, designing a plan for his newly purchased farm of 500 acres, wished to allot some acreage to pasture land, some to timber, and some to crops. From the lay of the land he has determined minimum and maximum acreage according to the information given in the table below. The estimated gross profit per acre from each type of land is pasture $100, timber $150, and crops $50. What plan should he follow to realize the maximum gross profit?

| Land use | Minimum | Maximum |
|----------|---------|---------|
| Pasture  | 125     | 200     |
| Timber   | 75      | 175     |
| Crops    | 150     | No maximum determined |

9. In preparing a mixture of two types of basic food materials, $F_1$ and $F_2$, the desire is to satisfy certain minimum food requirements at a minimum cost. The known food-value content per pound of $F_1$ is 275 g of protein, 1.5 g of fat, and 250 g of carbohydrates. The known food value content of $F_2$ is 100 g of protein, 5 g of fat, and 500 g of

carbohydrates. The desired minimum requirements per batch of the mixture are 1,375 g of protein, 30 g of fat, and 3,500 g of carbohydrates. The price per pound of $F_1$ is 75 cents, and for $F_2$ it is 50 cents. How many pounds of each type of foodstuff should be used to meet the specified minimum-food-value requirements at the lowest price per pound for the mixture? The minimum price?

## Invitations to Extended Study

**1.** For $a$, $b$, $c$, and $d$ real numbers and $bd > 0$, prove that

$$\frac{a+b}{b} \geq \frac{c+d}{d}$$

if and only if $a/b \geq c/d$.

**2.** For $a$ and $b$ any real numbers, prove that

$$\frac{a+b}{2} \leq \left(\frac{a^2+b^2}{2}\right)^{1/2}$$

Under what conditions does the equality hold?

**3.** For $a$ and $b$ any real numbers, prove that

$$ab \leq \left(\frac{a+b}{2}\right)^2$$

**4.** Prove for $x$ and $y$ any two real numbers that

(a) if $x > y > 0$, then $1/x < 1/y$;
(b) if $x < y < 0$, then $1/x > 1/y$.

**5.** If for any two positive real numbers $a$ and $b$ the *arithmetic mean* is $A = (a+b)/2$, the *geometric mean* is $G = \sqrt{ab}$, and the harmonic mean is $H = 2ab/(a+b)$, prove that $A > G > H$.

**6.** Prove the Cauchy-Schwartz inequality for any four real numbers $a$, $b$, $c$, and $d$:

$$(ac + bd)^2 \leq (a^2 + b^2)(c^2 + d^2)$$

**7.** If $\alpha$ (alpha) and $\beta$ (beta) are the two complex numbers $\alpha = a + bi$ and $\beta = c + di$, prove the triangle property for complex numbers:

$$|\,|\alpha| - |\beta|\,| \leq |\alpha \pm \beta| \leq |\alpha| + |\beta|$$

*Hint:* See Sec. 5-5.

**8.** Prove that if $x$ and $a$ are real numbers and $|x+a| + |x-a| < 2$, then $^-1 < x < 1$.

9. Sketch the graph of the inequality $|x + y| \leq 1$, where $x$ and $y$ are real numbers.

10. Sketch the graph of the inequality $|x - y| \leq 1$, where $x$ and $y$ are real numbers and $^-2 \leq x \leq 2$.

11. Prove Theorem 9-7.

12. Pursue the extension of linear programming to three-variable problems.

# BIBLIOGRAPHY

**Allendoerfer, Carl B., and Cletus O. Oakley:** "Fundamentals of College Algebra," McGraw-Hill Book Company, New York, 1967.

**Banks, J. Houston, and F. Lynwood Wren:** "Elements of Algebra," Allyn and Bacon, Inc., Boston, 1962.

**Beaumont, Ross A.:** "Linear Algebra," Harcourt, Brace & World, Inc., New York, 1965.

—— **and Richard S. Pierce:** "The Algebraic Foundations of Mathematics," Addison-Wesley Publishing Company, Inc., Reading, Mass., 1963.

**Beckenbach, Edwin, and Richard Bellman:** "An Introduction to Inequalities," Random House, Inc., New York, 1961.

**Bell, E. T.:** "Development of Mathematics," McGraw-Hill Book Company, New York, 1940.

**Bellman, Richard:** On the Concepts of a Problem and Problem-solving, *The American Mathematical Monthly,* **67:** 119–134 (1960).

**Burton, David M.:** "An Introduction to Abstract Mathematical Systems," Addison-Wesley Publishing Company, Inc., Reading, Mass., 1965.

**Byrkit, Donald R.:** Linear Indeterminate Equations, *School Science and Mathematics,* **60:** 627–631 (1960).

**Commission on Mathematics:** "Report of the Commission on Mathematics," Appendices, College Entrance Examination Board, New York, 1959.

**Diamond, Louis E.:** Introduction to Complex Numbers, *Mathematics Magazine,* **30:** 233–249 (1957).

**Eves, Howard:** "An Introduction to the History of Mathematics," rev. ed., Holt, Rinehart and Winston, Inc., New York, 1964.

—— **and Carroll V. Newsom:** "An Introduction to the Foundations and Fundamental Concepts of Mathematics," rev. ed., pp. 128–165, 196–238, Holt, Rinehart and Winston, Inc., New York, 1965.

**Exner, Robert M., and Myron Rosskopf:** "Logic in Elementary Mathematics," McGraw-Hill Book Company, New York, 1959.

**Fehr, Howard F., and Thomas J. Hill:** "Contemporary Mathematics for Elementary Teachers," D. C. Heath and Company, Boston, 1966.

**Hall, H. S., and S. R. Knight:** "Higher Algebra," Macmillan & Co., Ltd., London, 1950.

**Hammel, Arnold:** Verifying the Associative Property for Finite Groups, *The Mathematics Teacher,* **61:** 136–139 (1968).

**Johnson, Richard E.:** "Vector Algebra," Prindle, Weber, & Schmidt, Inc., Boston, 1966.

**Jones, Burton W.:** Miniature Number Systems, *The Mathematics Teacher,* **51:** 226–231 (1958).

**Jones, Phillip S.:** Complex Numbers: An Example of Recurring Themes in the Development of Mathematics, *The Mathematics Teacher,* **47:** 106–114, 257–263, 340–345 (1954).

**Kane, Robert B.:** Linear Programming, An Aid to Decision Making, *The Mathematics Teacher,* **53:** 177–179 (1960).

**Keedy, Mervin L.:** "Number Systems: A Modern Introduction," Addison-Wesley Publishing Company, Reading, Mass., 1965.

**Kelley, John L.:** "Algebra: A Modern Introduction," D. Van Nostrand Company, Inc., Princeton, N.J., 1965.

**Kinsolving, May Risch:** "Set Theory and the Number Systems," International Textbook Company, Scranton, Pa., 1967.

**Levi, Howard:** "Elements of Algebra," Chelsea Publishing Company, New York, 1956.

**Lichtenberg, Donovan, and Marilyn Zweng:** Linear Programming for First-year Algebra, *The Mathematics Teacher,* **53:** 171–176 (1960).

**MacLane, Saunders, and Garrett Birkhoff:** "Algebra," The Macmillan Company, New York, 1967.

**McGaughey, A. W.:** The Imaginary Number Problem, *The American Mathematical Monthly,* **64:** 193–194 (1957).

**Maskewitch, D.:** On the Equation $ax + by = c$, *School Science and Mathematics,* **60:** 288–290 (1960).

**Mostow, George D., Joseph H. Sampson, and Jean-Pierre Meyer:** "Fundamental Structures of Algebra," McGraw-Hill Book Company, New York, 1963.

**National Council of Teachers of Mathematics:** "Twenty-third Yearbook" (1957); "Twenty-fourth Yearbook" (1959); "Twenty-eighth Yearbook" (1963); "Twenty-ninth Yearbook" (1964), Washington, D.C.

**Newsom, Carroll V.:** "Mathematical Discourses: The Heart of Mathematical Science," Prentice-Hall, Inc., Englewood Cliffs, N.J., 1964.

**Ohmer, Merlin M., Clayton V. Aucoin, and Marion J. Cortez:** "Elementary Contemporary Mathematics," Blaisdell Publishing Company, New York, 1964.

**Parker, Francis D.:** "The Structure of Number Systems," Prentice-Hall, Inc., Englewood Cliffs, N.J. 1966.

**Pedley, Arthur H.:** Complex Numbers and Vectors in High School Mathematics, *The Mathematics Teacher,* **53:** 198–201 (1960).

**Peterson, John A., and Joseph Hashisaki:** "Theory of Arithmetic," 2d ed., John Wiley & Sons, Inc., New York, 1967.

**Polya, G.:** "How to Solve It," 2d ed., Anchor Books, Doubleday & Company, Inc., Garden City, N.Y., 1957.

———: "Mathematical Discovery," vols. I (1962) and II (1965), John Wiley & Sons, Inc. New York.

**Sanders, Paul:** "Elementary Mathematics: a Logical Approach," International Textbook Company, Scranton, Pa., 1964.

**School Mathematics Study Group:** "Introduction to Matrix Algebra," rev. ed., Yale University Press, New Haven, Conn., 1961.

**Selby, Samuel M., and Leonard Sweet:** "Sets-Relations-Functions," McGraw-Hill Book Company, New York, 1963.

**Tomber, Marvin L.:** "Introduction to Contemporary Algebra," Prentice-Hall, Inc., Englewood Cliffs, N.J., 1967.

**Ward, Morgan, and Clarence F. Hardgrove:** "Modern Elementary Mathematics," Addison-Wesley Publishing Company, Inc., Reading, Mass., 1964.

**Whitesitt, J. Eldon:** "Principles of Modern Algebra," Addison-Wesley Publishing Company, Inc., Reading, Mass., 1964.

**Wren, F. Lynwood:** "Basic Mathematical Concepts," McGraw-Hill Book Company, New York, 1965.

# GLOSSARY

The notation listed in Part 1 is assumed known from previous background but is included for reference. The page number refers to the first significant usage of this notation. The Greek alphabet is also included in Part 1.

**Part 1**

| Symbol | Page | Interpretation | |
|---|---|---|---|
| $s \in S$ | 11 | $s$ is an element of the set $S$ | **Set notation** |
| $s \notin S$ | 31 | $s$ is not an element of the set $S$ | |
| $\{s_1, s_2, s_3, \ldots\}$ | 8 | The set whose elements are $s_1$, $s_2$, $s_3$, and so on | |
| $\{n \mid n$ is a natural number$\}$ | 10 | The set of all $n$ such that $n$ is a natural number | |
| $\phi$ | 13 | The null set | |
| $S = T$ | 12 | The sets $S$ and $T$ consist of the same elements | |
| $S \subseteq T$ | 13 | $S$ is a subset of $T$ | |
| $S \subset T$ | 9 | $S$ is a proper subset of $T$ | |
| $S \cup T$ | 30 | The union of sets $S$ and $T$ | |
| $S \cap T$ | 34 | The intersection of sets $S$ and $T$ | |
| $a = b$ | 8, 291 | $a$ is the same as $b$ | **Number relations** |
| $a \neq b$ | 12, 291 | $a$ is not the same as $b$ | |
| $a < b$ | 8, 291 | $a$ is less than $b$ | |
| $a \leq b$ | 14, 291 | $a$ is less than or equal to $b$ | |
| $a > b$ | 8, 291 | $a$ is greater than $b$ | |
| $a \geq b$ | 14, 291 | $a$ is greater than or equal to $b$ | |
| $|x|$ | 144n | The absolute value of $x$ | **Miscellaneous** |
| $\overline{PR}$ | 170 | The line segment connecting points $P$ and $R$ | |

# The Greek Alphabet

| Letters | Names | Letters | Names |
|---------|-------|---------|-------|
| $\alpha$ | Alpha | $\nu$ | Nu |
| $\beta$ | Beta | $\xi$ | Xi |
| $\gamma$ | Gamma | $o$ | Omicron |
| $\delta$ | Delta | $\pi$ | Pi |
| $\epsilon$ | Epsilon | $\rho$ | Rho |
| $\zeta$ | Zeta | $\sigma$ | Sigma |
| $\eta$ | Eta | $\tau$ | Tau |
| $\theta$ | Theta | $\upsilon$ | Upsilon |
| $\iota$ | Iota | $\phi$ | Phi |
| $\kappa$ | Kappa | $\chi$ | Chi |
| $\lambda$ | Lambda | $\psi$ | Psi |
| $\mu$ | Mu | $\omega$ | Omega |

## Part 2

| | Symbol | Page | Interpretation |
|--|--------|------|----------------|
| **Specific sets** | $N$ | 8 | The set of natural numbers |
| | $Z$ | 45 | The set of integers |
| | $Q$ | 117 | The set of rational numbers |
| | $R$ | 128 | The set of real numbers |
| | $C$ | 142 | The set of complex numbers |
| | $R_n$ | 135 | The set of all $n$-tuples of real numbers |
| | $P_n$ | 211 | Set of all polynomials of degree $n$ or less over a field |
| | $Z_p$ | 110 | Set of integers reduced, modulo $p$ |
| | $P$ | 211 | Set of all polynomials over a field |
| **Logical notation** | $p \rightarrow q$ | 12 | If $p$, then $q$ |
| | $p$ or $q$ | 12 | Either $p$ or $q$ |
| | $p$ and $q$ | 12 | Both $p$ and $q$ |
| | not-$p$ | 12 | Negation of $p$ |
| | $p \leftrightarrow q$ | 25 | $p$ if and only if $q$ |
| **Systems** | $<G,*>$ | 64 | The group with set $G$ and binary operation $*$ |
| | $<Z,+,\cdot>$ | 94 | The ring with set $Z$ and binary operations $+$ and $\cdot$ |
| | $<F,*,\circ>$ | 112 | The field with set $F$ and binary operations $*$ and $\circ$ |

| | | | |
|---|---|---|---|
| $a \mid b$ | 35 | a divides b | **Operations and relations** |
| $a * b$ | 63 | Binary operation, a star b | |
| $a \circ b$ | 65 | Binary operation, a circle b | |
| $ab$ | 66 | Product of a and b | |
| $a \, \Delta \, b$ | 113 | a del b | |
| $S \, \# \, T$ | 77 | The mapping $S$ followed by the mapping $T$ | |
| $a * \boldsymbol{\alpha}$ | 133 | The product of scalar a and vector $\boldsymbol{\alpha}$ | |
| $\ominus$ (circle equals) | 98, 116 | Circle equals | |
| $\oplus$ (circle not equal) | 101 | Circle not equal | |
| $\oplus$ | 98, 108, 117,132 | Circle plus | |
| $\ominus$ | 123 | Circle minus | |
| $\odot$ | 100, 108, 120, 154 | Circle times | |
| $\oslash$ | 122 | Circle divides | |
| $\oslash$ (circle less than) | 123 | Circle less than | |
| $\nless$ | 15, 291 | Is not less than | |
| $\nleq$ | 291 | Is not less than or equal to | |
| $\ngtr$ | 291 | Is not greater than | |
| $\ngeq$ | 291 | Is not greater than or equal to | |
| $\begin{pmatrix} a & b & c \\ d & e & f \end{pmatrix}$ | 77, 78 | Mapping which carries a to d, b to e, and c to f | **Matrices** |
| $(a_{ij})$ | 97 | The matrix of $m$ rows and $n$ columns | |
| $a_{ij}$ | 97 | Element in the $i$th row and $j$th column of $(a_{ij})$ | |
| $(0)$ | 98 | Zero matrix | |
| $E$ | 101 | Identity matrix | |
| $\alpha, \beta, \gamma, \delta, \epsilon, \iota$ | 133 | Symbols for vectors | **Vectors** |
| $\mathbf{V}(F)$ | 133 | Vector space $\mathbf{V}$ over field $F$ | |
| $\lvert \boldsymbol{\alpha} \rvert$ | 136 | Length of vector $\boldsymbol{\alpha}$ | |
| $\mathbf{I}$ | 142 | Ordered pair (1,0) | |
| $\mathbf{i}$ | 142 | Ordered pair (0,1) | |
| $a + b\mathbf{i}$ | 148 | The complex number $a\mathbf{I} + b\mathbf{i}$ | |
| $y = x\phi$ | 83 | $y$ is the image of $x$ under the mapping $\phi$ | **Functions and mappings** |
| $y = f(x)$ | 83n | $y$ is the value of the function $f$ at $x$ | |
| $f\colon X \rightarrow Y$ | 163 | $f$ is a function from $X$ into $Y$. | |

| | | | |
|---|---|---:|---|
| | $f(x) = c$ | 169 | Constant function |
| | $f(x) = mx + k$ | | |
| | $\quad (m \neq 0)$ | 171 | Linear function |
| | $ax + by + c = 0$ | | |
| | $\quad$ (a and b not both | | |
| | $\quad$ zero) | 173 | General equation of straight line |
| | $f(x) = ax^2 + bx + c$ | | |
| | $\quad (a \neq 0)$ | 178 | Quadratic function |
| | $x = \dfrac{-b \pm \sqrt{b^2 - 4ac}}{2a}$ | 185 | Zeros of quadratic function |
| | $b^2 - 4ac$ | 186 | Discriminant of quadratic function |
| | $y = \dfrac{1}{x}$ | 192 | Reciprocal function |
| | $p(x)$ | 225 | Polynomial function in $x$ |
| | $(a,b)$ | 63n | Ordered pair |
| **Intervals** | $(a,b)$ | 164, 297 | Open interval $a < x < b$ |
| | $[a,b]$ | 164, 297 | Closed interval $a \leqslant x \leqslant b$ |
| | $[a,b)$ | 164 | The interval $a \leqslant x < b$ |
| | $(a,b]$ | 165 | The interval $a < x \leqslant b$ |
| **Miscellaneous** | $a \equiv b \pmod{m}$ | 6 | $a$ is congruent to $b$ modulo $m$ |
| | $a\ R\ b$ | 159 | $a$ is $R$-related to $b$ |
| | $P_S$ | 13 | The power set of $S$ |
| | $S_n$ | 88 | The symmetric group on $n$ objects |
| | $\sqrt{\phantom{x}}$ | 127 | Principal square root |
| | $\dfrac{a}{b}$ | 116 | The equivalence class containing all ordered pairs equivalent to $(a,b)$ |
| | $\dfrac{{}^{-}a}{b}$ | 118 | The additive inverse of $\dfrac{a}{b}$ |
| | $P \times Q$ | 159 | Cartesian product of sets $P$ and $Q$ |
| | $S'$ | 160 | The inverse relation of a relation $S$ |
| | $n!$ | 84n | $n$-factorial |
| | $a'$ | 64 | Inverse of $a$ |
| | ${}^{-}a$ | 68 | Additive inverse of $a$ |
| | $a^{-1}, \dfrac{1}{a}$ | 68 | Multiplicative inverse of $a$ |

# CHAPTER 1

## Section 1-2. Page 7

**7.** 44 years    **9.** *a, f*

## Section 1-3. Page 14

**1.** Term: *a, b, c, e, g, m, n*
Simple proposition: *d, f, h, i, k, l*
**7.** $a \in N$ and $b \in N \rightarrow a + b = b + a$
**9.** $a \in N$ and $b \in N$ and $c \in N$ and $a < b \rightarrow a + c < b + c$
**11.** $a \in N$ and $b \in N$ and $c \in N$ and $a < b \rightarrow ac < bc$

# CHAPTER 2

## Introduction. Page 22

**1.** An equality relation is reflexive, symmetric, and transitive.
**3.** *e*

## Section 2-1. Page 34

**1.** (a) Either two integers are the same or one is larger than the other.
(b) If two integers are the same then their respective products by a third integer are the same.
(c) If each of two pairs of integers are the same, then their respective products are the same.
(d) If one integer is smaller than a second integer, and each is added to a third integer, then the first sum is smaller than the second sum.

329

3. (a) $ab = 0$    (b) $a = 5$    (c) $ac = bc$
   (d) $a + c \neq b + c$    (e) $a = b \leftrightarrow a + c = b + c$
   (f) $a = b$ and $b < c$    (g) $b \leq a$
   (h) $a > b$ or $b > a$    (i) $a \neq b$ and $b \neq a$
   (j) $ac = bc$ and $a \neq b$    (k) not-($ac = bc \rightarrow c = 0$)

5. (a) $a < c$    (b) $ab \neq ac$    (c) $a = b$
   (d) $a^2 < b^2$    (e) not-($c < 0$)    (f) $c = 6$
   (g) $a = 5$    (h) $a = 0$ or $b = 0$    (i) $a|bc$

7. (a) No
   (b) If a student has an A paper, then that student is sitting on the front row.
   (c) The student has an A paper.
   (d) The student sits on the front row.

11. Sufficient. If the number $n$ is divisible by 6, then it is divisible by 3.

13. Necessary and sufficient. The exponent $n$ is a positive even integer if and only if the binomial $x^n - y^n$ is divisible by $x + y$.

15. Necessary and sufficient. The integer $n$ is divisible by 9 if and only if the sum of its digits is divisible by 9.

16. $c, e$

## Section 2-2. Page 44

3. If $a$ and $b$ are real numbers, and they are both positive, then $\sqrt{ab} = \sqrt{a} \sqrt{b}$.

## Section 2-3. Page 59

1. Morning flight, 516 mph; afternoon flight, 528 mph
3. 2 to 1
5. Electricity, \$12.42; water, \$8.28
7. \$8,604,700,000
9. \$629,200,000

# CHAPTER 3

## Section 3-1. Page 69

1. (a) $c$    (b) Yes    (c) Yes    (d) Yes    (e) Yes    (f) G-2
3. (a) Yes    (b) G-3
   (c) Since $b * b = d \notin G$, G-1 fails. Since $b$ has no inverse, G-4 fails.
5. (a) No    (b) Only G-1 holds.

**7.** Not a group. G-2 fails.

**9.** $\langle G, * \rangle$ is an abelian group, of order 4, with no generator.

**11.** (c), (d), and (f) are the only groups; each is abelian and infinite.

**13.** (a) Among others, let $a = s$ and $b = t$.

**17.** (a) $u$    (b) $s$    (c) $u$    (d) $s$    (e) $u$    (f) $s$

## Section 3-2. Page 81

**1.** With the operation #, each of the following sets form a subgroup: $\{R\}$, $\{R,S\}$, $\{R,T\}$, $\{R,U\}$, $\{R,V,W\}$, and $\{R,S,T,U,V,W\}$.

**3.** Is not a rotation but is a reflection in the diagonal joining vertices 1 and 3.

**7.**
$$E = \begin{pmatrix} 1 & 2 & 3 & 4 \\ 1 & 4 & 3 & 2 \end{pmatrix} \qquad F = \begin{pmatrix} 1 & 2 & 3 & 4 \\ 3 & 2 & 1 & 4 \end{pmatrix}$$

$$G = \begin{pmatrix} 1 & 2 & 3 & 4 \\ 2 & 1 & 4 & 3 \end{pmatrix} \qquad H = \begin{pmatrix} 1 & 2 & 3 & 4 \\ 4 & 3 & 2 & 1 \end{pmatrix}$$

**9.**

| # | A | B | C | D | E | F | G | H |
|---|---|---|---|---|---|---|---|---|
| A | A | B | C | D | E | F | G | H |
| B | B | C | D | A | H | G | E | F |
| C | C | D | A | B | F | E | H | G |
| D | D | A | B | C | G | H | F | E |
| E | E | G | F | H | A | C | B | D |
| F | F | H | E | G | C | A | D | B |
| G | G | F | H | E | D | B | A | C |
| H | H | E | G | F | B | D | C | A |

The group is not abelian.

With respect to #, each of the following sets form a subgroup:

$\{A\}$, $\{A,C\}$, $\{A,E\}$, $\{A,F\}$, $\{A,G\}$, $\{A,H\}$, $\{A,B,C,D\}$, $\{A,C,E,F\}$, $\{A,C,G,H\}$, and $\{A,B,C,D,E,F,G,H\}$.

**13.** Label the diamond as follows:

$$\text{Let } O = \begin{pmatrix} 1 & 2 & 3 & 4 \\ 1 & 2 & 3 & 4 \end{pmatrix} \qquad I = \begin{pmatrix} 1 & 2 & 3 & 4 \\ 3 & 4 & 1 & 2 \end{pmatrix}$$

$$J = \begin{pmatrix} 1 & 2 & 3 & 4 \\ 1 & 4 & 3 & 2 \end{pmatrix} \qquad K = \begin{pmatrix} 1 & 2 & 3 & 4 \\ 3 & 2 & 1 & 4 \end{pmatrix}$$

Let $G = \{O,I,J,K\}$ with table:

| # | O | I | J | K |
|---|---|---|---|---|
| O | O | I | J | K |
| I | I | O | K | J |
| J | J | K | O | I |
| K | K | J | I | O |

Then $<G,\#>$ is the group of symmetries of the diamond.

### Section 3-3. Page 88

**1.** See answer to Exercise 1, Sec. 3-2.

**3.** Using the notation of page 80, the inverses of $R,S,T,U,V,$ and $W$ are, respectively, $R, S, T, U, W,$ and $V$. In $S_2$, each element is its own inverse.

**5.** If numbers in the first row of the permutation symbol are in natural order, the second rows are:
(a) 1  3  2  5  4
(b) 6  5  4  3  2  1
(c) 4  5  3  6  2  7  1
(d) 5  1  3  2  4
(e) 4  1  5  2  6  3
(f) 1  3  5  7  6  4  2

**7.** $\begin{pmatrix} 1 & 2 & 3 & 4 \\ 1 & 2 & 3 & 4 \end{pmatrix}$ and $\begin{pmatrix} 1 & 2 & 3 & 4 \\ 1 & 3 & 2 & 4 \end{pmatrix}$ $<A,\#>$ is a group.

# CHAPTER 4

## Section 4-1. Page 95

**3.** (d) 2,3,4

## Section 4-2. Page 102

**3.** Let $S_1 = \{a\}$; $s_2 = \{b\}$. Then $P_S = \{S, S_1, S_2, \phi\}$.

| $\cap$ | $S$ | $S_1$ | $S_2$ | $\phi$ |
|---|---|---|---|---|
| $S$ | $S$ | $S_1$ | $S_2$ | $\phi$ |
| $S_1$ | $S_1$ | $S_1$ | $\phi$ | $\phi$ |
| $S_2$ | $S_2$ | $\phi$ | $S_2$ | $\phi$ |
| $\phi$ | $\phi$ | $\phi$ | $\phi$ | $\phi$ |

| $\cup$ | $S$ | $S_1$ | $S_2$ | $\phi$ |
|---|---|---|---|---|
| $S$ | $S$ | $S$ | $S$ | $S$ |
| $S_1$ | $S$ | $S_1$ | $S$ | $S_1$ |
| $S_2$ | $S$ | $S$ | $S_2$ | $S_2$ |
| $\phi$ | $S$ | $S_1$ | $S_2$ | $\phi$ |

$<P_S, \cap, \cup>$ is not a ring. $\phi$ and $S$ are annihilators with respect to $\cap$ and $\cup$, respectively.

## Section 4-5. Page 109

**1.**

| + | 0 | 1 | 2 | 3 | 4 | 5 |
|---|---|---|---|---|---|---|
| 0 | 0 | 1 | 2 | 3 | 4 | 5 |
| 1 | 1 | 2 | 3 | 4 | 5 | 0 |
| 2 | 2 | 3 | 4 | 5 | 0 | 1 |
| 3 | 3 | 4 | 5 | 0 | 1 | 2 |
| 4 | 4 | 5 | 0 | 1 | 2 | 3 |
| 5 | 5 | 0 | 1 | 2 | 3 | 4 |

| $\cdot$ | 0 | 1 | 2 | 3 | 4 | 5 |
|---|---|---|---|---|---|---|
| 0 | 0 | 0 | 0 | 0 | 0 | 0 |
| 1 | 0 | 1 | 2 | 3 | 4 | 5 |
| 2 | 0 | 2 | 4 | 0 | 2 | 4 |
| 3 | 0 | 3 | 0 | 3 | 0 | 3 |
| 4 | 0 | 4 | 2 | 0 | 4 | 2 |
| 5 | 0 | 5 | 4 | 3 | 2 | 1 |

**3.**

| + | 0 | 1 | 2 | 3 | 4 |
|---|---|---|---|---|---|
| 0 | 0 | 1 | 2 | 3 | 4 |
| 1 | 1 | 2 | 3 | 4 | 0 |
| 2 | 2 | 3 | 4 | 0 | 1 |
| 3 | 3 | 4 | 0 | 1 | 2 |
| 4 | 4 | 0 | 1 | 2 | 3 |

| · | 0 | 1 | 2 | 3 | 4 |
|---|---|---|---|---|---|
| 0 | 0 | 0 | 0 | 0 | 0 |
| 1 | 0 | 1 | 2 | 3 | 4 |
| 2 | 0 | 2 | 4 | 1 | 3 |
| 3 | 0 | 3 | 1 | 4 | 2 |
| 4 | 0 | 4 | 3 | 2 | 1 |

There are no zero divisors. The system is an integral domain.

**5.** (c)

| + | $A_0$ | $A_1$ | $A_2$ | $A_3$ | $A_4$ | $A_5$ |
|---|---|---|---|---|---|---|
| $A_0$ | $A_0$ | $A_1$ | $A_2$ | $A_3$ | $A_4$ | $A_5$ |
| $A_1$ | $A_1$ | $A_2$ | $A_3$ | $A_4$ | $A_5$ | $A_0$ |
| $A_2$ | $A_2$ | $A_3$ | $A_4$ | $A_5$ | $A_0$ | $A_1$ |
| $A_3$ | $A_3$ | $A_4$ | $A_5$ | $A_0$ | $A_1$ | $A_2$ |
| $A_4$ | $A_4$ | $A_5$ | $A_0$ | $A_1$ | $A_2$ | $A_3$ |
| $A_5$ | $A_5$ | $A_0$ | $A_1$ | $A_2$ | $A_3$ | $A_4$ |

| · | $A_0$ | $A_1$ | $A_2$ | $A_3$ | $A_4$ | $A_5$ |
|---|---|---|---|---|---|---|
| $A_0$ | $A_0$ | $A_0$ | $A_0$ | $A_0$ | $A_0$ | $A_0$ |
| $A_1$ | $A_0$ | $A_1$ | $A_2$ | $A_3$ | $A_4$ | $A_5$ |
| $A_2$ | $A_0$ | $A_2$ | $A_4$ | $A_0$ | $A_2$ | $A_4$ |
| $A_3$ | $A_0$ | $A_3$ | $A_0$ | $A_3$ | $A_0$ | $A_3$ |
| $A_4$ | $A_0$ | $A_4$ | $A_2$ | $A_0$ | $A_4$ | $A_2$ |
| $A_5$ | $A_0$ | $A_5$ | $A_4$ | $A_3$ | $A_2$ | $A_1$ |

# CHAPTER 5

## Section 5-1. Page 115

**1.** Let $F = \{0,1\}$ with operations $+, \cdot$ defined by the tables:

| + | 0 | 1 |
|---|---|---|
| 0 | 0 | 1 |
| 1 | 1 | 0 |

| · | 0 | 1 |
|---|---|---|
| 0 | 0 | 0 |
| 1 | 0 | 1 |

**3.** Let $F = \{0,1,2,3,4\}$ with operations $+, \cdot$ defined by the tables:

| + | 0 | 1 | 2 | 3 | 4 |
|---|---|---|---|---|---|
| 0 | 0 | 1 | 2 | 3 | 4 |
| 1 | 1 | 2 | 3 | 4 | 0 |
| 2 | 2 | 3 | 4 | 0 | 1 |
| 3 | 3 | 4 | 0 | 1 | 2 |
| 4 | 4 | 0 | 1 | 2 | 3 |

| · | 0 | 1 | 2 | 3 | 4 |
|---|---|---|---|---|---|
| 0 | 0 | 0 | 0 | 0 | 0 |
| 1 | 0 | 1 | 2 | 3 | 4 |
| 2 | 0 | 2 | 4 | 1 | 3 |
| 3 | 0 | 3 | 1 | 4 | 2 |
| 4 | 0 | 4 | 3 | 2 | 1 |

## Section 5-2. Page 125

**9.** $\dfrac{7}{12}$    **11.** $\dfrac{7a - 2}{12}$    **13.** $\dfrac{^-14a - 18}{9}$

**15.** $\dfrac{1 - a^2}{a}$    **17.** $\dfrac{7bc}{2}$    **19.** $\dfrac{^-1}{1}$

**21.** $\dfrac{3a^2 - 1}{8a}$    **23.** True    **25.** True

## Section 5-3. Page 131

**3.** (a) $\{x \,|\, x \in R, x \geqslant 7\}$    (b) $\{x \,|\, x \in R, x \geqslant 4\}$
(c) $\{x \,|\, x \in R, x \geqslant 4\}$    (d) $\{x \,|\, x \in R, x \geqslant {}^-2\}$
(e) $\{x \,|\, x \in R, x \geqslant {}^-2\}$    (f) $\{x \,|\, x \in R, x \geqslant 0\}$
(g) $\{x \,|\, x \in R, x \geqslant {}^-2\}$

## Section 5-4. Page 141

**1.** (a) 8    (c) $\{(1,0,0), (0,1,0), (0,0,1)\}$    (d) 3
**3.** (a) 9    (c) One basis is $\{(1,0), (0,1)\}$    (d) 2
**7.** One basis is $\left\{ \begin{pmatrix} 1 & 0 \\ 0 & 0 \end{pmatrix}, \begin{pmatrix} 0 & 1 \\ 0 & 0 \end{pmatrix}, \begin{pmatrix} 0 & 0 \\ 1 & 0 \end{pmatrix}, \begin{pmatrix} 0 & 0 \\ 0 & 1 \end{pmatrix} \right\}$.
The dimension is 4.

## Section 5-5. Page 151

**1.** (a) $x = 3, y = 3$    (b) $x = 5, y = 2$    (c) $x = 9, y = 7$

(d) $x = \frac{2}{5}, y = \frac{1}{5}$   (e) $x = \sqrt{29}$   (f) $x = 5, y = {}^-7$

(g) $x = 4, y = 4$   (h) $x = 3, y = {}^-2$   (i) $x = \frac{2}{5}, y = \frac{1}{5}$

(j) $x = 4$ or $x = {}^-4$

5.  (a) $\frac{-3}{5} + \frac{4}{5}\mathbf{i}$   (b) $4 - 3\mathbf{i}$   (c) $1 + 2\mathbf{i}$

(d) $\frac{-3}{5} - \frac{4}{5}\mathbf{i}$   (e) $\frac{2}{5} - \frac{33}{10}\mathbf{i}$   (f) $\frac{-51}{85} + \frac{68}{85}\mathbf{i}$

(g) $3 - \mathbf{i}$   (h) $\frac{4}{25} + \frac{3}{25}\mathbf{i}$   (i) $2 - \mathbf{i}$

(j) $4 + 0\mathbf{i}$   (k) $2 - 2\mathbf{i}$   (l) $\frac{2}{5} + \frac{9}{5}\mathbf{i}$

# CHAPTER 6

## Section 6-1. Page 165

1.  (a) Is the square of   (b) Is the same model as
    (c) Has the same area as   (d) Is a square root of
    (e) Is 3 more than 2 times   (f) Is one-half of
    (g) Is the positive square root of
3.  *Reflexive: b, c; symmetric: b, c; transitive: b, c*
5.  (a) One-to-many   (b) No   (c) No
7.  $W(x) = 0$, x even; $W(x) = 1$, x odd. W is a many-to-one mapping from Z onto $\{0,1\}$.
    S is not a mapping.
    C is a many-to-one mapping from P onto D.
9.  (a) $y = x$   (b) $y > x$   (c) $y = 2x + 1$
    (d) $y \le x$   (e) $y = |x|$   (f) $y = 5$
    (g) $y = 6 - \frac{1}{3}x$   (h) $y = \frac{2}{3}x + 1$
    (i) $y = \sqrt{x}$   (j) $y = {}^-x$
11. (a) $f(\ ) = 2(\ ) - 3$   (b) $f(\ ) = 3(\ )$
    (c) $f(\ ) = 6$   (d) $f(\ ) = 3(\ )^2 - 2(\ ) + 7$
    (e) $f(\ ) = \dfrac{4(\ ) - 2}{3(\ ) + 1}$   (f) $f(\ ) = \dfrac{[2(\ ) + 4][(\ ) - 1]}{5[(\ ) - 3][(\ ) + 2]}$
13. The respective values are:

    (a) $f(4)$: 5, 12, 6, 47, $\frac{14}{13}, \frac{8}{5}$
    (b) $f(-1)$: $^-5, ^-3, 6, 12, 3, \frac{3}{5}$

    (c) $f(\frac{2}{3})$: $\dfrac{-5}{3}$, 2, 6, 7, $\frac{2}{9}, \frac{1}{10}$

(d) $f(a - 1)$: $2a - 5$, $3(a - 1)$, $6$, $3a^2 - 8a + 12$, $\dfrac{4a - 6}{3a - 2}$,

$\dfrac{2(a + 3)(a - 2)}{5(a - 4)(a + 1)}$

**15.** One-to-one.

**17.** Yes; no

**21.** (a) The largest such proper subset $X$ is

$\{^-8, ^-6, ^-4, ^-2, 0, 2, 4, 6, 8\}$

(b) $Y = \{0, 1, 2, 3, 4, 5, 6, 7, 8\}$

(c) $\{(^-8, 8), (^-6, 7), (^-4, 6), (^-2, 5), (0, 4), (2, 3), (4, 2), (6, 1), (8, 0)\}$

(d)

| $x$ | $^-8$ | $^-6$ | $^-4$ | $^-2$ | 0 | 2 | 4 | 6 | 8 |
|------|------|------|------|------|---|---|---|---|---|
| $f(x)$ | 8 | 7 | 6 | 5 | 4 | 3 | 2 | 1 | 0 |

(e) (See graph.)

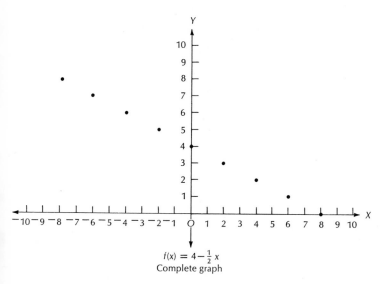

$f(x) = 4 - \frac{1}{2}x$
Complete graph

**23.**   (a)  $f(x) = x$:

| $x$ | ⁻9 | ⁻8 | ⁻7 | ⁻6 | ⁻5 | ⁻4 | ⁻3 | ⁻2 | ⁻1 | 0 | 1 | 2 | 3 | 4 | 5 | 6 | 7 | 8 | 9 |
|---|---|---|---|---|---|---|---|---|---|---|---|---|---|---|---|---|---|---|---|
| $f(x)$ | ⁻9 | ⁻8 | ⁻7 | ⁻6 | ⁻5 | ⁻4 | ⁻3 | ⁻2 | ⁻1 | 0 | 1 | 2 | 3 | 4 | 5 | 6 | 7 | 8 | 9 |

(See graph.)

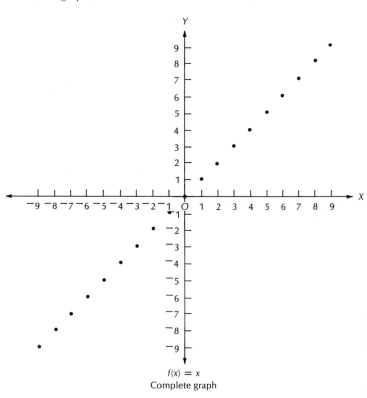

$f(x) = x$
Complete graph

(e)  $f(x) = |x|$

| $x$ | ⁻9 | ⁻8 | ⁻7 | ⁻6 | '5 | ⁻4 | ⁻3 | ⁻2 | ⁻1 | 0 | 1 | 2 | 3 | 4 | 5 | 6 | 7 | 8 | 9 |
|---|---|---|---|---|---|---|---|---|---|---|---|---|---|---|---|---|---|---|---|
| $f(x)$ | 9 | 8 | 7 | 6 | 5 | 4 | 3 | 2 | 1 | 0 | 1 | 2 | 3 | 4 | 5 | 6 | 7 | 8 | 9 |

(See graph.)

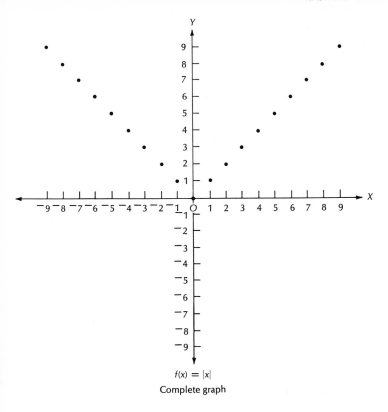

$f(x) = |x|$

Complete graph

(f)  $f(x) = 5$:

| x | ⁻9 | ⁻8 | ⁻7 | ⁻6 | ⁻5 | ⁻4 | ⁻3 | ⁻2 | ⁻1 | 0 | 1 | 2 | 3 | 4 | 5 | 6 | 7 | 8 | 9 |
|------|----|----|----|----|----|----|----|----|----|---|---|---|---|---|---|---|---|---|---|
| f(x) | 5  | 5  | 5  | 5  | 5  | 5  | 5  | 5  | 5  | 5 | 5 | 5 | 5 | 5 | 5 | 5 | 5 | 5 | 5 |

(See graph.)

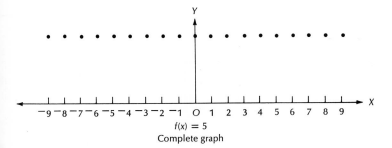

$f(x) = 5$

Complete graph

($j$) $f(x) = {}^-x$:

| x | ⁻9 | ⁻8 | ⁻7 | ⁻6 | ⁻5 | ⁻4 | ⁻3 | ⁻2 | ⁻1 | 0 | 1 | 2 | 3 | 4 | 5 | 6 | 7 | 8 | 9 |
|---|---|---|---|---|---|---|---|---|---|---|---|---|---|---|---|---|---|---|---|
| f(x) | 9 | 8 | 7 | 6 | 5 | 4 | 3 | 2 | 1 | 0 | ⁻1 | ⁻2 | ⁻3 | ⁻4 | ⁻5 | ⁻6 | ⁻7 | ⁻8 | ⁻9 |

(See graph.)

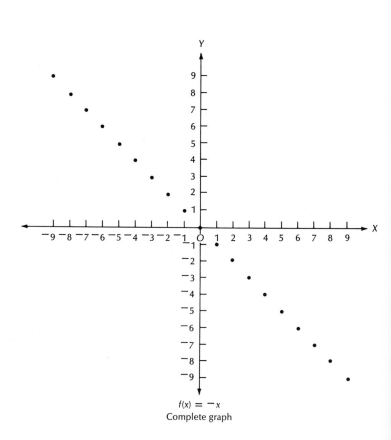

$f(x) = {}^-x$
Complete graph

**25.** (a) Yes    (b) Yes    (c)

| x | ⁻4 | ⁻2 | 0 | 2 | 4 |
|---|---|---|---|---|---|
| f(x) | 6 | 5 | 4 | 3 | 2 |

(See graph.)

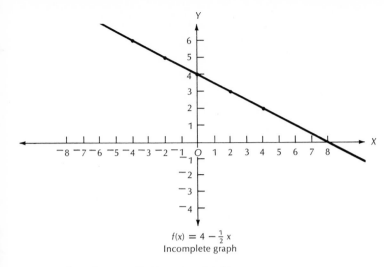

$f(x) = 4 - \frac{1}{2}x$
Incomplete graph

**27.** (a) $[^-2,3]$ (b) Yes (c) Yes
(d) Complete (See graph.)

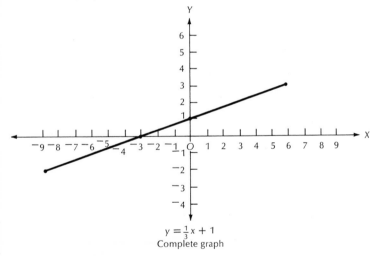

$y = \frac{1}{3}x + 1$
Complete graph

(e) Domain $(^-9,6)$, range $(^-2,3)$; domain $[^-9,6)$, range $[^-2,3)$;
domain $(^-9,6]$, range $(^-2,3]$

**Section 6-4. Page 175**

**1.** (a) $y = ^-3x + 2$ (b) $y = \frac{2}{3}x - \frac{1}{2}$
(c) $y = 5x + 3$ (d) $y = (^-9/5)x - 7/5$

    (e) $y = 2x - 4$              (f) $y = 6x + 5$

    (g) $y = (^-3/5)x - 5$

**3.**  (a) $3x + 2y + 6 = 0$       (b) $4x - 6y - 9 = 0$

    (c) $y - 2 = 0$            (d) $4x + 3y - 2 = 0$

    (e) $4x + y + 2 = 0$        (f) $y - 4 = 0$

    (g) $x + 6 = 0$           (h) $y - 1 = 0$

    (i) $3x + y - 6 = 0$        (j) $x - 3 = 0$

    (k) $x - y + 1 = 0$        (l) $x - 5 = 0$

**5.**  (See graphs.)

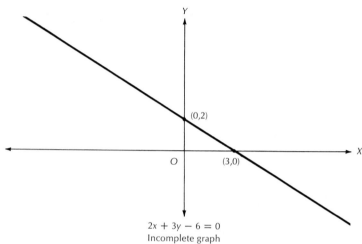

$2x + 3y - 6 = 0$
Incomplete graph

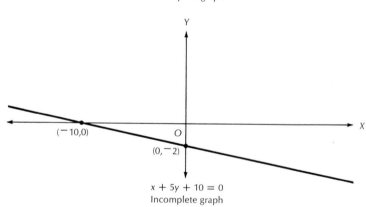

$x + 5y + 10 = 0$
Incomplete graph

**7.**  30 square units

**9.**  (a) $2x + y - 13 = 0$     (b) $3x - 2y - 6 = 0$

    (c) $x + 5y - 6 = 0$      (d) $2x - 3y = 0$

**11.**  (a) $f(x) = mx$    (b) $f(x) = mx + 1$    (c) $f(x) = mx$

**13.**  168       **15.**  .00038 sec      **17.**  1944

**19.**  8 in.      **21.**  8 ft

**Section 6-6. Page 188**

3. To find the points of intersections of the curve with the x axis.
5. (a) Positive            (b) Negative            (c) Zero
7. (a) ⁻3, ⁻2              (b) ⁻1, 2              (c) ⁻7, ⁻2
   (d) ⁻2, 5              (e) ⁻9, 2              (f) ⁻1/3, $\frac{1}{2}$
   (g) ⁻4/5, $\frac{2}{3}$    (h) ⁻5/3, ⁻3/4         (i) ⁻5/7, $\frac{2}{3}$
9. (a) $(x + 6)(x - 2)$          (b) $(x - 22)(x + 6)$

   (c) $\left(x + \dfrac{5 + \sqrt{13}}{2}\right)\left(x + \dfrac{5 - \sqrt{13}}{2}\right)$

   (d) $(2x + 1)(2x - 5)$    (e) $\left(x - \dfrac{2 + \sqrt{5}i}{9}\right)\left(x - \dfrac{2 - \sqrt{5}i}{9}\right)$

11. (a) $(x - 18)(x + 2)$          (b) $(x + 23)(x - 8)$

    (c) $(2x - 5)(x + 1)$     (d) $\left(x + \dfrac{7 - \sqrt{85}}{6}\right)\left(x + \dfrac{7 + \sqrt{85}}{6}\right)$

    (e) $\left(x + \dfrac{1 - \sqrt{7}}{2}\right)\left(x + \dfrac{1 + \sqrt{7}}{2}\right)$

    (f) $\left(x + \dfrac{5 - \sqrt{7}i}{2}\right)\left(x + \dfrac{5 + \sqrt{7}i}{2}\right)$

    (g) $\left(x - \dfrac{7 + \sqrt{33}}{8}\right)\left(x - \dfrac{7 - \sqrt{33}}{8}\right)$

    (h) $[x - (3 - \sqrt{3})][x + (3 + \sqrt{3})]$
    (i) $[x - (3 - 2i)][x + (3 + 2i)]$
    (j) $(x + 11i)(x + i)$          (k) $(2x - \sqrt{2})(x + 3\sqrt{2})$
13. 1030.4 in.
15. (a) 5538.96 cu in.           (b) 1130.40 cu in.
    (c) 27,129.60 cu in.          (d) 83,084.40 cu in.
17. (a) $ax^2 + c$                  (b) $ax^2 + ax + c$
    (c) $ax^2 - 5ax + c$            (d) $4a^2x^2 + 4abx + b^2$
19. (a) ±18              (b) ±12         (c) 2
    (d) ⁻4 or 0      (e) ⁻3 or 13     (f) ⁻3 ± 2√3


**Section 6-7. Page 195**

1. (a) 40 cu ft                    (b) 40 lb/sq in.
3. (a) 12 amp                     (b) 0.2 ohm
5. With depth of 6 in. it will support 288 lb more.
7. (a) 8.1 ft          (b) 2.7 ft
9. y varies inversely as x may be stated in the form y varies directly as the reciprocal of x.


**Section 6-8. Page 203**

3. Yes

**5.** No

**7.** (a) No solution          (b) No positive solution

(c) $x = 2$, $y = 2$ only positve solution

**9.** $x = 5s + 2$, $y = {}^-6s - 1$ (for each $s \in Z$). *Note:* An equivalent solution is $x = 5k - 3$, $y = {}^-6k + 5$ (for each $k \in Z$).

**11.** $x = 9$, $y = 2$

**13.** 5 suckers and 2 cones; or 0 suckers and 5 cones

**15.** (a) $x = 2s + 1$, $y = 9s - 8$, $z = {}^-11s + 29$ for each $s \in Z$

(b) $x = 3$, $y = 1$, $z = 18$ for $s = 1$

$x = 5$, $y = 10$, $z = 7$ for $s = 2$

**17.** 0 cocks, 25 hens, 75 chickens; or 4 cocks, 18 hens, 78 chickens; or 8 cocks, 11 hens, 81 chickens; or 12 cocks, 4 hens, 84 chickens

**19.** 12 television sets, 15 stereo sets, 23 radio sets

# CHAPTER 7

## Section 7-3. Page 215

**1.** (a) $6 + 2x$     (b) 6     (c) $x - x^4$

(d) $1 + 6x + 8x^2 - 6x^3$          (e) $^-2 - x + 3x^2 + x^4 - 4x^6$

(f) $^-2 - x + 5x^3 + x^4$

**7.** $P_n \subset P$

**11.** (a) 4; 7     (b) at most 2; 4     (c) 0; 0

(d) 1; 1     (e) 5; 7

## Section 7-4. Page 223

**1.** (a) $ac + ab + a^2$             (b) $6 + 4a - 2b$

(c) $6a^2 + 9ab + 3ac$         (d) $a^2bc + ab^2c + abc^2$

(e) $^-ab^2 + b^3 + b^2c$         (f) $ac + ad - bc - bd$

(g) $ac - ad - bc + bd$         (h) $^-a^2 + 2ab - b^2$

(i) $ac - ab - bc + b^2$         (j) $2a^2 - 2b^2$

(k) $^-a^3 - 2a^2b - ab^2$         (l) $4a^2 - b^2$

(m) $9a^2 - 4b^2$                 (n) $a^2 - 2ab + b^2 - c^2$

(o) $a^2 - 2ab + b^2 - c^2 + 2cd - d^2$

(p) $a^2 - b^2 + 4bc - 4c^2$

(q) $8a^3 + b^3$     (r) $a^3 - 8b^3$     (s) $a^6 + b^6$

(t) $25a^2 + 20a + 4$          (u) $9a^2 - 30ab^2 + 25b^4$

(v) $a^4 + 2a^2b^2 + b^4$          (w) $5a^2 + 17a + 6$

(x) $18a^4b + 12a^2b^2 - 9a^3b^2 - 6ab^3$

**3.** Over the field $Q$:

    (a) $(x^2 + 2)(x^2 - 2)$

    (b) $2(x^2 + 4)(x + 2)(x - 2)$

    (c) $(x - 1)(x^2 + x + 1)$

    (d) Not factorable

    (e) $3(x + 2)(x^2 - 2x + 4)$

    (f) $(x + 2)(x - 2)(x^2 + 2x + 4)(x^2 - 2x + 4)$

    (g) $(x + 1)(x^2 - x + 1)$

    (h) $5(x + 3)(x^2 - 3x + 9)$

    (i) Not factorable

    (j) Not factorable

    (k) $(4x^2 + 3)(4x^2 - 3)$

    (l) $3x(3x - 2)(9x^2 + 6x + 4)$

Over the field $R$:

    (a) $(x^2 + 2)(x + \sqrt{2})(x - \sqrt{2})$

    (b) $2(x^2 + 4)(x + 2)(x - 2)$

    (c) $(x - 1)(x^2 + x + 1)$

    (d) Not factorable

    (e) $3(x + 2)(x^2 - 2x + 4)$

    (f) $(x + 2)(x - 2)(x^2 + 2x + 4)(x^2 - 2x + 4)$

    (g) $(x + 1)(x^2 - x + 1)$

    (h) $5(x + 3)(x^2 - 3x + 9)$

    (i) Not factorable

    (j) Not factorable

    (k) $(4x^2 + 3)(2x + \sqrt{3})(2x - \sqrt{3})$

    (l) $3x(3x - 2)(9x^2 + 6x + 4)$

Over the field $C$:

    (a) $(x + \sqrt{2}i)(x - \sqrt{2}i)(x + \sqrt{2})(x - \sqrt{2})$

    (b) $2(x + 2i)(x - 2i)(x + 2)(x - 2)$

    (c) $(x - 1)\left(x + \dfrac{1 + \sqrt{3}i}{2}\right)\left(x + \dfrac{1 - \sqrt{3}i}{2}\right)$

    (d) $(x + i)(x - i)$

    (e) $3(x + 2)(x - 1 + \sqrt{3}i)(x - 1 - \sqrt{3}i)$

    (f) $(x + 2)(x - 2)(x + 1 + \sqrt{3}i)(x + 1 - \sqrt{3}i)$
        $(x - 1 + \sqrt{3}i)(x - 1 - \sqrt{3}i)$

    (g) $(x + 1)\left(x - \dfrac{1 + \sqrt{3}i}{2}\right)\left(x - \dfrac{1 - \sqrt{3}i}{2}\right)$

    (h) $5(x + 3)\left(x - \dfrac{3 + 3\sqrt{3}i}{2}\right)\left(x - \dfrac{3 - 3\sqrt{3}i}{2}\right)$

    (i) $(x - \sqrt{3} + i)(x - \sqrt{3} - i)$

(j) $\left(x + \dfrac{1 + \sqrt{7}i}{2}\right)\left(x + \dfrac{1 - \sqrt{7}i}{2}\right)$

(k) $(2x + \sqrt{3}i)(2x - \sqrt{3}i)(2x + \sqrt{3})(2x - \sqrt{3})$

(l) $3x(3x - 2)(3x + 1 + \sqrt{3}i)(3x + 1 - \sqrt{3}i)$

7. $(a^6 - b^6)(a^6 + b^6) = (a^3 - b^3)(a^3 + b^3)(a^6 + b^6)$
$= (a - b)(a^2 + ab + b^2)(a + b)(a^2 - ab + b^2)(a^2 + b^2)(a^4 - a^2b^2 + b^4)$

### Section 7-6. Page 234

1. (a) $^-35/8$, $^-52/9$, $0$, $^-24 - 12i$, $^-24 + 12i$, $0$
   (b) $3x^2 + 18x - 15$; $3x^2 + (19 + 3i)x - (12 - 19i)$

3. (a) $\{3, ^-2, ^-1\}$     (b) $\{^-1\}$ where $^-1$ is of multiplicity four.
   (c) $\{1, \frac{1}{3}\}$ where $1$ is of multiplicity two.
   (d) $\{^-2, \frac{1}{2}, \frac{3}{2}\}$ where $\frac{1}{2}$ is of multiplicity two.

5. (a) $x^4 - 10x^3 + 35x^2 - 50x + 24$
   (b) $2x^4 - 7x^3 - 17x^2 + 10x$
   (c) $2x^5 + x^4 - 4x^3 - 3x^2$
   (d) $x^5 - 2x^4 - x + 2$
   (e) $x^4 - 4x^3 + x^2 + 8x - 6$
   (f) $x^4 - 2x^3 + 3x^2 - 2x + 2$

11. $7, 8, 9$     13. $10$ in.

17. $x^3 - 3x^2 + x + 5$

19. $x^4 - 2x^3 + 3x^2 - 2x + 2$

## CHAPTER 8

### Section 8-2. Page 245

1. $\{(1, ^-3)\}$ (See graph.)

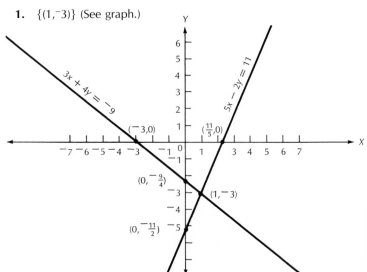

**3.**   $\{(8,0)\}$ (See graph.)

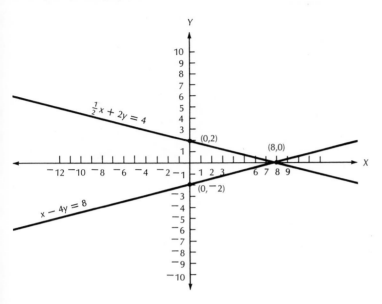

**5.**   Inconsistent (See graph.)

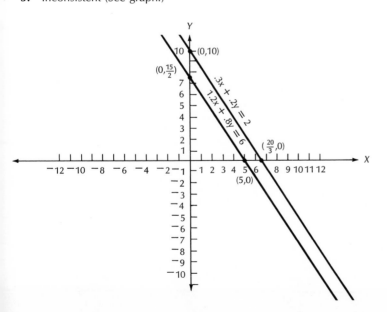

**7.** $\{(10,5)\}$ (See graph.)

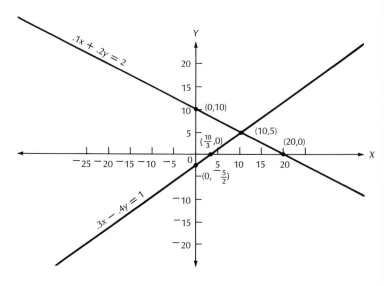

**9.**  $x = {}^-8$, $y = \frac{8}{5}$
**11.**  $x = \frac{1}{2}$, $y = \frac{1}{3}$
**13.**  First class: 2,000 @6 cents; airmail: 1,000 @10 cents
**15.**  Local charge: $7.94; long distance charge: $7.77
**17.**  $f(x) = x + 7$
**19.**  $2\frac{1}{4}$ miles from first boy's home, $1\frac{1}{4}$ miles from second boy's home
**21.**  6 ohms and 12 ohms

### Section 8-3. Page 254

**1.**  Each element is 0     **3.**  2          **5.**  2     **7.**  3
**9.**  3                     **11.**  4         **13.**  3    **15.**  1
**17.**  $^-1$ or $\frac{1}{2}$     **19.**  $^-\frac{1}{2}$ or 1

### Section 8-5. Page 269

**1.**  At least the value 0 for each of its variables will satisfy each equation.

**3.**  $\{(1,3)\}$ (See graph.)

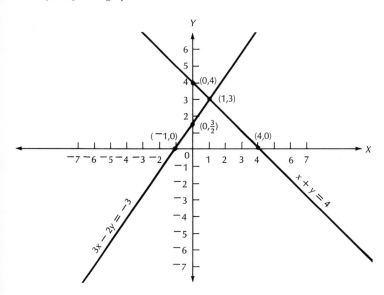

**5.**  $\left\{\left(x, \dfrac{3x-5}{2}\right) \middle| x \in R\right\}$ (See graph.)

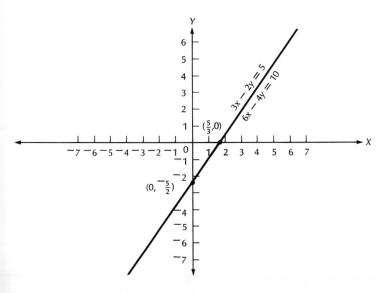

  **7.**  $\{(2,4)\}$ (See graph.)

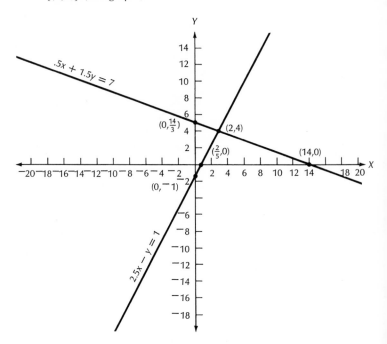

  **9.**  Consistent; $\{(1,2,3)\}$
  **11.**  Inconsistent
  **13.**  Consistent; $\{(5,^-2)\}$
  **15.**  Inconsistent
  **17.**  Consistent;
       $\{(8 + u - 3v,\ 10 - 2u - 2v,\ ^-2 - u + v,\ u,\ v)|u,v \in R\}$
  **19.**  $\{(1,0,2)\}$
  **21.**  Inconsistent
  **23.**  Consistent; $\left\{\left(\dfrac{12 + x_4}{15},\ \dfrac{^-12 - 11x_4}{15},\ \dfrac{^-x_4}{15},\ x_4\right)\middle|\ x_4 \in R\right\}$
  **25.**  (a) $5x - y - 7 = 0$
  **27.**  $4y = ^-3x^2 + 5x + 16$
  **29.**  $x^2 + y^2 - 31x - 23y + 106 = 0$
  **31.**  $x - 2y + 4z - 3 = 0$
  **35.**  \$10,000 @4.5 percent; \$7,500 @5 percent; \$6,500@4 percent;
       #26,000 @5.5 percent
  **37.**  $3x - y - 3 = 0$
  **39.**  $\{(0,^-3),\ (1,0),\ (2,3)\}$
  **41.**  The line of Exercise 37. The coordinates of points of intersection
       of pairs of circles of the configuration do not satisfy the equation
       of this line.

**Section 8-7. Page 285**

1. The solution set of the system is the null set.
3. Tangent    5. Do not intersect
7. Intersect in two distinct points    9. Do not intersect
11. Tangent    13. Intersect in two distinct points
15. $\{(^-1,5)\}$ (See graph.)

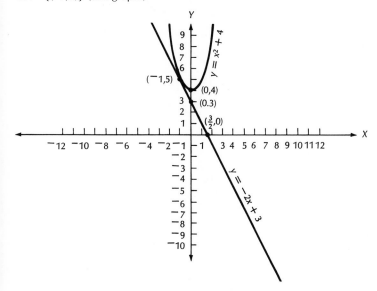

17. $\left\{\left(\dfrac{^-3 + \sqrt{15}i}{4}, \dfrac{19 + 3\sqrt{15}i}{4}\right), \left(\dfrac{^-3 - \sqrt{15}i}{4}, \dfrac{19 - 3\sqrt{15}i}{4}\right)\right\}$

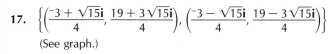

(See graph.)

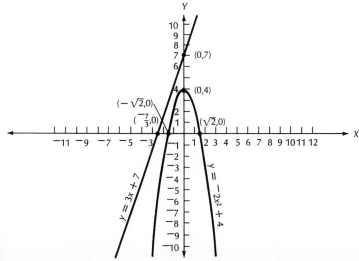

**19.** $\left\{ \left( \dfrac{1 + \sqrt{37}}{6}, \dfrac{7 + \sqrt{37}}{6} \right), \left( \dfrac{1 - \sqrt{37}}{6}, \dfrac{7 - \sqrt{37}}{6} \right) \right\}$ (See graph.)

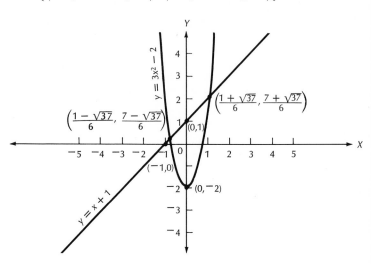

**21.** $\left\{ \left( \dfrac{^-1 + \sqrt{63}\mathbf{i}}{8}, \dfrac{35 - 3\sqrt{63}\mathbf{i}}{8} \right), \left( \dfrac{^-1 - \sqrt{63}\mathbf{i}}{8}, \dfrac{35 + 3\sqrt{63}\mathbf{i}}{8} \right) \right\}$
(See graph.)

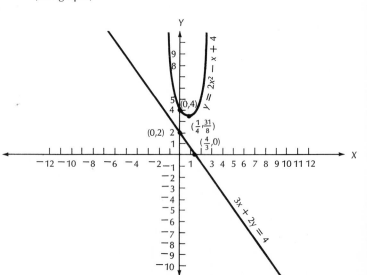

**23.** $\{(1, {}^-2)\}$. (See graph.)

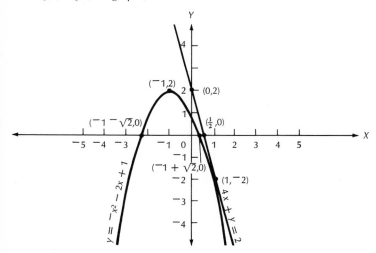

**25.** $\left\{ \left( \dfrac{{}^-5 + \sqrt{29}}{2}, 8 - \sqrt{29} \right), \left( \dfrac{{}^-5 - \sqrt{29}}{2}, 8 + \sqrt{29} \right) \right\}$ (See graph.)

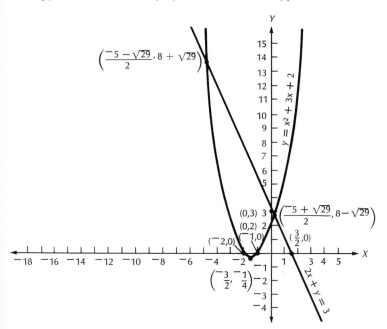

**27.** Radical axis: $x + y + 3 = 0$; circles have no points in common
**29.** Radical axis: $x + y - 8 = 0$; tangent
**31.** Radical axis: $3x - 4y = 0$; intersect in two distinct points

**33.** $\left\{\left(\dfrac{-3+i}{2},\dfrac{-3-i}{2}\right),\left(\dfrac{-3-i}{2},\dfrac{-3+i}{2}\right)\right\}$

**35.** $\{(4,4)\}$   **37.** $\{(4,3),(-4,-3)\}$

**39.** (See graph.)

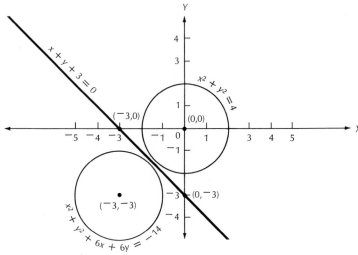

**41.** (See graph.)

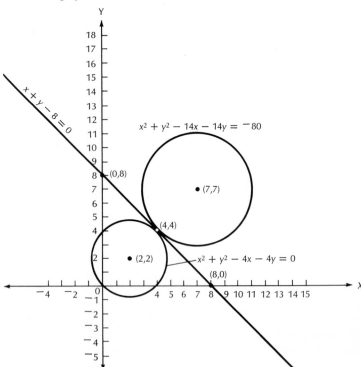

**43.** (See graph.)

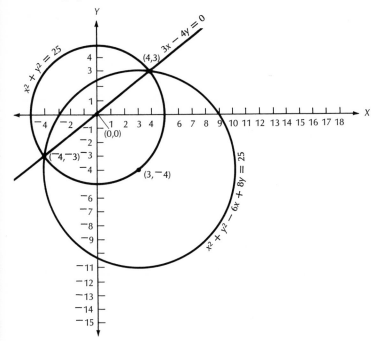

**45.** $\{(0,^-2), (0,2), (3,^-1), (^-3,1)\}$
**47.** $\{(^-1,1), (1,^-1), (3\mathbf{i},2\mathbf{i}), (^-3\mathbf{i}\ ^-2\mathbf{i})\}$
**49.** $\{(^-2,0), (^-2,2)\}$
**51.** $\{(^-2,^-3), (2,3), (\mathbf{i},4\mathbf{i}), (^-\mathbf{i},^-4\mathbf{i})\}$
**53.** The sides are of equal length.
**55.** No such real numbers exist.
**57.** No
**59.** $^-2, \frac{2}{3}$

# CHAPTER 9

## Section 9-3. Page 304

**1.** $^-2 < x < 2$
**3.** $s \leq ^-8$ or $s \geq 8$
**5.** $x < ^-3$ or $x > 7$
**7.** $0 \leq a \leq 2$
**9.** Impossible
**11.** Impossible
**13.** $|a| \leq 4$
**15.** $|x + 7| < 2$
**17.** $|r + \frac{1}{2}| \leq \frac{5}{2}$
**19.** $|x - 2| < 1$
**21.** $|x - 1| \leq 5$
**23.** $|x - \frac{7}{2}| < \frac{7}{2}$
**25.** $x \leq 8$
**27.** Impossible

**29.** $x > 2$

**31.** $x \leqslant 1$ or $x \geqslant 2$ (See graph.)

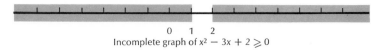

Incomplete graph of $x^2 - 3x + 2 \geqslant 0$

**33.** $^-2 \leqslant x \leqslant 5$ (See graph.)

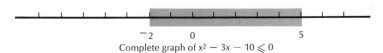

Complete graph of $x^2 - 3x - 10 \leqslant 0$

**35.** $x < ^-2$ or $x > \frac{3}{2}$ (See graph.)

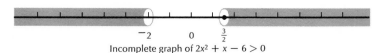

Incomplete graph of $2x^2 + x - 6 > 0$

**37.** $x < ^-1$ or $x > 2$ (See graph.)

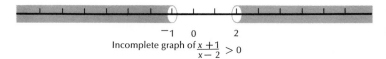

Incomplete graph of $\dfrac{x+1}{x-2} > 0$

**39.** $^-5 \leqslant x < 1$ (See graph.)

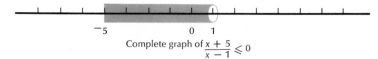

Complete graph of $\dfrac{x+5}{x-1} \leqslant 0$

**41.** (See graph.)

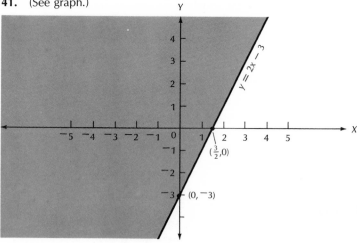

Incomplete graph of
$y \geqslant 2x - 3$
(shaded, closed half plane)

**43.** (See graph.)

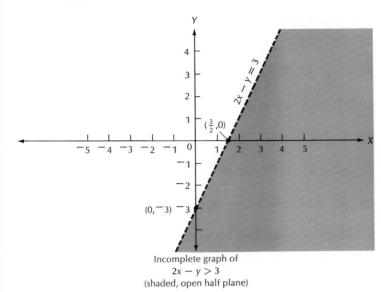

Incomplete graph of
$2x - y > 3$
(shaded, open half plane)

**45.** (See graph.)

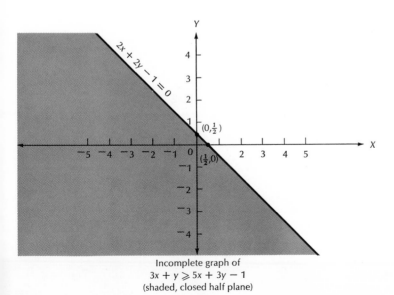

Incomplete graph of
$3x + y \geqslant 5x + 3y - 1$
(shaded, closed half plane)

**47.** (See graph.)

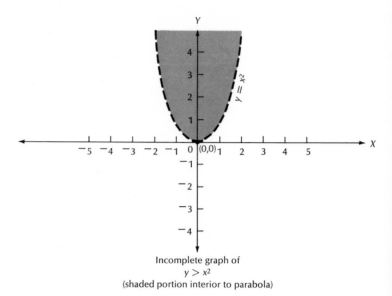

Incomplete graph of
$y > x^2$
(shaded portion interior to parabola)

**49.** (See graph.)

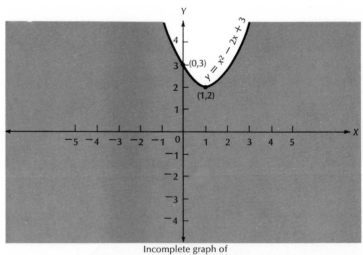

Incomplete graph of
$y \leqslant x^2 - 2x + 3$
(shaded portion exterior
to and including parabola)

**51.** (See graph.)

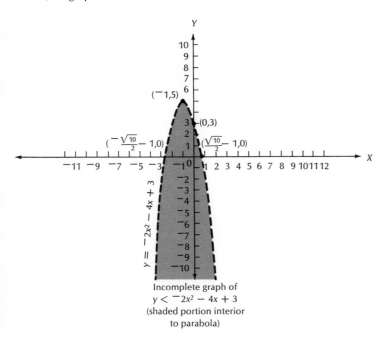

Incomplete graph of
$y < {}^-2x^2 - 4x + 3$
(shaded portion interior
to parabola)

**53.** (See graph.)

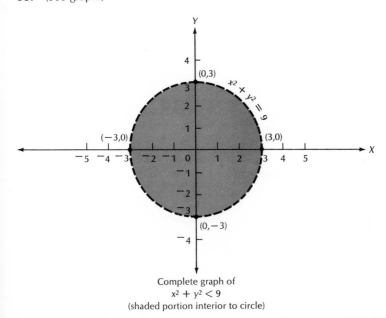

Complete graph of
$x^2 + y^2 < 9$
(shaded portion interior to circle)

**55.** (See graph.)

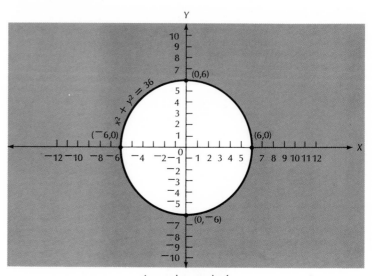

Incomplete graph of
$x^2 + y^2 \geqslant 36$
(shaded portion exterior
and including circle)

## Section 9-5. Page 311

**1.** (See graph.)

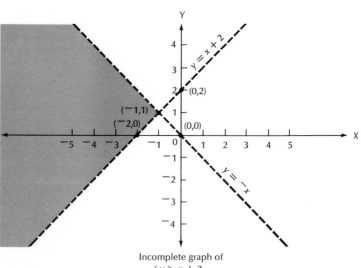

Incomplete graph of
$$\begin{cases} y > x + 2 \\ y < -x \end{cases}$$
(shaded portion excluding
boundary lines)

**3.** (See graph.)

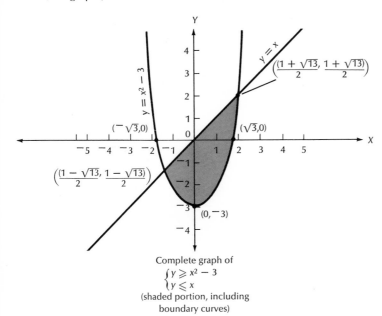

Complete graph of
$$\begin{cases} y \ge x^2 - 3 \\ y \le x \end{cases}$$
(shaded portion, including
boundary curves)

**5.** (See graph.)

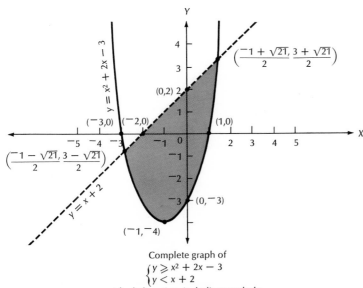

Complete graph of
$$\begin{cases} y \ge x^2 + 2x - 3 \\ y < x + 2 \end{cases}$$
(shaded portion, including parabola,
excluding boundary line)

7.   (See graph.)

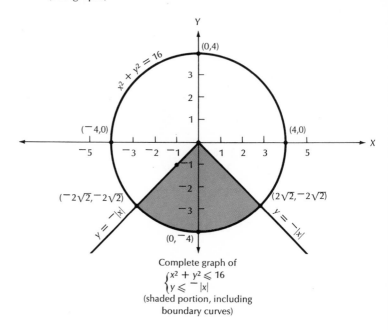

Complete graph of
$$\begin{cases} x^2 + y^2 \leqslant 16 \\ y \leqslant {}^-|x| \end{cases}$$
(shaded portion, including
boundary curves)

9.   (See graph.)

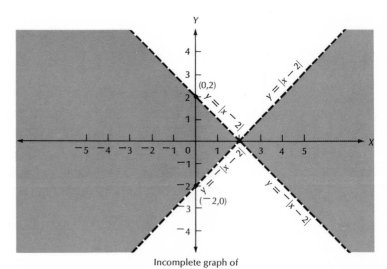

Incomplete graph of
$$\begin{cases} y < |x - 2| \\ y > {}^-|x - 2| \end{cases}$$
(shaded portion excluding
boundary lines)

**11.** (See graph.)

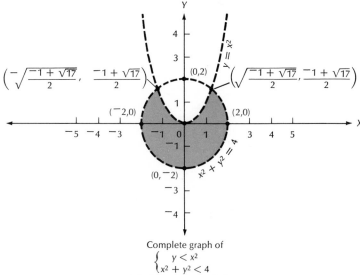

Complete graph of
$$\begin{cases} y < x^2 \\ x^2 + y^2 < 4 \end{cases}$$
(shaded portion, excluding
boundary curves)

**13.** $\phi$

**15.** (See graph.)

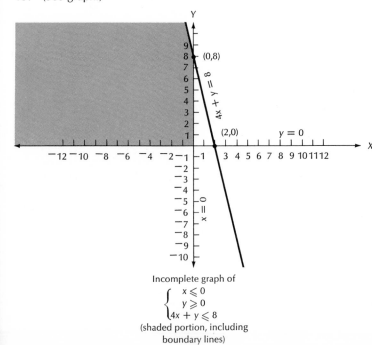

Incomplete graph of
$$\begin{cases} x \leqslant 0 \\ y \geqslant 0 \\ 4x + y \leqslant 8 \end{cases}$$
(shaded portion, including
boundary lines)

**17.**   (See graph.)

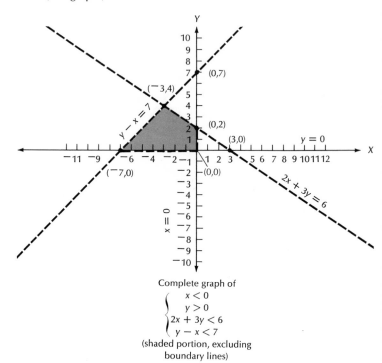

Complete graph of
$$\begin{cases} x < 0 \\ y > 0 \\ 2x + 3y < 6 \\ y - x < 7 \end{cases}$$
(shaded portion, excluding
boundary lines)

**Section 9-6. Page 317**

1. Lowest price, 40; medium price, 25; highest price, 15; profit, $81,000

3. Yes; model $M_1$, 6; model $M_2$, 3

5. Yes; 14 units of $G_1$ and 4 units of $G_2$

7. (a) $\frac{70}{3}$ lb   (b) $\frac{80}{3}$ lb
   (c) 50 lb; cost: 12.87 cents/lb or $12.87/100 lb

9. $F_1$, $\frac{310}{98}$ lb, or approximately 3.2 lb; $F_2$, $\frac{495}{98}$ lb, or approximately 5.1 lb; minimal price, 60 cents/lb

# INDEX